EARLY CHILD CARE

Bettye M. Caldwell

Caroline A. Chandler

Catherine S. Chilman

Laura L. Dittmann

Jacob L. Gewirtz

Dorothy S. Huntington

Reginald S. Lourie

Allen E. Marans

Dale R. Meers

Lois Barclay Murphy

Peter B. Neubauer

Eleanor Pavenstedt

Ann DeHuff Peters

Sally Provence

Julius B. Richmond

Halbert B. Robinson

Leon J. Yarrow

Early Child Care

THE NEW PERSPECTIVES

Caroline A. Chandler
Reginald S. Lourie
Ann DeHuff Peters

EDITED BY

Laura L. Dittmann

ATHERTON PRESS

NEW YORK · 1968

Address all inquiries to:
Atherton Press, Inc.
70 Fifth Avenue
New York 10011

Library of Congress Catalog Card Number 68–27526

FIRST EDITION

Second Printing 1970
Manufactured in the United States of America
Designed by JoAnn Randel

Foreword

This is a book about the very young child—infant, toddler, and early preschool—in today's world. It grew out of a series of four conferences sponsored jointly by the National Institute of Mental Health, the Children's Hospital of Washington, D.C., and the Committee on Day Care of the Maternal and Child Health Section of the American Public Health Association. The conferences, held in Bethesda, Maryland, covered a span of almost two years: April 1964 through October 1965.

Each of the three sponsoring agencies represents a focal point where pressures from many groups concerned with improving the care of the young child were being felt with increasing intensity. Faced with a common concern, the three sponsoring agencies brought together a number of experts in the field of early child development to pool information and experience and to review research findings as a basis for sound planning for children under three years of age. It was out of this context that the name of the conference series, *Early Child Care Re-examined*, emerged.

Conference members were drawn from the fields of pediatrics, psychology, child psychiatry, education, cultural anthropology, and research in child development. They were working in a wide range of backgrounds and settings: teaching hospitals, child guidance clinics, day-care centers, and university research centers; others came from centers of education, both community-based and those associated with teachers' colleges. Their work with children, whether research, clinical, or both, encompassed the advantaged as well as the disadvantaged, the handicapped and the emotionally disturbed as well as the normal—from premature infants to the preschool child.

The workshop discussions of the conferences were far-reaching in scope and depth, and from first to last were lively and stimulating. They were also, in the beginning, often stormy, highly charged, and anxiety producing. The papers brought to the meetings were subjected to the scrutiny and criticisms of the group as a whole, and these discussions provided the outline of this book. Many people contributed who are not directly represented in these final chapters, but their thinking has enriched the book. Those who participated most fully in the series of meetings are named on page x.

While consensus was finally reached on some of the fundamental principles of early development and on a few well-established research findings—a consensus on which this volume of guidelines is based—the series ended as it began: there were no final answers, no comforting conclusions, not even a few unequivocal *do's* and *don'ts*. Unsatisfying as this outcome may be, it seems singularly appropriate in an area of research and development where openendedness is not only desirable but absolutely prerequisite.

CAROLINE A. CHANDLER, M.D.
Center for Studies of Child and
Family Mental Health,
National Institute of Mental Health

ANN DeHUFF PETERS, M.D.
Chairman, Committee on Day Care,
Maternal and Child Health Committee,
American Public Health Association

Contributors

BETTYE M. CALDWELL, PH.D.
   Professor of Child Development and Education
   Director, Children's Center
   Syracuse University and
   Upstate Medical Center
   State University of New York
   Syracuse, New York

CAROLINE A. CHANDLER, M.D.
   Consultant in Child Mental Health and Early Child Care
   Center for Studies of Child and Family Mental Health
   National Institute of Mental Health
   Bethesda, Maryland

CATHERINE S. CHILMAN, PH.D.
  Research Division
  Welfare Administration
  Department of Health, Education and Welfare
  Washington, D.C.

LAURA L. DITTMANN, PH.D.
  Institute for Child Study
  University of Maryland
  College Park, Maryland

JACOB L. GEWIRTZ, PH.D.
  Chief, Section on Early Learning and Development
  Laboratory of Psychology
  National Institute of Mental Health
  Bethesda, Maryland

DOROTHY S. HUNTINGTON, PH.D.
  Research Director, Infant Rearing Study
  Department of Psychiatry
  Children's Hospital, Washington, D.C.

REGINALD S. LOURIE, M.D.
  Director, Department of Psychiatry
  Children's Hospital, Washington, D.C.
  Medical Director, Hillcrest Children's Center
  Professor of Pediatric Psychiatry,
  George Washington University

ALLEN E. MARANS, M.D.
  Psychiatric Consultant to Junior Village
  Formerly, Program Director, Infant Rearing Study
  Department of Psychiatry
  Children's Hospital, Washington, D.C.

DALE R. MEERS
  Research Associate, Infant Rearing Study
  Children's Hospital
  Washington, D.C.

LOIS BARCLAY MURPHY, PH.D.
  Senior Consultant, Infant Rearing Study
  Department of Psychiatry
  Children's Hospital, Washington, D.C.

PETER B. NEUBAUER, M.D.
    Director, Child Development Center
    Jewish Board of Guardians
    New York City

ELEANOR PAVENSTEDT, M.D.
    Clinical Professor of Psychiatry
    Boston University School of Medicine
    Lecturer, Tufts College Medical School
    Staff Child Psychiatry, Tufts-Columbia Point Health Center

ANN DeHUFF PETERS, M.D.
    Associate Professor of Maternal and Child Health
    School of Public Health
    University of North Carolina
    Chapel Hill, North Carolina

SALLY PROVENCE, M.D.
    Professor of Pediatrics
    Yale Child Study Center
    Yale University
    New Haven, Connecticut

JULIUS B. RICHMOND, M.D.
    Dean of Medicine and Chairman of Pediatrics
    Upstate Medical Center
    State University of New York
    Syracuse, New York

HALBERT B. ROBINSON, PH.D.
    Professor of Psychology
    University of North Carolina
    Chapel Hill, North Carolina

LEON J. YARROW, PH.D.
    Chief, Social and Behavioral Sciences Branch
    National Institute of Child Health and Human Development
    Bethesda, Maryland

Participants in the series of four conferences jointly sponsored by the National Institute of Mental Health, the Children's Hospital of Washington, D.C., and the Committee on Day Care of the Maternal and Child Health Section of the American Public Health Association, April 1964 to October 1965, Bethesda, Maryland.

Mrs. Mildred Arrill
Dr. Alfred Baldwin
Mrs. Frank Beck
Mr. Michael Begab
Dr. Herbert Birch
Dr. Ruth Blumenfeld
Dr. Samuel Braun
Dr. Caroline A. Chandler
Dr. Bettye M. Caldwell
Dr. Stella Chess
Dr. Catherine S. Chilman
Dr. Leon Cytryn
Dr. Laura L. Dittmann
Dr. Leon Eisenberg
Dr. Selma Fraiberg
Dr. Alfred Freedman
Dr. Helen Gee
Dr. Jacob L. Gewirtz
Dr. Charles Gershenson
Miss Cornelia Goldsmith
Dr. D. Wells Goodrich
Dr. Marianne Kris
Dr. E. James Lieberman
Dr. G. S. Laveck
Dr. Reginald S. Lourie
Dr. Allen E. Marans
Mr. Dale R. Meers
Dr. James Moss

Dr. Lois Barclay Murphy
Dr. Peter B. Neubauer
Dr. William J. Oberman
Dr. Eleanor Pavenstedt
Dr. Paul Penningroth
Dr. Ann DeHuff Peters
Dr. Sally Provence
Dr. Molly Putnam
Dr. Harriet Rheingold
Dr. Julius B. Richmond
Dr. Samuel Ritvo
Dr. Halbert B. Robinson
Dr. Earle Schaefer
Dr. Patricia Schloesser
Dr. Charlotte Silverman
Mrs. Edna Salant
Miss Pearl Shalit
Dr. William Stark
Dr. L. Joseph Stone
Dr. Lovisa Tatnall
Miss Mildred Tate
Dr. Eva Towns
Dr. Charles Wenar
Dr. Sidney Werkman
Dr. Marvin Wirtz
Dr. Helen Witmer
Dr. Leon J. Yarrow
Dr. Herbert Zimelas

Contents

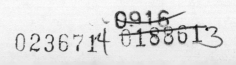

Introduction

LAURA L. DITTMANN

The contributors to this volume have undertaken a task which is as much the result of modern technology as tomorrow's moonshot, although it is considerably more earthbound. In their search for the right words to express their ideas, they often yearn for a technical vocabulary comparable to that available to the physical scientist. Lacking words which carry highly precise meaning, they are forced in some instances to use terms already well used: "mothering," "adjustment," or "relationship"; yet the ideas they seek to express may not have been conceptualized before. In other instances, they are seeking application for concepts generally accepted for some time, the implications of which have not been thought through for babies and very young children.

They are pioneers in the true sense of the word. Yet this book is about the most widespread, everyday process: taking care of babies

1

and toddlers. One might observe facetiously that it is the second oldest profession in the world, yet until very recently, no one has tried to specify exactly what goes on between mother and her baby, who does what to whom in the exchange, and what happens if, instead of one mother, there is no mother, an alternating day and night mother, or many different substitutes for her. Now it is realized that until all that transpires between the mother and her baby in the best of circumstances is comprehended in sufficient detail that it can be confidently reproduced in its entirety, it is impossible to make alternative plans with assurance that none of the essentials has been unwittingly omitted.

Throughout, the writers maintain a double focus. They are seeking to recognize and specify the conditions under which a young child can best develop. Once identified, they reason, it should be possible to re-create these conditions in a variety of situations and under different auspices. This book becomes, then, an effort to identify what is known about young children and apply it to the day-by-day programing—or "engineering," as Gewirtz puts it—of the lives of children.

For many reasons such a compilation is urgently needed today. Of course, millions of mothers give their babies a good start, providing devoted and painstaking care, exquisitely attuning to the baby, and delicately balancing giving and withholding so that the relationship becomes a kind of duet in which now one, then the other, calls the beat. Such mothers somehow know when a child needs to be let alone—to climb too high or work desperately to solve a baffling problem alone. And they respond instantly in the next moment, for reasons they can scarcely communicate, to an event which to the outsider appears to be similar in every respect.

Many keen observers have studied the development of children, watching and recording age-typical behavior. Others have tried to capture as many of the facets as possible of what goes on between a mother and her baby, and the fleeting unspoken exchanges and nuances ricocheting among other members of the family. Nevertheless, there has been a tendency to accumulate records on the atypical child or to become involved in scrutinizing family patterns which produce clinical symptoms of disruption, blunted potential, or communicative breakdown.

But there are thousands of babies today who are not cared for in the way considered ideal, at least by Western cultural standards: by a woman who is the child raiser and homemaker and a man who is the wage earner and provider, while the children happily bounce in and out of the kitchen with jam on their mouths.

Modern life places conflicting pressures on mothers in a way previously unknown. Dr. Catherine Chilman reminds us that the pressures are felt by *both* mothers and fathers. Margaret Mead (1947) also was thinking in terms of the two-adult family unit as she remarked:

> We now expect a family to achieve alone what no society has ever expected an individual family to accomplish unaided. In effect, we call upon the individual family to do what a whole clan used to do.

And the family delivers—*if* everything clicks. But if any one of the pieces falls out, the gap is bound to affect deeply each member of the family on several levels simultaneously. The base—two parents —is so narrow that when one of them is unable to perform the many tasks now expected by our society, the little unit threatens to topple immediately. It is not necessary here to trace the steps by which this state of affairs has come about in an industrialized, mobile, urban society such as ours. The pattern and the demands it generates are most certainly not confined to the United States, but rather are characteristic of all modern technological societies.

For a long time we have heard fragments about the experiments in other countries by which child care is underwritten by the state. In Chapter 10, Dale Meers and Allen Marans report in detail on the massive programs in the U.S.S.R., the East European Communist countries, and Israel. They also candidly evaluate the little-known but extensive efforts in France and Greece. In this country, we are just beginning to admit that there are thousands of babies and very young children whose care is far from ideal. There are many who lack two able-bodied parents, others who have only one. We must figure out a way to assist the parents of these children—in a manner consistent with our firm commitment to the right of parents to choose their own way—as they try to balance the demands and yet partake of the dividends of living in this age. There are thousands of other babies who quite literally have no parents at all, those for whom the community must devise a substitute family life. As this country accepts the challenge these many babies represent, it will have to come to terms with some of the issues explored in this book.

Officially, we know that a good many mothers leave their homes every day for work. In 1965, 4 million women with children under six years of age were employed in full-time jobs, and this number continues to grow. During the day many women leave their children with a relative; others arrange for a "sitter" to come; a few can hire a maid, or there is a friend down the street. For some there is a nursery or settlement house or a day-care center. Fewer than 10 per cent of these young children are placed in approved day-care centers or family day homes. In fact, licensed facilities of this nature are in such short supply that many of the children are tucked away in situations which are unsupervised and which may be operated by people who are either ignorant of the needs of children or simply too tired or indifferent. The shortage of suitable facilities for daytime care forces many mothers who must work to leave their babies in the care of friends, neighbors, relatives, or commercial ventures for the entire week, picking them up only on the weekends.

Our government spokesmen appear to be somewhat schizophrenic on the subject of the working mother. Some agencies have endorsed the philosophy that babies and very young children do much better at home, and seek to provide a mother's care in a family day-care home if the child's own mother cannot stay home herself. Other agencies are busily getting women out to work, to become technicians, teachers, secretaries, and to fill the host of other jobs necessary for the functioning of our economy. Even the woman who formerly was paid to stay at home with her children under the Aid to Families of Dependent Children program is now encouraged to get training so that she will be qualified to enter the labor market at the most favorable rung.

The economic and social pressures which drive mothers to work outside their own homes are responsible for the largest number of children for whom supplementary care is needed during the day. But there are other pressures too, which contribute to the sense of urgency felt by the writers of this volume. All professional persons dealing with the health and welfare of young children are currently deeply concerned about the *quality* of mothering a child receives, whether from his own mother or a substitute. In other words, we are engaged in upgrading the specifications for the dimensions of mothering. It is not enough that the baby be cared for in a physically intact home by his own mother. We need to know how to help all who care for children to do a better job, whether the caretaker is the child's own mother, a relative, a daytime caretaker, or a worker in a residential center or hospital where babies are cared for on a twenty-four-hour basis.

Historical Concepts of "Mothering"

Providing a maternal type of care for all babies and young children has long been a primary goal among experts in health and welfare fields in this country. This is not altogether the result of sentimentality. Most theories of child development advanced in this century have emphasized the importance of the maternal role. The specifics of what the mother should or should not do depend upon the social and cultural factors emphasized at any one time.

In the first decades of the century, professional emphasis was largely on physical health, and attention was focused on safe methods of infant feeding, of hygiene and sanitation in the nursery and the kitchen, culminating in the concept of prevention of disease through routine well-baby care, and immunization schedules. Somewhat later, the scientific ordering of the environment was extended to the realm of behavior. Watson and others sought to control the psychological milieu of the nursery in order to "nurture" the type of adult deemed desirable and functional in a scientific age. Mother was seen as the first and prime promulgator of sound habits. This naïve approach to the complexity of infant learning and behavior was tempered by the work of Piaget, Gesell, and others who, observing the behavior of infants and children outside the laboratory, watched their subjects "unfold" rather than become automated. These keen observers argued eloquently in favor of "nature," placing great weight on the maturing of function according to an inner genetic timetable relatively immune to the meddlesome trainer or conditioner. While they conceived of normative behavior in chronological terms, their commitment to the biologically determined origins of response implied the presence of individual differences, genetically dictated. Mother became the impatient watcher and waiter who read the signs of impending peace or turmoil in the nursery.

Psychoanalytic insights added a dimension to biological determinism with emphasis on the social context in which behavioral and instinctual transactions were fostered and manifested. From psychoanalytic theory came emphasis on the child's early experiences within the family, especially with the mother, as they through her shaped the child's concept of himself and colored the world as a comfortable or threatening and unpredictable place to be. As first developed, the infant was seen as an impressionable creature to whom things were done in more or less appropriate ways at different life stages. Sequentially unfolding, these phases were characterized by a core developmental task. The resolution of conflicting demands and wishes implicit in each phase was regarded as essential to forward movement; if the child failed to resolve the conflict, there was the possibility of becoming fixed in an earlier stage with subsequent impairment in adaptability and the possibility of later regression. Recently, increasing importance has been given to the part played by the infant himself as a contributor to the exchange. Mother is seen as the one who comforts and gratifies, while she in turn is reassured and comforted by the responses of her child.

Resting on the understandings of each of these modes of thinking, there is emerging today an eclectic model of child development which selects relevant components from many schools of thought, no one of which can stand alone. In its barest outlines, this model would include substantial agreement from all sides that every child:

Should receive regular health supervision, beginning before birth.

Should be seen as a unique individual.

Continually modifies and is modifiable by conditions surrounding him, including the significant persons in his environment.

Learns gradually about the dimensions of himself and the world through his experiences with a variety of sensations and stimuli, both animate and inanimate, internal and external.

Needs to be cherished, to be the recipient of the emotional investment of others.

These theories are fine, but as a working model they become woefully inadequate. If they are viewed as a kind of "super-checklist," the resultant blend may be thin and unbalanced. We are beginning to recognize the necessity for viewing these elements as an indivisible whole; at the same time we see more clearly that many of the elements themselves have been insufficiently conceptualized.

Take the first consensus, for example. We have done a good job of selling cleanliness as a virtue. As a result, parents looking for substitute care may be more apt to value the frilly dress and a spotless kitchen rather than a cheerfully disordered playroom. Dirt may be banished by a caretaker—mother or another—who keeps babies in cribs and playpens long past the time when they should be allowed to get their hands and knees dirty from investigations into the corners of their domain as they creep about.

Likewise, diaper rash has been equated with neglect in institutional or day care, but neglectful people who operate day nurseries could avoid it by leaving a baby without diapers. One conscientious caretaker pridefully pointed out that all her babies were wearing diapers, proof that they were changed sufficiently often. When all the babies were put into a wading pool later in the morning, the diapers stayed on, hanging low about the knees as they became soaked in the pool. The visitor's suggestion that the babies might be put into the pool naked was countered with shocked assurance that the health department wouldn't like *that*.

Such piecemeal application of health concepts does not add up to a healthful day for children. How can we interpret to parents and other caretakers the need for and the meaning of "judicious neglect"? How can we keep standards for health and cleanliness high, yet be realistic about the anachronisms of practice? In Chapter 5, Dr. Lois Barclay Murphy gives many practical suggestions, both for mothers and teachers, for resolution of these dilemmas.

We may be getting somewhere, too, with the second area of consensus: babies should be seen as unique individuals. Each of the authors in Part One expresses dissatisfaction with chronological age as a determinant of behavior. The dynamic interplay between hereditary and environmental factors has been confirmed and elaborated. Dr. Sally Provence starts with the premise that "development, and the learning which is an integral part of it, comes about through an interaction of the infant's inborn maturing system and the forces of the environment. Both somatic and mental innate factors are called successively into play according to a biological timetable unique to the human being."

It is perhaps appropriate to speak of developmental changes under the heading of individual differences because, over time, the child becomes a vastly different person in the normal sequence of growth. There is a marked change in behavior and in the responses elicited when the child begins to walk. A mother may "love" little babies but find the autonomous toddler a nuisance. On the other hand, she may feel that the child who talks and socializes and has ideas of his own is a "person" but will leave an infant to spend much time alone in his crib. Dr. Neubauer speaks of the characteristic delight in sheer running (*funktionlust*). Can the child's caretaker stand such vigor? Possibly; her responses to the changes she must deal with will be dependent on the age assortment in her home at any one time. It may be a convenience when a child walks early if another baby is on the way, but it may be a real nuisance if there are already two or three preschool children in the home.

Furthermore, each child who comes along in a family presents a different problem in adaptation. If the mother takes the first baby as a norm, she may become quite upset if the second one differs. In addition, there appear to be some limits to the extent to which a mother can alter her conceptions of what a baby "should" be like. The nuances of a suitable match between substitute mother and child—or biological mother, for that matter—are very real and may determine the behavior of both to a large extent. In an unusual study of the environmental differences actually experienced by two children in the same foster home (twenty-four-hour care), Dr. Leon Yarrow (1963) cites two incidents. One, with two infants at different times, reveals that the actual behavior of the foster mother was vastly different at the two time-points checked.

In the second instance, two infants of the same age and sex were placed simultaneously. Although exposed to the same gross physical environment, the two were treated entirely differently. Infant A, a vigorous outgoing child, was met in kind. He was called by name in discussions about his progress. Infant B, quiet and passive, was progressively more ignored as the life of the family tended to flow on past him. He was referred to by the foster mother as "the other one." Conceptualizing such elusive aspects of the environment provides the theme for Leon Yarrow's contribution to this book.

Emphasis on Early Learning

This is the decade of revived interest in learning—the aspect mentioned fourth in the areas of consensus—especially in infant learning and the conditions which push a baby to begin to sort out meanings in his environment. Today we hear that by the age of two or three it is too late to begin to optimize the environment so that the baby can lay the groundwork for later school achievements. Five years ago, such a statement would have been attributed to a doting parent, who was reading into the behavior of his child a great deal more than was actually there. We are, however, far from reaching agreement on the ways in which an infant learns to monitor incoming information and guide correction strategies in perceiving, cognizing, and manipulating his environment. For example, watch a ten-month-old baby playing in his crib. He pulls up, then dares to let go and rush for the bars opposite. To vary the theme, he falls purposely en route, shouting in glee as he dives for the mattress. Suddenly, the observer realizes that the baby does not do this when he is on the floor. How did he learn the difference between hard and soft in such a superbly meaningful way? Or to use an even more refined example, in Chapter 6, Dr. Murphy looks at the principle behind an infant rattle. She sees the rattle, not as a plaything habitually offered to a baby, but "as a small object which the baby can grasp, and by inadvertent or deliberate movements evoke sounds. The baby will be stimulated to more goal-directed activity if pleasurable consequences follow his efforts."

At first blush, this appears to be an astonishing bit of embroidery over a commonplace object item in the nursery. Yet it is exactly this minute rethinking of the environment and what it offers to a child which must be done before we can hope to create culture-free settings in which young children can begin to use their minds and be stimulated to think. In Chapter 7, Dr. Jacob Gewirtz insists that we can only define environment in terms of what we are trying to produce in the way of behavior. Once our behavioral objectives are identified, the response we seek will determine how we go about specifying the behavior of adults or providing objects. His paper challenges the reader to some basic rethinking of the transactions between child and caretaker in terms of stimulation.

Finally, we have the need for every child to become the recipient of emotional investment of significant persons. Particularly in infancy, the baby needs one person of special significance to him, one on whom he depends for his security in a world which is otherwise chaotic or formless. Once he has such a person, he is upset at losing her. In fact, we are worried if the child is not threatened by the loss of one so vital to his sense of well-being. If he is "promiscuous," forming superficial attachments to any adult who comes along, we believe that the child has missed an essential experience. But, as Marans and Meers document in Chapter 10, the child's need to receive the emotional investment of another is exceedingly difficult to quantify. Furthermore, only exposition permits the conceptual differentiation of affective needs of the infant from his requirements for physical care and for stimulation of a sensory or cognitive nature. Rheingold (1964) poses the question: "Does the infant know if it's love or a routine?" Marans and Meers would rejoin, "Is love routine? Do babies fail to respond differentially to differences in nurture and care?"

If conditions are right for the desired "love affair" to take place on schedule, what happens when the lady leaves? This is the "separation" part of the story and the focus for a good deal of research interest. Much of the work reported has dealt with traumatic situations where separation is associated with death or illness of a parent, extreme neglect or rejection of the child, and illness or hospitalization. The extent to which the regular reappearance of the mother (as is the case in day care) mitigates potential trauma is not documented as yet.

Since the development of motherly feelings has been shown to be a product of the interaction between a child and his caretaker—each depending on the other to play an appropriate role—it is natural that in a day-care situation both mothers, the day and the night one, would depend upon appropriate responses from the child in order to function adequately. At least in our culture, it also may be natural for the child to orient himself to one or the other caretaker as the *right* one. Not enough is known about the manner in which a child relates to another person for us to be able to say how he selects. Over time, the child's own mother remains in the picture, so simple continuity may be one factor which aids him to decide who is "mother." Possibly nuances of dominance, possessiveness, degree of emotional involvement, and other factors are communicated to the child as well. Dr. Eleanor Pavenstedt in Chapter 3 suggests ways in which the day nursery can reassure the child that his mother still exists, although out of sight.

Probably the conflicts and crosscurrents in family day care are not the same as those in twenty-four-hour care. We have too little research to know. The quantitative differences represented may actually generate qualitatively differing stresses and tensions. At any rate, the problem is not simple. If the relationship between the day mother and infant is all that is implied in "good care," the infant should begin to respond to her intimately and become attached, finding in her presence his sense of security and contentment. At the normal developmental stage when he begins to become wary of "strangers" (which may include his own grandmother and father as well as his pediatrician or a casual passerby), he may pull away from his own mother in the process.

To the extent that they are a factor in day care, separation problems can occur over the weekend for example. Rejection by her own child is hard for any mother to accept and even harder if the circumstances under which she has placed the baby are such that she is in conflict over the placement, feels guilty over her employment, is troubled by marital or economic pressures, or is in any other way especially vulnerable. To many young mothers, a group care center which is not so highly personal as care in a home or with a friend is more acceptable. In some instances, the child's mother may remove her child from a loving day-care mother because she views the growing attachment between her child and the substitute as a threat to her primary position. In others, the day-care mother may ask to have the arrangement terminated because of her deepening involvement with the child, or she may withdraw symbolically, anticipating the pain of separation later.

Licensing of Facilities

The pressure for a book such as this comes from still a third quarter. In our eagerness to upgrade the experiences of all children in their earliest years, more and more communities are regulating the conditions under which children can be cared for outside their own homes. For some time, all states have had laws specifying what can be done, by how many people, and where, for children cared for in groups for the day or on a residential basis. Less generally, states have regulations to specify suitable conditions for children who are cared for in families, where fewer than five or six children, including the mother's own, are cared for by a mother in the pattern known as family day care. More and more people are agreeing that licensing for these homes is essential if the rights of young children are to be protected. Since it is the youngest children who usually receive care in family homes, the pressure becomes even stronger.

Licensing can be used to stimulate improvements in existing facilities, but too often mandatory licensing regulations have served merely to establish stereotyped patterns of day care with minimal levels of program quality. To be truly effective, the standards must go beyond safety and hygiene. The major emphasis must be placed on the total living of the children themselves within the premises; it must not be focused on the premises alone. The suitability of training and temperament of the caretakers becomes as important as their age or health. Children may be kept alive when provided with food, clothing, and shelter, but they require more than this if their spirits are to thrive. It is the "more than this" which the authors of this volume have earnestly attemped to define.

REFERENCES

Mead, M. What is Happening to the American Family? In *New Emphasis on Cultural Factors*. Reprinted from *Journal of Social Casework* by Family Service Association of America, 1947.

Rheingold, H. Remarks made at Conference on Early Child Care Re-Examined. Bethesda, Maryland, May 1964.

Yarrow, L. J. Research in Dimensions of Early Maternal Care. *Merrill-Palmer Quarterly*, 9(2): 101–114, 1963.

PART I

A New Look at the Young Child: Development and Individuality

Texts on growth and development of children abound and appear at about the same rate of increase as the children themselves. It is not the intention of this book to present in abridged form the steps by which a child grows. Rather, certain psychosocial factors have been selected for a fresh examination. As background for the focus on the first three years the reader is asked to begin with Leon Yarrow's thoughtful reconceptualization of the factors and transactions in the environment as they affect and are affected by the child. In the following chapters, Sally Provence, Eleanor Pavenstedt, and Peter Neubauer discuss the development of the child in each of his first three years. Finally, Lois Barclay Murphy specifies in meticulous detail how any one of the elements in the child's environment —the child himself, the people around him, and the psychological climate—can be selectively manipulated by a sensitive caretaker.

1

Conceptualizing the Early Environment

LEON J. YARROW

Programs for the care of young children outside their own homes have usually been developed on a purely pragmatic basis and often in a somewhat haphazard way. This has been true with regard to congregate care of young infants in institutions, as well as group care of toddlers and preschool children in day-care centers.

The development of programs for substitute and supplemental care of infants and young children has been hampered by a lack of clarity about the significant parameters of the environment. It is time that we became more articulate about the theoretical rationale underlying the kinds of environmental conditions and the specific experiences provided young children in institutionalized child-care programs. We need to establish some links between theoretical concepts and practical details of programming. Such conceptual links should provide an orderly framework within which to plan programs and to experiment with specific environmental variables.

15

There are many different levels on which the environment can be conceptualized. It can be analyzed on a simple descriptive level in terms of physical properties, such as the intensity of light or the decibels of sound at a given moment in time. In relation to the experiencing child, the physical dimensions of the environment can be described in terms of perceptual characteristics, such as brightness or loudness. Finally, the environment can be conceptualized from a more complex phenomenological orientation in terms of psychological dimensions, such as warmth or permissiveness. These higher order properties can be defined in terms of variations in simpler physical and perceptual dimensions. Each of these levels of environmental analysis has meaning and relevance for different purposes.

In recent years there have been major developments in theoretical thinking about organism-environment relationships. Several concepts are of special relevance to developing bridges between programs and theory: the concepts of the effective environment, the direction of action of environmental influences, and environmental contingencies. The rigid separation of organism and environment which has characterized psychological theories in the past is giving way to a recognition of an interdependence on many levels. Although we can define environmental events objectively in terms of their physical properties, we recognize that the effective environment at any moment must be considered in relation to the characteristics of the responding organism. The impact of any given set of environmental conditions will depend on the child's sensory thresholds for specific kinds of stimulation, his capacity for discriminating differences among stimuli, his level of cognitive complexity, and his immediate motivational state. Thus, for a two-week-old infant, a complex, multicolored visual stimulus may have no different value than a dull, black cube in eliciting attention. Similarly, a three-month-old infant may be relatively unresponsive to a rattle or a bell when hungry; whereas these same stimuli may elicit strong approach responses when he is well fed.

Traditionally, analysis of environmental influences has been in terms of a unidirectional model—that is, the environment has been seen as a set of antecedent conditions acting *on* the child to elicit behavior. Only recently have we begun to shift from this simple antecedent-consequent orientation to an interactional framework. From this orientation, the environment is conceptualized as a medium in which there is a constant bidirectional flow with the organism. In more concrete terms, this means that the child responds selectively to stimulation and uses certain aspects of the environment discriminatively for gratification of drives. With regard to the human environment, the implications of an interactional orientation are profound. It recognizes that the child is not simply a recipient of caretaker actions, but rather he elicits responses from others. Moreover, the kinds of responses he elicits are significantly influenced by his own physical and psychological characteristics, his own unique stimulus properties.

One of the most significant theoretical developments in recent years has been the growth of a more differentiated conception of the early environment based on an analysis of the components of early experience. Such differentiation is necessary if we are to understand more completely the relationship between environmental influences and the development of the child. Such an analytic approach provides a basis for systematically examining natural home environments, as well as different kinds of substitute care—foster homes, day care, and institutional settings for children of various ages. For purposes of systematic analysis we can distinguish three major aspects of the environment: the properties of the inanimate environment, the characteristics of the human environment, and the conditions under which these stimuli are provided.

The Inanimate Environment

The importance of adequate sensory stimulation for the development of cognitive and problem-solving abilities in young children has now been well documented. Among the significant dimensions of stimulation are amount, intensity, variety, and complexity. It is likely that there are optimal levels on all of these dimensions. The optimal level of intensity, the degree of complexity, the amount of stimulation per time unit in a given modality probably varies significantly at different developmental levels, and depends also on individual differences in thresholds.

For the very young infant, stimuli have important evocative functions. They arouse him, they direct and focus his attention on the external environment, they elicit active approach or avoidance responses. For stimuli to be effective in eliciting responses and maintaining behavior, it is essential that they be of appropriate intensity, above the child's threshold of awareness but not so intense as to be physiologically disruptive or painful.

Variety in stimulation has been emphasized from both neurophysiological and psychological perspectives. During the period when the underlying neurological structures are developing, young children need stimulation in a variety of sensory modalities. Central to Piaget's concept of differentiation of schemata is the notion of a gradation of variation in properties of stimuli. Stimuli that vary in a number of dimensions enable the child to develop and consolidate concepts through the processes of assimilation and accommodation. It is likely that monotonous, unvaried stimulation leads to habituation, so that a given level of stimulation or a given degree of complexity loses its evocative power.

Intensity and amount of stimulation are fairly simple dimensions to manipulate. Consequently, we know much more about the effects of variations in these dimensions on capacity to elicit behavior and to sustain attention and goal-directed activity. The effects of complexity, patterning and degree of structure of materials are less well known. We might assume that the degree of structure is an important determinant of the degree of stereotypy or creativity of the response elicited. Unstructured stimuli that provide a variety of response possibilities are likely to elicit responses of a higher level of creativity than highly structured stimuli. Similarly, the degree of complexity of a stimulus is probably directly related to the amount and quality of exploratory behavior evoked. Stimuli of limited complexity are likely to elicit less exploratory behavior than are highly complex stimuli.

In analyzing the stimulus properties of the environment, we must consider not only the stimulation from specific objects, events, and experiences, but also the stimulation derived from the general environmental context. The context in which any given stimulus is provided is important to the extent that it influences the distinctiveness or cue value of stimulation and important to the extent that the value of any given level or pattern of stimulation may be modified by background stimulation. In the emphasis on the harmful effects of deprivation there is danger in assuming an intrinsic value in quantity and intensity of stimulation. It is clear that there is a point beyond which stimulation itself may become traumatic. Stimuli that are too complex, too intense, or inappropriately timed may be as harmful as lack of sufficient stimulation. Excessive or inappropriate stimulation may result in the development of defenses, resulting in varied forms of withdrawal or an elevation in the threshold of responsiveness. The concept of optimal levels of perceptual and sensory stimulation is an important one. The intensity, the complexity, and the patterning of stimulation that is optimal will vary at different developmental levels and will depend also on individual sensitivities and vulnerabilities.

From a somewhat different theoretical perspective, we can analyze the human as well as the inanimate environment in terms of predominant functional characteristics. We can distinguish the following kinds of conditions: conditions which elicit or evoke responses; stimulus conditions which facilitate expression of certain kinds of behavior; conditions which inhibit the expression of specific behavior patterns; environmental conditions which sustain given levels or kinds of responses; stimuli which enhance the intensity or level of a response; conditions which reinforce or increase the probability of reoccurrence of certain kinds of responses; and conditions which decrease the probability of the reoccurrence of certain kinds of behavior. Some of these conditions are determined primarily by the properties of the stimuli; others are based on contingency relationships; others are dependent on the interaction between a specific stimulus event and a cumulative historical sequence—for example, permissive attitudes which facilitate exploratory behavior or the expression of feelings.

The Human Environment

The human environment can be conceptualized in terms similar to the inanimate environment, that is, the amount, quality, and intensity of stimulation in different sensory modalities. In addition, there are variables distinctive to the human environment: the affective and affectional characteristics of interaction; the level or depth of relationship with caretakers and other significant persons; the extent of individualized sensitivity to the child; the behavior and personal characteristics of caretakers and peers as identification models; the consistency and predictability of the behavior of caretakers; and the continuity of significant people.

With regard to stimulation, the caretaker's activities can be conceptualized along a number of dimensions. She is an initiator of stimulation (tactile, kinesthetic, visual and auditory), a mediator of stimulation, and an agent of response. In her capacity as an initiator, we can distinguish two broad categories of stimulation provided by the caretaker to an infant: stimulation derived from physical contact with her body and stimulation involving behavior directed toward eliciting responses from the child. During the very earliest months of life, simple contact stimulation seems to be most important; with increasing age, evocative stimulation becomes increasingly significant.

Stimulation associated with physical contact serves several functions. It has an arousal function, that is, it raises the infant's general level of awareness and responsiveness to his environment. The tactile-kinesthetic stimulation derived from holding probably also serves a very primitive need-gratifying function. To the extent that this kind of stimulation reduces tension, it frees the infant to become aware of and to respond to perceptual stimuli in his environment.

The second type of stimulation involves more active manipulation of the environment by the caretaker. It includes bringing the child in contact with appropriate materials and objects, manipulating situations in order to elicit appropriate intellectual and personal-social responses, as well as varied forms of indirect and focused teaching—that is, encouraging the child to attempt his own solution of problems as well as demonstrating and guiding him in the solution of problems.

With regard to modes of stimulation, the significance of given modalities changes at different points during infancy and early childhood. The importance of tactile-kinesthetic stimulation probably decreases rapidly after the first few months of life when more directed and active stimulation takes on increasing importance. Nevertheless, during the period from eighteen months to three years, physical contact with the mother still provides a very basic form of gratification. Visual and auditory stimulation become increasingly important in later infancy and early childhood.

The mediational activities of the caretaker are extremely important for the young child. Because of the infant's extreme helplessness, the caretaker must bring him in contact with appropriate stimuli. A most important aspect of maternal mediation in early childhood is the regulatory function. The mother or caretaker can enhance or reduce the intensity of stimuli by regulating the ways in which the child comes in contact with stimuli. She determines the context of events by regulating the background conditions. In addition to being a direct source of gratification, she serves as a source of frustration, providing aversive as well as reinforcing stimuli. In distinction to the inanimate environment, which may be rewarding or unrewarding indiscriminately, the human environment responds selectively to the child. This is perhaps one of the most significant aspects of the human environment: the active interaction with the child which involves *response* to his behavior rather than simply doing things for him. This selective responsiveness is the basis for very important learning in the young child. In addition to providing conditions for learning appropriate behavior, as, for example, rewarding the child when he responds appropriately, this kind of interaction provides the basis for the child's acquisition of the response patterns involved in the development of reciprocal relationships with people.

The aspects of early experience that are most distinctive for the human environment are the affectional components of interaction with caretakers. These components of the environment are part of a complex of interpersonal variables. The elements of maternal behavior described under the protective, buffering, gratifying, and responsive functions are the basic behavioral units of affectional interchange. These variables traditionally have encompassed both personal characteristics of the caretaker, underlying feelings and attitudes, as well as specific categories of behavior. Included are such variables as the degree of emotional involvement (the gratifications which the caretaker derives from the relationship with the child); the degree of individualization (the extent to which the caretaker is aware of the uniqueness of the infant and the extent to which she differentiates his characteristics and responds to him with an awareness of his individuality); and acceptance (the degree to which she is able to respond positively to the infant and all of his characteristics). From this perspective, affectional interchange becomes definable in terms of specific behavior characteristics rather than being a vague, global entity. It is likely that the child's capacity to respond to inanimate stimulation is significantly influenced by the broader context of affectional relationships.

Separation-Continuity of Persons

After a time, the caretaker acquires distinctive properties for the infant. To the extent that her responses become predictable to him, the environment acquires continuity for the child. Such continuity in infancy is thought to be extremely important in the earliest development of concepts of object permanence and object constancy. There is some speculation that development of the concept of time is intimately related to continuity of person and general environmental predictability.

Recent research and theoretical writings have emphasized the importance of continuity in maternal care. The harmful effects of discontinuity have been dramatized by the studies of young infants who have been suddenly separated from their mothers and placed in institutional care. This is one extreme form of discontinuity. In planning programs for the child, several aspects of continuity need to be distinguished. It is important to distinguish between continuity in the person who is the major source of gratification for the child; continuity in the qualitative patterns of stimulation and gratification; continuity in the timing and scheduling of experiences; and continuity in the broader background environment. Much of the concern about the harmful effects of separation has assumed that lack of continuity in person is inevitably accompanied by the other kinds of discontinuities.

Studies of institutional care have pointed up some of the consequences of lack of continuity of person under circumstances where there is no one caretaking person who has the major responsibility for the child. The caretaker has little opportunity to become sensitized to the individualized characteristics and vulnerabilities of a given child under her care. With the dispersion of mothering functions among several caretakers, the likelihood of their developing feelings of attachment to an individual child is diminished. Sensitive, individualized adaptation of the caretaker's behavior to a child and associated feelings of positive emotional involvement are among the major deficiencies of group care situations for young children.

In planning programs for young children, where it is not always feasible to maintain complete continuity in person, it may be possible to minimize the degree of discontinuity experienced by the infant or young child by planning carefully the scheduling of routines, the patterns of gratification, and the modalities in which gratifications are provided. In addition, caretakers may be trained to be sensitive to the individualized needs of young children. It may be possible to maximize the predictability of the environment for the young child and to foster individualized adaptations to his special characteristics, even with changing caretakers.

We must distinguish between discontinuity associated with separation or loss of the mother and discontinuity that may be associated with having several mother-figures. The implications for personality development of multiple mother-figures are not nearly so clear-cut as the effects of inadequate maternal care involving deprivation of contact or loss of a mother-figure. There has been some speculation that the greater variety of stimulation provided by several close mother-figures may be intellectually stimulating and promote flexibility. Although the importance for the young child of a primary mother-figure is generally accepted, it is likely that the intensity of this relationship may be diluted by being spread among several mother-figures without serious consequences to the child. It is thought that the child takes on behavior patterns, attitudes, and sentiments of other human beings in his environment through the process of identification. In general, we have assumed that learning through identification is facilitated if the child has developed positive feelings toward the identification object. On the basis of available data we cannot assume that children are unable to develop strong positive cathexes concurrently with several mother-figures.

In programs of substitute care, there has been particular emphasis on the importance of the caretaker establishing as close a relationship as possible with the child. At our present state of knowledge, it seems desirable that if the child is exposed regularly to several mother-figures, he should have discriminably different levels of relationships with them. This suggests that in full-time care of young children, one person should assume major responsibility for an infant and should be encouraged to develop a special relationship with this infant. Such a relationship increases the likelihood that one caretaker will develop particular sensitivity to the individual characteristics and needs of this infant. In this way, it is likely that the infant will experience different levels of relationship and will learn to establish discriminating relationships.

With regard to temporary separation, such as in day care, the problems are quite different from those involved in long-term separation. In the day-care setting, while it may be desirable to avoid disruptive anxiety in the child by carrying over similar patterns of maternal care from the home to the school environment, to do so may in many instances be defeating the basic purpose of the day-care program, namely, providing increased stimulation and more adequate interpersonal relationships. Under these circumstances, traumatic effects may be avoided by introducing significant changes gradually. It is important too that there be some continuity between the child's school and home experiences. To achieve this continuity, it may be necessary to work with the parents in attempting to influence the child-care patterns.

In planning day-care programs, it is necessary to consider, from the orientation of the young child, the optimal period of being away from the mother. Aside from practical considerations governing the length of the day, we need to consider optimal periods for children of different ages in terms of their concepts of time. For very young children with very limited time concepts, a long period away from the mother may maximize separation feelings.

Environmental Factors and the Characteristics of the Organism

There has been growing recognition that the impact of environmental influences must be considered in relation to the characteristics of the organism. A concept of great theoretical importance and correspondingly great practical significance is that of the "state" of the organism at the time of any environmental input. This concept can be broken down into several different types of organismic variables:

1. Degree of receptivity or sensitivity to stimuli determined by developmental characteristics.
2. Response capabilities based on developmental level.
3. Individualized receptivity, sensitivity or vulnerability related to
    a. Basic biological or constitutional factors.
    b. Cumulative changes in the organism resulting from the unique past history of the organism.
4. Receptivity to stimuli based on immediate past experiences, e.g., the level of attentiveness of a hungry infant will differ from that of a satiated one.

The recognition that the environment does not simply act on the passive child, eliciting or inhibiting responses, but that to some extent the child determines his effective environment has many implications for programs of child care. For example, children who have a low activity level or manifest little curiosity are likely to elicit a lower level of responsiveness from their caretakers and are likely to be given fewer opportunities for spontaneous exploration than highly active and highly exploratory children. Similarly, babies who are responsive to cuddling, who show their enjoyment of it by their postural adaptations as well as by cooing and smiling, are likely to elicit more of this kind of behavior from their caretakers.

In a sense, the caretaker is adapting her behavior to the child's overt indication of need. There is some apparent conflict between the concept of sensitive adaptation to the child's characteristics and needs, and a therapeutic orientation of attempting to change the level of responsiveness of a child who does not interact appropriately with his environment.

Goals for the Early Years

There exists some consensus about the general goals for which we are striving in child-care programs. These can be stated most appropriately in terms of the behavior patterns and characteristics we wish to develop in young children:

1. The development of language skills and problem-solving and cognitive skills to enable the child to handle effectively the requirements of his world at each developmental stage.

2. The development of capacities for appropriate and enduring relationships with people.

3. The development of appropriate reality orientation and appropriate and constructive use of fantasy.

4. The development of initiative and spontaneity.

5. Development of controls for appropriate handling of drives, e.g., capacity to delay gratification and constructive use of aggression.

6. The development of gratification in goal-directed activities, precursors of the development of appropriate achievement motivation.

We have a considerable amount of knowledge to enable us to design environments in day-care and group care settings to foster the development of these characteristics and behavior patterns; but we need more precise knowledge than now exists of the relationship between specific kinds of experiences and personality, and adaptive functions and intellectual capacities. Only for extreme effects are the data convincing. The research findings point mainly to the limiting conditions, that is, to the critical levels of stimulation below which effects of deprivation become evident. It is more difficult to define optimal levels of stimulation. These can only be approximately specified in terms of our knowledge of the developmental level of the child and his individual idiosyncratic characteristics. In part, we can begin to define optimal levels and qualities of stimulation in relation to the central issues with which the child is faced at each developmental point. Ultimately, more precise definition of early environments should provide us with a clearer understanding of the important stimulus conditions on the basis of which we can design environments to elicit or control desirable behavior patterns.

Some of these issues are discussed in detail in the next four chapters.

❧ 2 ❧

The First Year of Life: The Infant

SALLY PROVENCE

This chapter proposes some general principles and concepts to be used as a framework for organizing some of our knowledge of children. Hopefully, such a framework will provide a practical approach to the care of young children in day care settings. The views expressed on the development of infants and young children come in part from clinical experience, in part from research, and in part from knowledge human beings have accumulated over centuries of living with and caring for their children. No claim is made that the presentation is a complete theory of child development or that it answers more than a few of the many important questions. Indeed, the need for continuing the search for greater understanding has never been more widely recognized.

The approach used here rests on a theoretical position which holds that development and the learning, which is an integral part

27

of development, come about through an interaction of the infant's inborn maturing system and the forces of the environment. Both somatic and mental innate factors are called successively into play according to a biological timetable unique to the human being (Hartmann, 1958). One of the needs of the infant is for an environment, that is, for a variety of stimuli and experiences, in which these maturing systems can be organized into action units and integrated with other functions and systems and successively higher levels serving adaptation and learning.

We take it for granted that innate characteristics play a role in respect to the body and its organ systems. But the influence of innate factors should be recognized in regard to mental development as well. The infant's constitution includes primitive forms of the mental equipment serving perception, motility, thinking, memory, and other abilities which help the individual gradually to perceive and deal with reality. The infant's constitution includes also instinctual (psychic) drives which have characteristic phases and go through various developments that are codetermined by endowment factors and by interaction with the environment. In the understanding of the personality development of the individual child as well as his physical development, therefore, it is essential to take into account both the innate characteristics and the environmental influences.

In speaking of the very young infant's environment, we refer mainly to the quantity and quality of maternal care under which the wide variety of sensorimotor experiences and the social and affective communications are subsumed. As the infant grows older, his environment enlarges to include his father and other family members, the "things" that are part of the physical world, and a rapidly growing variety of increasingly complex experiences that constitute his daily living. In this prolonged helplessness, the child is dependent upon the family, that is, upon a social structure for protection, care, and education. The role of the human parent as compared with other species is unique in the extent to which it influences the present and future development of the child (Erikson, 1959; Greenacre, 1960). The mother-child relationship is both a biological and social one. The crucial role of adequate nurturing care as a stimulating and organizing influence in the child's physical and psychological development has been amply documented (Chapin, 1915; Bowlby, 1951; Provence and Lipton, 1962; Spitz, 1945).

The concept of typical sequences and typical phases in a child's development has gained general acceptance. Each developmental phase is characterized by certain qualities and certain changes; there are tasks to be solved in each phase and there are specific vulnerabilities (Hartmann, 1958). Sequences in motor development are well known (Gesell and Amatruda, 1947; McGraw, 1943). The sequence of phases of psychosocial development has been outlined and linked to the developmental tasks that should be solved within each phase (Erikson, 1959). In respect to vulnerabilities, the common causes of anxiety in the child are also related to the phases of development: anxiety about the stranger in the early months, separation anxiety a little later, still later the fear of loss of love, and so on. We assume, moreover, that difficulties in the child's development occur when something disrupts the usual sequence. Each capability, each function, has an optimal time for its appearance and for its integration into the whole. While permanent problems do not necessarily result from interference with the optimal condition, clinical and research observations support the view that development may be temporarily or permanently distorted by experiences which are grossly "out of phase" with the child.

In summary, we have a threefold concept which can be stated as follows: The determinants of a child's development are (1) his innate characteristics, (2) the characteristics of the environment with all that this implies, and (3) the phase of the child's development in which a particular stimulus or experience occurs.

A General Observation

The translation of theory into recommendations for child care which can be put into practice (whether in the home or in other child-care situations) is not always an easy step. The concepts and principles to be presented here have to do with the need of the child for *continuity* of experience, with the *appropriateness* of the care and stimulation to his needs (quantity and quality of care), and with *timing*. The child's needs vary according to his stage of development, his individuality, and his previous experiences. These variations do not allow us to talk about a specific amount of care as being adequate or inadequate for all children. What is adequate for one child may be not nearly adequate for another. An experience that imposes a task which one child masters successfully and that strengthens him may be traumatic for another, and so on. Nevertheless, there are enough similarities in the needs and capacities of children of comparable ages, living under comparable conditions, to allow us to make some general recommendations about how their needs can be met. One can state rather generally what adults should provide infants and young children in any setting in order to promote healthy growth and development. No attempt is made here to specify how these recommendations could be followed in planning day-care programs. In Chapter 5, Lois Murphy translates them into operational definitions.

Fundamentals of Child Care

The most basic need of the infant is for a person, one who will respond to his distress signals, his need for comfort, for relief of tension, and for an interactive social partner. Emotional communication can be established with such a need-satisfying adult. The model is a devoted mother caring for her own child. By providing for her baby's bodily needs for food, rest, warmth, and relief from discomfort, she promotes his development. A host of stimuli and communications are implicit in this care. In addition, there is also a large component of protection. For example, she tones down what would be excessive stimuli, modifying the environment so as to introduce experiences that are appropriate for an infant of a particular age. She prevents him from getting into danger when he becomes mobile. What the mother or her substitute provides constitutes the most important experiences of the infant's life and affects not only his immediate development and learning, but also his developmental process over time. In early infancy, the kind of care that is given to satisfy bodily needs also stimulates emotional and cognitive development. Later, as there is increasing maturation and differentiation of the psychic and somatic systems, the child has both the capacity and need for more differentiated experiences.

The importance of this primary-attachment relationship to a specific person in infancy can hardly be overemphasized if one is concerned with optimal care. In the course of the first year, once the primary attachment is formed the infant develops the ability to relate to substitutes for the mother. He can benefit from outside contacts as long as they are firmly anchored in a tie to a maternal figure. In the day-care situation, the necessity of providing a main caretaker to whom the infant is encouraged to form a primary attachment will be influenced by the extent to which his own mother provides or can be helped to provide this kind of relationship. If she can do so, the day-care center will complement her care by widening and providing experiences and activities for the infant in her absence. If she is unable to care for him in a way that promotes his development and cannot be helped to do so, the child's best interest will be served if a main caretaker with a personalized interest in him can be provided during the time he is in the center.

Good "nurturing" or adequate care is a global term which needs amplification. The points which follow exemplify specific experiences and forms of stimulation which we believe to be of special significance for the child's development in his first year.

Adequate nourishment for the child's growth and health: The prevention of physical illness through protective measures. Seen broadly, nurture includes both the intake of sufficient calories and other nutrients to support growth and physical health, as well as the prevention of physical illness through immunizations and other measures. It means also attentiveness to symptoms of illness or delay in development. The provision for the physical health and growth of infants and young children in day-care centers is a subject of considerable importance in planning, but no attempt is made to deal with it in this chapter, since it is dealt with in detail by experts in the health field in other publications.*

A speaking social partner. It is not likely that language can develop adequately if the infant is not spoken to. The speech of the adult is one of the principal ways through which information comes to the infant about himself and his world, what he is, how he feels, and what he is doing. It provides information about people, objects, and experiences he encounters. At first, the adult responds to the child's meaningless babbling, reinforcing and interpreting it in such a way that his repertoire of sounds with specific meanings steadily increases. It is believed also that the verbal communications of the adult provide essential elements in the development, differentiation, and organization of the infant's inner world of thought, imagery, and emotions. Thus, both the child's own speech and his inner world of thought and general awareness are beneficially influenced by a speaking social partner and suffer in the absence of such a partner.

* See, for example, the pamphlet prepared by the Day Care Committee, Maternal and Child Health Section, American Public Health Association, *Children in Day Care with Focus on Health*, publication No. 444, Department of Health, Education, and Welfare, Children's Bureau, Washington, D.C., 1967.

An atmosphere which includes a reasonable amount of consistency and repetition. Quality and timing of care received from the familiar adults are involved in producing such a climate. Consistency and repetition in the child's experience help to create in him a physical and psychic state conducive to learning; that is, the child needs significant periods of time when he is free from major discomfort and excessive tension and is able to give attention to people and things in his environment. Such an atmosphere of consistency and repetition exists in most families and in most group care settings. However, situations on either side of this "reasonable" consistency and repetition are not uncommon. In the group care setting in particular, there is often excessive routinization and rigidity in schedules and programs, which tends to stifle the child's interests, play, and physical activity. On the other hand, it is not unusual for the other extreme to exist in many of the families of children who will be in day-care programs; namely, there is such a state of disorganization and inconsistency in the home environment that the child's development suffers.

Variety and contrast within the atmosphere created by consistency and repetition. Variety and contrast, we believe, sharpen the perceptions and create in the child *mild* tension states that call for an adaptive response. As long as a tension state is not so massive as to be disorganizing or paralyzing, it can serve as a stimulus to development. This concept has its practical applications in such things as the introduction of new activities, variety in toys, play experiences, and so on.

Toys and other playthings. Toys provide a variety of stimuli, challenges, and satisfactions because of their structure, texture, color, configuration, and other physical qualities. Thereby, they enhance perception and intellectual development. Toys are also important as objects upon which an infant can actively, physically discharge feelings of aggression or pleasure and excitement *without* evoking a response. While a responsive partner is essential to the infant's development, he also needs experience with materials in which his independent action and manipulation allow him to discover causal relationships, qualities of matter, and his own capacities for exploitation, experimentation, and self-regulation. Play, both with toys and with people, adds an important dimension to the child's life.

Physical handling through holding, cuddling, bathing, lifting, and touching. The stimulation provided in this way is especially significant for the development of gross motor skills and for the development of the body image. It is also one of the elements in the child's ability to become *active* in relation to the external environment, a capacity which is of great importance in his developmental progress. Action influences mental development and is, of course, in turn influenced by it. The development of methods of defending oneself against danger requires action: first, motoric; later, psychic. Action is essential to progress in the ability to master many of the developmental tasks of the first year of life.

Opportunities to move about, to play, and to utilize emerging skills and dispositions in a supportive and safe atmosphere. A combination of freedom and protection becomes increasingly important toward the end of the first year in the child's development toward independence and self-determination. Opportunities to enter actively into the possibilities afforded by the surroundings influence the child's development of the sense of self as distinct from others. They also are important in enlarging his inner world and stimulating the level of bodily development.

Limits and prohibitions appropriate to the age of the child. The support of self-regulation and cooperative behavior from the child. We must often deal with children who have experienced excessive tension and stress, when parental controls and education have either been too severe or too lax. However, we also recognize situations in which a young child's development is impeded because his environment has not supported and required of him the skills, controls, and adaptations of which he is capable.

The infant is born with the capacity to develop the ability to tolerate tension, to delay discharge of impulse, and to postpone gratification. These inhibitory mechanisms are a part of the infant's endowment and their antecedents are seen from the early days onward. However, these capacities are influenced in very important ways by the learning process and, of course, by the parents as the child's first educators. The process of education and socialization gives rise to tension and conflict within the child by requiring of him that he learn to adjust to some of the expectations and demands of society. Therefore, experiences of tension, inner conflicts, and frustrations are as essential to the development of the child as are the experiences of gratification and comfort referred to earlier.

The question of how much tension and conflict are favorable to optimal development is an important consideration for which we have as yet no definite answer. It appears safe to state that in infancy, at least, the necessary education and training of the child should take place in an atmosphere of loving attention. Two aspects are worth restatement: First, the environment should provide appropriate limits and prohibitions in a supportive atmosphere; second, the child himself brings to this situation a considerable capacity—partly innate, partly learned—for self-regulation.

Achievements of the First Year

Many of the characteristics in a child's development in the first year have been referred to or implied in the preceding pages. However, it seems appropriate to describe a few areas of development in order to illustrate developmental steps and to begin to sketch a picture of the living child, a sketch which is developed further in subsequent chapters.

Much of the muscle activity of a newborn baby is diffuse and random; he flails his arms, wriggles, and kicks. Yet some muscle activity is already organized into patterns that serve survival: for example, the sucking and rooting behavior. The first set of muscles over which the baby gains control are those of the eyes. During the first three months of life, he develops the ability to focus and follow; in short, he learns to look. Visual following stimulates the turning of his head, and he changes the position of his body in order to look at people or things or his own hand.

After three and one-half to four months, the baby is able to clasp his hands together when lying on his back. He uses his hands with increasing skill from this time on to touch, grasp, explore, and control things. By the time he is six to seven months old, he has gained control over the muscles which support his head and move his eyes well enough to pick up a toy, bang it, and pass it from one hand to another. He can easily get his thumb to his own mouth, reach his toes and all other parts of his own body, and hold tightly to something he wants. He also can roll over from back to front and back again, and keep his trunk and head erect when placed in a standing position. He learns to creep on hands and knees when about nine months old, and about this time he can pull himself into a standing position independently. Skill in creeping increases steadily, so that by the end of the first year most babies creep rapidly about the house or yard.

Learning to walk upright after having walked with support comes toward the end of the first year or shortly thereafter. At the same time, the infant has developed precision and control of his arms and hands and can pick up tiny objects such as crumbs or bits of fuzz with almost adult precision. He uses his forefinger to poke into things and a bit later to point to what he wants. His control over trunk, arms, and hands permits him to reach, grasp, pluck, poke, throw, and hit. Coordination of hand and eye is well developed (Gesell and Amatruda, 1947). The infant who is developing normally mentally and physically uses his motor capacities in a variety of ways which reflect his learning and some aspects of his personality development. By the end of the first year, he moves forward or away from things and people; he uses his hands to make contact and explore things, as well as to get rid of them. The development of body and hand skills, therefore, not only reflects the mastery of certain motor functions, but also provides him with some of the skills through which he copes with his environment and which facilitate further learning.

Speech, like other steps in development of the infant, comes about as a result of maturation of the neurologic apparatus stimulated in crucial ways by interaction with the environment. By the time he is a year of age, the infant usually has two or three specific words and can make all of the sounds he will ever require for speech. At this time he can recognize a number of common objects when they are named for him: car, light, cup, bottle, etc. The first phases of what later will be speech are spontaneous and responsive vocalizations and vocal signals of the infant. In the first months, the earliest noncrying vocalizations are throaty noises and gurgling sounds (Lewis, 1959). In the second and third months, the infant produces delightful, musical cooing sounds and chuckles in response to being talked to by the adult; in the fourth month, he laughs aloud. By six to seven months, there are recognizable vowel sounds and soon clearly enunciated consonants appear (Gesell and Amatruda, 1947). There are also vocal signals which the infant uses voluntarily and with increasing specificity to indicate his feeling state. By age seven to eight months, the vowels and consonants are combined in such sounds as *mama, baba, dadda*. When these sounds first appear they are not used as names, but they gain specific meaning in the last quarter of the first year. Integrity of the sensory and motor apparatus is essential to the development of speech. It is assumed to be important to speech development when the infant hears his own voice. A circular reaction is postulated in which an infant vocalizes, hears himself, and is stimulated to further vocalization. He also experiences body sensations that are a part of the act of phonation.

In addition, the presence and attention of the mother appear to influence the development of speech in several ways in the child's first year. The general stimulation associated with acts of mothering promotes the child's vocalization. Mutual imitation develops, which encourages the use of an ever-increasing variety of sounds. The mother's speech is important as one of the carriers of emotional communications. Through her response to the infant—in her actions and in her speech—she also identifies elements of his world for him. He gradually learns to recognize many aspects of inner and outer reality —people, objects, actions, and feelings—because she provides the appropriate experiences. The syllables that become the child's first words probably gain their meaning primarily because of the response of the parents to the infant's vocalizations. For example, the *mama* and *dadda* sounds, which are at first nonspecific, become names probably because of the strong affective response to these sounds (Escalona, 1953). Adults react as though the infant intends these sounds as names and in so doing give them meaning. The process through which these syllables gain specific meaning in the language development of the infant is presumed to be an example of one way in which the adult influences the process of differentiation in the infant's mental functioning. In other words, the parents' repetition, labeling, and affective response to the baby's reactions, feelings, interest, and vocalizations are very important not only to the development of meaningful speech, but also to his recognition of himself, of other persons, and of many things in his world.

In addition to the development of language there is an enormous amount of nonverbal communication that goes on between the infant and other people. In the beginning the mother "reads" the infant's behavior, interprets how he feels, and does something with or for him. For example, she responds to his feeling state, deciding that he is hungry, cold, or in some other way uncomfortable, or that he is comfortable and happy. As the child's own ability to perceive, to discriminate, and to remember develop through combined effects of maturation and experience, especially in interactions with people, he begins in turn to be able to "read" the mother. He recognizes and reacts in quite selective ways to her nonverbal communications. This is most easily visible in respect to the mother's affective state. Feelings of anxiety or distress, pleasure or calmness, are impressively "contagious" for the infant (Escalona, 1953). In addition, however, he also learns to recognize various expressions, gestures, and actions that signal a certain event, such as preparation of his meal or an outing, arrival of another person, leave taking and so on.

The growing awareness of these signals is implicit in what we call normal development and reflects the development of the perceptual apparatus, the ability to discriminate, the capacity for anticipation and memory, as well as progress in the child's relationships with people. In his relationships with people, the well-cared-for infant changes markedly in the period of a year. Whereas in the very beginning there is no evidence of recognition or feeling for another person, by the time he is one year old the infant recognizes his mother as a person of special importance, can remember her for a brief period when she is absent, and has developed what has been called a sense of confidence or trust that she will take care of him (Erikson, 1959; Benedek, 1938). With the growing awareness of her importance to him, there comes also a reaction of anxiety at being separated from her. It is important to note that he has also developed some capacity to accept substitutes for her, as long as they are able to meet his needs. Relationships with others develop gradually, becoming steadily more complicated and more specific. However, the early stages in this development are easily observable in infancy. One can be fairly confident that the infant can correctly interpret observations of his feelings, preferences, and dependency upon others. The infant's behavior reflects not only his ability to perceive and interact, but also the quantity and quality of the nurturing. The baby's relationships to others are also permanently colored by the fact that the essential role of those he loves includes experiences which frustrate him as well as experiences which give him pleasure. His most intense feelings, therefore, in the early years, both positive and negative, are attached to those who are closest to him.

In the first year, the infant also develops an interest in toys and in play. This is rooted in his relationships to people but develops its own characteristics and functions. The child's play provides him not only with experiences of pleasure, but also with an avenue to the solving of problems through activity and through fantasy. It is also one of the ways by which he begins to understand and communicate with others. More is said about play in the next three chapters. It is sufficient to describe here some of the early phases (see also Provence and Ritvo, 1961).

The first steps in the development of play occur in the social interaction between infant and adult, and the earliest playthings of the baby are parts of his own body and that of the mothering person. The first toys that are given are usually rattles, "cradle gyms," and other objects that are suspended over the crib for an infant to look at and, later, to reach for. Play with his own body and with toys, and social play with the adult develop together in the first year. The infant of four months plays with his hands and a little later with his feet. During the first six months he gradually develops the ability to reach out and grasp a toy which he mouths, bangs, inspects, and manipulates with steadily increasing skill. In the second six months he is able to handle more than one toy at a time and to combine them in various ways: He can put a block inside a box, bang two toys together, etc. He also develops the ability to remember a toy long enough to find it when it is out of sight and may also develop strong preferences for some toys over others. His play with the adult also goes through various stages. Beginning in the early months with smiling and cooing to the adult, he later initiates contact with another person by smiling, vocalizing, or reaching out to touch or tug. By eight to nine months, he plays such social games as Peek-a-boo, So-big and Bye-bye with great glee and shortly later develops other little "tricks" with which he captures the attention of others for the pleasure in their response. His laughter, his first words, and many other sounds also become part of a playful interchange with others. Play then has many meanings and many functions. In addition, a study of a child's play reveals much about his intellectual and emotional development.

Other aspects of the development during the first year might be described, but the foregoing brief descriptions of these four—motor development, speech, relationships with others, and play—have permitted us to specify some of the important areas and to suggest their interdependence.

REFERENCES

Benedek, T. 'Adaptation to Reality in Early Infancy. *Psychoanalytic Quarterly,* 7: 200–214, 1938.
Bowlby, J. *Maternal Care and Mental Health.* World Health Organization Monograph No. 2. Geneva: World Health Organization, 1951.
Chapin, H. D. Are Institutions for Infants Necessary? *Journal of the American Medical Association,* 64: 1–3, 1915.
Erikson, E. H. Identity and the Life Cycle. *Psychological Issues,* vol. 1, no. 1. New York: International Universities Press, 1959.
Escalona, S. K. Emotional Development in the First Year. In M. J. E. Senn (Ed.), *Problems of Infancy and Childhood.* New York: Josiah Macy, Jr., Foundation, 1953, pp. 11–92.

Gesell, A., and C. S. Amatruda. *Developmental Diagnosis.* 2d ed. New York: Hoeber, 1947.

Greenacre, P. Considerations Regarding the Parent-Infant Relationship. *International Journal of Psychoanalysis,* 41: 571–584, 1960.

Hartmann, H. *Ego Psychology and the Problem of Adaptation.* New York: International Universities Press, 1958.

Lewis, M. M. *How Children Learn to Speak.* New York: Basic Books, 1959.

McGraw, M. B. *The Neuromuscular Maturation of the Human Infant.* New York: Columbia University Press, 1943.

Provence, S., and R. C. Lipton. *Infants in Institutions.* New York: International Universities Press, 1962.

———, and S. Ritvo. Effects of Deprivation on Institutionalized Infants: Disturbances in Development of Relationships to Inanimate Objects. *The Psychoanalytic Study of the Child,* vol. 16. New York: International Universities Press, 1961, pp. 189–205.

Spitz, R. A. Hospitalism: An Inquiry into the Genesis of Psychiatric Conditions in Early Childhood. *The Psychoanalytic Study of the Child,* vol. 1. New York: International Universities Press, 1945, pp. 53–74.

Development During the Second Year: The One-Year-Old

ELEANOR PAVENSTEDT

In discussing the developmental status of children during the second year, we cannot make a rigid delimitation of time. Actually, the second year cannot stand alone. If development is viewed as an epigenetic process, what the child achieves during the second year rests upon the growth of the first year and might well be lost without further strengthening in the third year.

Children, even from the same family, differ in their achievements during the first and second years. For example, the onset of walking occurs anywhere between nine and fifteen months. Cultural differences further widen the range of achievements. When it comes to eating, some children eat what their parents eat; but in other cultures, Japan for instance, the child is still at the breast. Toilet-training customs also vary widely. In some countries, the child is trained in infancy; as yet, we have no way of estimating what proportion of these children have to be retrained when innervation of the sphincters matures sufficiently to permit voluntary control. In Western countries, the psychoanalytic school of thought advocates postponing training to the age when voluntary control is possible, approximately fifteen to sixteen months. (The rationale behind this recommendation will be discussed later.)

Disregarding cultural differences for the time being and averaging the differences among children in our own culture, we can identify certain areas of development which are expected during this second year. The areas of most rapid growth are locomotion and the refinement of other motor skills, socialization, speech, the development of initiative and autonomy, and of a sense of self. In addition, there comes the recognition that persons and objects remain constant, that is, they continue to exist when out of sight. Progress in each of these areas arouses specific conflicts which require certain adaptations on the part of the adult. Mastery can be supported and sometimes stimulated, aided and abetted by certain behaviors on the part of the adult and by specific pieces of equipment. Each of these areas will be discussed in the context of the care a child might receive outside his own home, although the expectations of the adult are in many instances a conscious replication of responses which might be more or less unconsciously produced by the child's own mother. Finally, however, a few suggestions will be made which will pertain only to the situation where care outside the home is being undertaken.

The socialization process that takes place during the second year does not easily proceed unless an adult to whom the child has developed a strong tie is available, at least a part of each day, and is responsive to the child as an individual. The importance of this key relationship cannot be overemphasized. The feeling of trust and deepening affection, the gradual fusing of ambivalent emotions, the establishment of controls, the growing awareness of the self, and the distinction between the self and the outside world are seriously impaired and fail to become stable integrated parts of the personality unless this condition is fulfilled.*

The primary adult—the mother or her surrogate—must be a source of affection, appreciation, and security. She becomes so only

* Such a statement seems analogous to suggesting a "critical period" in socialization, but the concept does not apply during the second year of life. The concept of critical periods, coming as it does from ethology and referring to a brief period during which imprinting takes place, has been applied to the period of "supraindividual smiling" early in the infant's life. Even there, the concept has been disputed (Ambrose, 1963; Gray, 1958).

when her handling of the child and her expectations and prohibitions are consistent over time. Unless the child can anticipate her reactions, he becomes confused. When there is mutual understanding, the caretaker will know how much change from his ordinary routine the small child can tolerate, in what way he reacts to strange events and new stimulations, and what ministrations on her part will help him reconstitute his psychic balance. By consistency we do not mean sameness, but rather an inner consistency, a gradation of the demands made on the child in keeping with his development and a careful timing and dosage of frustrations.

There is a considerable body of clinical evidence to support these contentions. One well-known clinical experiment involving children at this age took place in a war nursery directed by Anna Freud (Freud and Burlingham, 1944). Children were cared for—dressed, bathed, served food, etc.—by any worker who cared for their group. Noting that "certain steps in development were slow in coming [and] baby habits were not outgrown," the staff followed the lead given by a number of the children who "suddenly showed strong preference for certain workers." They established six small family groups of four children, each with its own substitute mother. The result of this arrangement was astonishing in its force and immediacy. At first, jealousy and possessiveness led to considerable anxiety and unhappiness. The weeping and fighting that ensued lasted two to three weeks. However, as soon as the children learned to trust the return of their substitute mother and experienced the feeling that she belonged to them, they quieted down. Freud and Burlingham note the salutary effect of this move on the toilet training of several particularly recalcitrant children and "a remarkable effect on the development of speech" in the entire group.

If a child is cared for by others than his own mother, the extent of his need for a strong consistent tie with someone in his second "home" will vary with several factors:

1. The length of time the toddler is separated from his own mother in terms of number of hours daily. Qualitative differences emerge with such quantitative differences as a half day, a full day or, the full twenty-four hours. In addition, the span of time over which the daily or continuous separations occur.

2. The mothering capacity of the toddler's own mother.

3. The age at which separation first takes place, the length of separation at that time, and the adequacy of the early surrogate mother.

4. Innate or acquired reaction to separation in the child; his capacity for deep attachments.

5. The mother's attitude to recurrent or prolonged separation and her observable reaction to each separation and reunion.

6. The degree to which the child's tie to his own mother is respected by her surrogates.

We have little idea concerning minimal needs of different children. And even when the above factors are weighed and evaluated, a recurring question must be faced: Minimal needs for what? To prevent delinquency sometime in the future? To facilitate school learning ability? To further the degree of maturation to the equivalent of an average middle-class child between one and two years old? We have to establish goals before we can consider minimal requirements.

Since research evidence will not be available for many years to come, evidently our safest procedure is to approximate the home environment that seems to have contributed to the steps in development which we will describe and which have repeatedly been noted by others. These steps appear to occur in the average middle-class child in our culture. If a child is in a situation which necessitates shuttling back and forth between two environments, accomplishment of this timetable with a second set of adults is a considerable task that calls for the most thoughtful planning and experimentation followed by responsible assessment. To complicate this task, attempting to *optimize* certain functions not only makes the analysis of what has happened infinitely more complex, but also may further jeopardize the individual's normal harmonious progress.

Locomotion and Other Motor Skills

Some children may still be crawling or hitching themselves along at one year; others, although they have learned to stand and walk, will still be tottering and unsure of themselves; they too will crawl when tired, when they have fallen down, or when they want to get somewhere in a hurry. The progression from tottering to steady walking and then to running and climbing, from throwing away to pursuing what is thrown, and from pushing to pulling proceeds in keeping with the child's thirst to conquer the unknown, when he is granted freedom to explore and is protected only when there is real danger of his hurting himself.

Increasing separation anxiety is the conflict that ensues from this development. The child frequently expresses this conflict by alternately moving away and returning again to his mother. Sometimes he clings and cries in a most demanding way; sometimes he wants to be held for a moment to cuddle or sit on her lap. It may be enough just to be in her orbit to "refuel," as Margaret Mahler (1963, p. 314) puts it. Often the child will want to run after her or imitate her.

Most children need little stimulation toward locomotion and thrive with praise for gains in proficiency, however small. Some children are slow to walk and prefer to remain closer to the ground. There is no evidence that slow walkers develop more slowly in general. Nevertheless, since delayed walking may be a sign of over-all retardation, the cause should be carefully assessed. When called for, appropriate treatment can be instituted. Encouragement must be carefully timed and dosed so as not to have the opposite effect. (See Chapter 8 on individuation of the environment.)

At first helping hands should be available, to be withdrawn whenever the toddler is ready to venture forth by himself. Sturdy chairs and sofas with soft rounded corners, some within arm's length, others at a gradually more challenging distance, are helpful to the cruising child. Later they can be climbed on. A low ladder with several steps and a wide platform on top serves climbing efforts as well. Shchelovanova and Aksarina (1960) advocate a "mountain" with steps leading up and a graded descent on the other side. By providing needed support, doll carriages, trucks, and other wheel toys with handles at appropriate heights permit the tottering child to venture further.

When plenty of space is available, the child spends most of his time in gross motor activity. His urge to explore can be utilized to lead him into many different experiences. Boys tend to be more active and more experimental in their approach to things; the urge to take apart and to put back together begins early. Girls, on the other hand, are more restrained and dependent on mother's approval. This is a generalization, of course, and the reverse should be no cause for alarm. In the perceptual field, Montessori-type material can introduce tactile experiences, such as the feeling of different materials, shapes, and weights. Music and other rhythmic sounds are enjoyed by one-year-olds, and they will readily imitate simple songs, rhythmic noise making, and movements to music. They will learn to push objects of different shapes through the appropriate holes in a box. At this age, it will do no harm to introduce concepts of simple grouping when toys are put away. At this age, also, children enjoy searching for small objects hidden behind a chair or drape while they look on; later, they learn to cover their eyes while the object is being hidden.

At home, one-year-olds particularly enjoy getting into things used by adults: pots and pans, ashtrays, waste baskets, and boxes of detergent. The staff in a day-care center would do well to set aside certain of these items for the child to play with and should likewise see that harmful substances are not accessible.

Toward the latter part of the second year, the child can be introduced to toys that require a finer degree of muscle coordination. Ring pegs serve this purpose, as well as screw toys. Simple building with large blocks also develops skill; subsequent destruction gives the child a happy feeling of power. Here again boys take the lead. Hammering pegs through holes on a pegboard can be a good outlet for discharge of aggression. Differences in sizes of objects can be pointed out and verbalized for the child, even though it will be some time before he can apply his recognition of sizes in a meaningful way. Other pieces of equipment should be available for gradual presentation. These would include push and pull toys, simple figures that are put together with three or four pieces, simple jigsaw puzzles with large pieces, sturdy doll furniture, plastic dishes, plastic tools, large balls, carts, trucks, cars, wooden trains, simple guns or pistols, and child-size fireman or cowboy hats. Soft animals and large rag dolls should be available for cuddling and maltreating.

Wax crayons and paper should be available for less active periods. Bright colors, particularly red, are attractive to most children. It comes naturally to the caretaker interested in the child's productions to name the colors, even though children under two will seldom be able to make the verbal distinctions.

Play at this age serves various functions. It is principally imitative and seeks to re-create in miniature what the child sees about him, what the adults do. During this year children have a great urge to do actively what they have experienced passively. This has begun already during the first year and continues throughout life. In the second year, such play is often particularly intense. In the process, objects are put to many uses and explored for their qualities by all the perceptual channels. Beneath the children's activities one can perceive a constant stream of fantasy that makes the activity so absorbing.

Care must be taken not to overstimulate children. Every child has his pace and tolerance, his own style of moving ahead. In addition, lightning-like shifts in mood should be expected from the children. After a period of great activity the child may quite suddenly need some intimate contact. The caretaker may move by the child's side at a table while he scribbles or looks at a sturdy picture book. The child may want to be in her lap to be fondled. Here again the individual child differs and these differences should be responded to.

Self-protection

As running and climbing begins, most children have to be helped to learn to protect their bodies. Toddlers venture out before they recognize distances and heights. Caretakers must be alert to catch them before they really hurt themselves, at the same time putting into gestures and words that they care about and want to protect the child's body. Very gradually the child assumes this care himself, but many have not developed awareness of danger or feelings of self-protection by their second birthday.

Development of the Concept of Object Permanence

In the course of the second year, the child normally learns that when mother disappears from his perceptual field, she continues to exist. If he is away from his home, the caretakers can assist him to verify this discovery by making frequent reference to the child's mother during the day. Simultaneously, he watches for objects, such as balls, to reappear from under furniture. This awareness of a trajectory in space enlarges his whole concept of space. The realization that his mother continues to exist spreads over to other people. Thus, he learns to gradually ascribe a separate existence to all adults who are important to him and also to distinguish himself from them. He slowly evolves a sense of self which consists of his growing perceptions, his feelings, his experiences, his capacities, and his awareness of his body and its functions.

Autonomy and Reality Testing are Fostered by Constructive Controls

Once a child has a grasp of the constancy of people and objects and is aware of himself as a separate entity he can begin to adapt to the world of reality, its opportunities and limitations, its pleasures and frustrations. In order to explore with zest, the permanency of a "home base" must be a certainty. It will not be home base unless he feels that his urgent needs are understood and responded to specifically and with feeling. When granted initiative to explore, he will be increasingly self-propelling and will strengthen his feeling of autonomy, the cornerstone of much later achievement.

The one-year-old's persistent "no" is an emphatic expression of autonomous feelings. As Fraiberg (1959, p. 64) writes:

> He says "no" with splendid authority to almost any question addressed to him. Very often it is a "no" pronounced in the best of spirits and doesn't even signal an intention. . . . It's a political gesture, a matter of maintaining party difference while voting with the opposition on certain issues. . . . It's a kind of declaration of independence, but there is no intention to unseat the Government.

Fear of masculine aggression and sexuality, particularly as it is expressed in delinquency, may lead mothers to stifle autonomy strivings, especially in their boys, and to exercise "smothering" controls on their behavior at a very early age, sometimes as early as the first year. Curiosity and initiative seem to be innate, but we have seen them practically stifled by an overcontrolling adult. The means of control can vary: withdrawal of the person, of love, of assistance and reassurance, or just the threat of these can serve this purpose.

The initial battle for autonomy may take place over bedtime, self-feeding or any other form of constraint. Stifled autonomous urges may be the foundation of the passivity seen in so many fathers whose children are brought to child-guidance clinics. Toddlers should not be frustrated or coerced beyond their individual tolerance. Frustration should serve a constructive not suppressive purpose.

However, at least in our culture, an occasional clash of wills is a necessary ingredient for the development of a healthy character. When the toddler is obliged to adapt himself to a few consistent limits, his self-concept and his reality-testing function are thereby strengthened. When judiciously managed, these obligations will not threaten his autonomy; in fact, one can begin now to invoke a sense of partnership in him. The experience of transgression against the adult's prohibition and of incurring anger is also necessary. When the child and the adult emerge from such a clash unscathed, the child is reassured that his own and the adult's aggression are not too dangerous or destructive.

The child is apt to express his autonomy in activities of self-care, such as dressing and eating. In day care, allowances have to be made not only for the child's inherent pace, but also for the kind of experience and training he has had at home. Whereas individual achievement should be encouraged and praised, periods of regression, frequent at this age, should be allowed for. Some toddlers have little opportunity to get their hands on (or into) food. They make up for lost time when free to do so outside the home. Giving the child a chance to mess with other materials, such as mud or paints, will reduce his desire to use food in exploring textures or for rebelling. One-year-olds will need help in learning to drink from a cup and in eating with a spoon. Again, assistance should be supportive rather than intrusive.

Socialization

We have stressed the one-year-old's concern with adults that are important to him, because the child does not perceive his peers as little "people" like himself. He treats them like dolls; he pushes and pulls at them and attacks them when they get in his way or have something he wants. He may be brought to understand that he is hurting them by patient explanation and by being helped to recognize the feelings that give rise to certain facial expressions and cries in his little victim. Before long it may be possible to help him control his anger by verbalizing his own feelings. Gradually, the adult has to express some disapproval which must be gauged to the child's sensitivity. Separating him from another child may be necessary for a time. Praise for generous gestures may be voluble. Calling an act of generosity to the attention of the other children may substitute for adult praise.

The presence of a pet increases the children's interest in observation and conveys some further notion of solicitude. They can first observe at a distance, watching as the adults or older siblings feed and otherwise care for the pet. Eventually they learn to handle gently and assist in caretaking themselves. An adult should be present to protect an animal whenever it is outside its cage, as a child may be thoughtless or accidentally rough. The adult is needed also because sadistic impulses may break through at any time. The child's impulse to hurt, however, need not be regarded as alarming, unless, of course, it is carried to extremes.

Besides rapid mood changes and petulant demands for attention and possession, the caretaker must be prepared for the child's repeated testing of her endurance and of the limits she sets. In a group, even more than at home where infinite concessions are apt to be made, the one-year-old has to learn to live with others in a world full of things that cannot be touched, pulled, climbed on, or knocked over. He has to discover that the beloved adult can firmly check him and nevertheless remain available for soothing caresses. He also needs the experience of occasionally transgressing limits and of incurring the anger of his caretaker without thereupon losing his or her love. He has to be able to hit her on occasion and to discover that he does not demolish her. The security of flexible routine assists in the socialization process. Shchelovanova and Aksarina (1960) believe that the routines should run in a sequence of sleeping–feeding–playing–sleeping, etc. They believe that well-rested children eat better and that they become tired as they play. The sequence seems reasonable and is worth exploring. However, the pattern usually followed in the American culture is eating–sleeping–playing.

Toilet Training

Control of bowels and urine is such an important component of the socialization process that it deserves to be discussed separately. The conflict of giving or withholding in relation to mother's expectation and the struggle of wills may become quite intense. Finally, acceptance of cleanliness in toilet habits signifies the child's willingness to give up certain pleasures in order to obtain approval and love of the cherished adult. At the least, the child substitutes something akin to thoughtful control for previous disregard of the related physiological functions.

Advocates of the psychoanalytic point of view consider the child's willingness to accede to the wishes of others—at a time when he himself can make the decision and choose between two alternatives —an important model for the entire process of socialization. One might call it an early decisive exercise in self-control. For the sake of a loved person, he gives up infantile disregard—and often pleasure— and learns to open and close his sphincters at an appropriate place and time. It is not surprising that a burst of speech often follows this attainment, since by voluntarily accepting the symbolic vocal form in use by those who surround him, he becomes a member of the community as he does when he accepts the necessity for cleanliness.

If the training process is rigidly uncompromising and fails to take into account other stresses bearing down on the child, such character traits as stubbornness, negativism, possessiveness, great cleanliness, and painstaking orderliness may at this time be consolidated. In some cultures, these personality traits are valued; in others, they interfere with congenial adaptation in later life.

The sense of shame often appears at this time, and in many cultures it is capitalized upon to bring about conformity to social usages. In other cultures where self-confidence and the assurance of one's value is an important attribute, it may be very hampering. Adult teasing at this age may be experienced as a sadistic act and be unnerving to the child, or it may be responded to in turn.

Actually, children living in groups are more easily trained than those at home. However, recent emphasis that every child develop a relationship with one particularly important adult in the group setting has introduced the conflict of giving or withholding in relation to this adult. Even so, the struggle will, in most instances, not be as intense as with his own mother.

In a day-care center it is easier to provide for endless hours of play with water and sand than at home. This messy play may substitute for the welcome feelings of wet and soiled diapers and for the urge to play with excrement. Caretakers should be informed that feces play is a normal form of experimentation, however, so that they do not overreact when it occurs. Nevertheless, they need not suppress distaste for the smell and sight of feces, since these are normal sentiments of the people that surround the child and he may as well acquire them. The caretakers should also be helped to be tolerant of excessive reactions on the part of some children. Occasionally, for example, the child's developed disgust spreads over to certain foods and materials, such as modeling clay or finger paints. These items can be temporarily avoided.

Plaintive concern over injuries often appears now. Fear of haircuts or of going down the toilet or the drain in the bathtub requires comforting reassurance. Possessiveness of toys as well as of adults and sometimes of another child is a normal characteristic, and the training to yield something or to take turns may suffer a severe setback. Many children collect a number of articles which they want to carry around with them wherever they go. Filling and emptying becomes a great preoccupation and toys that satisfy this need are essential.

Children are temperamentally different in regard to the urgency of their needs and demands, as well as in their willfulness and domination of others. Caretakers need to recognize that although these traits make for difficulty at this age, they may, when patiently modified, be valuable characteristics in later life. When a child seems to be embattled with a particular adult, it will be easier to introduce another into the situation to whom the child can accede without "losing face."

Development of Speech

Children between twelve and eighteen months usually carry on with a continual stream of jargon in the course of their play. Occasional phrases can be distinguished as comprehensible words. However, when directly in contact with an adult, the child can verbalize many of his simple wishes, can designate objects, and can imitate adult speech, often after a delay. Sometime during the second half of this year, there is a marked push forward in the use of speech. The child substitutes words in general use around him for the jargon he previously enjoyed in an autistic way. As previously noted, the acquisition of toilet controls and communicative speech frequently coincide. According to Piaget (1926) the child at this point abandons his egocentric position and accepts the use of words used by those around him for the sake of communication. It is an enormous step forward in the socialization process. Since children who spend most of their time in groups of peers tend to be slow talkers, it is important for the adults in charge to encourage verbal communication. They will be obliged to listen carefully to understand the child's first speech as many mothers or more often older siblings do.

Unless words spoken to young children are in tune with their thoughts and feelings and excited interest at that moment, they will pass over him as water over pebbles. A child eating at a table may be thinking of his mother or the rabbit he fed that morning or some anticipated play, while the teacher points out the colors of the cups or exclaims upon their round shape. Most middle-class mothers will make a sentence from one or two words the toddler says and gradually help him elaborate his sentences and correct his pronunciation. Since the staff will be preoccupied with many menial tasks, it may be well to remind them to do this at times. It would be unfortunate, though, to rob them of spontaneity in their interaction with the children by overemphasis on teaching. Mutual pleasure in a child's discovery or achievement, enthusiastic response to the endless "Look at me's," and acclamations that draw in the entire peer group are the best stimuli to further effort. They have the additional value of enhancing the child's self-esteem.

There seems to be some evidence that by eighteen months, when most children begin to talk in simple and combined phrases, they have already absorbed some notions of syntax. These will be supported by the adults' attention to completing the child's verbalizations and making simple well-structured sentences with them.

Development of the Sense of Self

The development of autonomy is interwoven with and supports a growing sense of self. We have already spoken of the child's gradual ability to conceive of an object's or a person's existence even when it is outside his perceptual range. Piaget has assigned this advance to the child's now having a mental representation of the object or person. Likewise, mental representation plays a vital role in the development of the child's self-concept.

The nucleus of a self-concept is a representation of the physical self. In the first year of life, the child's image of his body is gradually formed as he is held, fondled, and caressed, as he encounters the sides of his crib, discovers his hands, strokes his face and hair, plays with his feet, and slaps his stomach and genitals. During the second year, vocabulary games indicating parts of the body can be introduced during body care. Children can be helped to strengthen their sense of self by the caretaker's appreciative comments of their looks, their bodily skills and their productions. Safeguarding and displaying their crayon and paint work enhances a child's self-image. The feeling of having a desirable self is supported by "hide-and-seek" games in which the adult actively looks for the child and exclaims joyfully when he is found.

In the second year, most children become very defensive about having their bodies manipulated by others. They will fight having to lie down, being diapered and dressed. While such resistance is a nuisance to the caretaker, it should be recognized as a healthy expression of self-protection and autonomy, and procedures should be adapted to it. A general tendency of adults to tease the child must be guarded against. Family members can be helped to control this tendency when they participate in the care of the children at the center.

Children who spend much of their lives in a group are especially in need of a place of their own, a cubby or locker with shelves and hooks for their clothes and other precious possessions. These items become transitional objects linking home and center. Safeguarding them helps a child master the anxiety inherent in separations and gives him a sense of continuity (Winnicott, 1953).

Even though parents may not recognize the importance of a plaything as a transitional object, the center should be educated to understand its value. A treasured item may well be used in reverse, being taken home from the center and back again. This device and similar techniques can help a child to maintain an undivided sense of self despite his two very different environments. As many family members as possible can be introduced into the center's life and given positions of authority in keeping with their age.

In speaking of himself, the one-year-old may not progress beyond "me" in the course of this year. When he arrives at "I," we can be sure that some experience has taken place which gives rise to a feeling of self-respect, of conflict mastered, of autonomy expressed against opposition. The growing recognition of the self may depend in large measure on the toddler's identification with an individual who is exceptionally important to him.

Sexual Differentiation

Unless he has a twin of the opposite sex or grows up in close proximity to a child of a different sex close to his own age, the child who is at home during his second year of life usually has little awareness of the difference in sexes. At this age, children play quite indiscriminately with material which usage ascribes to one sex or the other.

Awareness of differences in sex may come earlier for the child in group care, since the children are free to observe each other during toileting. Every center should have several men (janitor, psychologist, or administrator) on its staff who mingle freely with the children and serve as models for identification. They will find themselves very much in demand. Play material serving sexual roles should be available. Plastic tools, nuts, and bolts serve for masculine identification; dishes and dolls with clothes that can be easily taken off and put on, stand for women's work. However, both types will be used by both boys and girls. As they approach the age of two, children of both sexes will enjoy a doll corner with large dolls and sturdy furniture, pots and pans, etc. In this intimate setting, play will be more representational. While often playing out roles indiscriminately and alternately, the children may gradually assume and feel more comfortable with the role that is appropriate to their sex. Even though they do not stress the difference, caretakers may comment on the fact that someday the child will be a "daddy" or a "mommy."

Accompanying the growing awareness of their bodies, toddlers will increasingly express concern about any bruise or blemish, often imaginary, which can be magically healed by a kiss or a bandage. Reassurance concerning bodily strength, wholeness, and capacity for restitution is helpful in building the child's trust in his body.

Summary

Before the age of two, only beginnings are made in logical, ordered thinking, the ability to generalize, categorize, and abstract. In later years, education of the preschool child concerns itself with supplanting the expression of instinctual strivings, feelings of omnipotence, and magical thinking with control and appreciation of the feelings of others as well as an acceptance of one's own limitations.

Special Needs Outside the Home

We come now to a few specific requirements for the everyday life of the one- to two-year-old in a group setting. As a start, there should be a basic framework. A routine free from compulsive rigidity helps one-year-olds to learn to anticipate what is coming and to get a sense of order and security, which is a necessary foundation for planning, postponing, and modifying basic urges. It is helpful when the adult verbalizes what is going on, as well as what comes before and after. Often children enjoy hearing songs about the daily happenings, spiced with personal touches about the behavior of each child. Gradually, one or another will join in the singing about the rhythms of life and the center.

Since breakfast in the homes of many children may be disorganized if not altogether absent, the day at the center should begin with warm cereal, a warm drink, and crackers or toast. The children will not all arrive at the same time, so the person in charge can be particularly responsive to each child as he comes in. The child will need some help with feeding. When the mother or other family member has time, she can be included in the breakfast conversation, possibly in the meal, and actually help the child with his food. Breakfast can probably be served in the playroom, so that each child can slip away and play when he is finished. Whatever medical checkups are needed can be taken care of by the appropriate person in the course of this play time. A nap will soon be in order. Many children from families needing day care are accustomed to lying in their cribs, playing and napping alternately while the adult sleeps well into the morning.

The prenap preparation may include cleaning, changing, and diapering some children. The area set aside for sleeping should be kept well aired and at low temperature (60°–65°). Sleeping children should always be supervised.

As the children awaken one by one they can be changed, cleaned, and diapered individually with attention to their idiosyncrasies and acceptance of each child's mood and pace on awakening. An exchange of caresses, body games, mirror games, and all forms of communication should be introduced at this time. During the first months of the second year, most children do not like to be held down or restrained in the course of changing clothes or during other routines. Patient respect for the child's need for body integrity should dictate tactics for body care.

When all the children are up and dressed, a midday meal is served. Beginning at about sixteen to eighteen months, the little girls can help bring the plastic dishes to the table. The staff can unobtrusively assist the children as they independently climb in their chairs, feed themselves, and drink from their cups. Eating is usually not a problem for these children in a group setting unless toilet training stimulates a reaction of disgust to foods of certain colors or consistencies. Appetites may vary a good deal from day to day. If a child is not eating well, he can be given encouragement and help with feeding, but ups and downs in appetite should not arouse concern. The consultation of a dietitian in the center will assure well-balanced meals and can have a beneficial effect on the diet served in the homes.

After toileting, the main play period for children of sixteen to eighteen months begins, indoors or outdoors as weather and opportunity provide. Those who are walking and running freely require enough space to permit these activities. Following the play period the children who are not picked up to return home will require another nap, preceded and followed by the usual toileting procedure. Many children will have been called for during the latter part of the afternoon. Despite their recent nap, the length of the separation from mother and home will be taking its toll. Activities at this time will need to be more sedentary with increased intimacy and physical closeness to the adults. Infantile behavior such as mouthing objects and demanding attention will occur. Such behavior should not be corrected. Instead, simple ways of meeting the children's needs should be found.

When mothers carry a full-time job, the center can offer an evening meal to the family which they will serve themselves. Such a practice serves as a transitional function during which day care and family care overlap. Furthermore, the parents are then free to spend the few hours they have with their children in mutual interests and concerns, undisturbed play, and communication.

REFERENCES

Ambrose, J. A. The Concept of a Critical Period for the Development of Social Responsiveness. In B. M. Foss (Ed.), *Determinants of Infant Behaviour*, vol. 2. New York: Wiley, 1963, pp. 201–226.

Fraiberg, S. *The Magic Years*. New York: Scribner's, 1959.

Freud, A., and D. T. Burlingham. *War and Children*. New York: International Universities Press, 1944.

Gray, P. H. Theory and Evidence of Imprinting in Human Infants. *Journal of Psychology*, 46: 155–166, 1958.

Mahler, M. Thoughts about Development and Individuation. *The Psychoanalytic Study of the Child*, vol. 18. New York: International Universities Press, 1963, pp. 307–342.

Piaget, J. *The Language and Thought of the Child*. New York: Harcourt, Brace & World, 1926.

Shchelovanova, N. M., and N. M. Aksarina. *The Upbringing of Young Children in Children's Establishments*. 4th Ed. Moscow: Medgiz, 1960.

Winnicott, D. W. Transitional Objects and Transitional Phenomena. *International Journal of Psycho-Analysis*, 34: 89–97, 1953.

❧ 4 ❧

The Third Year of Life: The Two-Year-Old

PETER B. NEUBAUER

One is struck by the expansion which takes place in all areas of psychic development when the child is between two and three years of age. Locomotion becomes more refined and more under control of ego activities, and is, therefore, more smooth. Separation from the human object—and with it, individuation—is one of the major tasks during this period. Speech proceeds from simple sentence structure to elementary differentiation. Play becomes more elaborate as spatial orientation, weight of inanimate objects, and surface qualities are recognized and used for fantasy expression. Thus, in this third year, expansion, quality of refinement, specialization of function, and increased integration take place in faculties already acquired.

57

Developmental Steps

Except for increasing control of body function and separation from the human object, the period between two and three years of age does not represent any new developmental characteristics that are qualitatively different from those which emerged in the previous year and which will be again observed in the fourth year. Actually, chronological age is not the most suitable way to categorize developmental process. It may well be that the reader, after following the progression of development in the first three years of life, would propose a subdivision of the process into segments other than annual age periods.

LOCOMOTION AND MOTOR SKILLS

As the toddler grows more and more assured of his upright position, and as his central nervous system achieves control of movement, he becomes equipped to expand his areas of physical activity. He becomes an explorer of space. He is more and more in control of running, jumping, and banging activities originating in the second year. He adds new motor achievements, such as climbing the jungle gym and sitting on vehicles which can be propelled and steered. Running in itself is experienced as singularly pleasurable (*funktionlust*) and gives rise to vocal outbursts of pleasure which sound as if the child were in a mood of elation and all-encompassing gratification.

This intensity in the function of the body is rather unique for this period and never reaches the same height again. This pleasure seems to give endless energy for the repetition of physical activities so that running, jumping, and rolling are incessantly repeated until exhaustion. Children run before they can walk. Walking is a measured, aim-oriented activity. Motor activity during this period of life appears aimless and seems propelled by the pleasure that action itself provides. Open space for freedom of movement is thus a requirement of this age. Small rooms which inhibit explorations and motor activity of the child may interfere with these important developmental experiences. Space limitation may therefore have important consequences during this period. It may interfere with the child's sense of pleasure, and he may force himself toward "wild" activities which will continuously lead to more interference or restrictions by the adults; whatever he does runs into prohibition. He may become unmanageable and destructive and often respond to these limitations of his pleasure strivings with another less-acceptable activity discharge, namely, the temper tantrum. Under undue restrictions, some children may tie themselves too much to the adults with increasing dependency or negativism, instead of moving away from them; others may be led to precocious verbal or fantasy substitution for action. The joyfulness may give way to caution; and trust of himself and his function, to overcontrol and restriction. The explorer becomes prematurely harnessed, his self-image and his body image impaired.

At this age, the child will increasingly work on developing his finer motor skills. He learns about size, form, and spatial relations, as well as the stability and instability of materials. Learning how to build so that the blocks can support each other becomes a continuous, ever-fascinating task. Exploration of texture, color, and smell supports the child's need for differentiation of the outside world. There is the need for large spatial exploration; yet, at the same time, there is the need for equipment which enables him to discover the details of objects.

These steps in differentiation which accompany learning in the necessary motor fields are directly related to the development of concepts of "you" and "I," which in turn are basic to the development of causative thinking. In this manner, these play exercises become essential ingredients in the development of psychic structure. Once there is differentiation of the "you" and "I," an insistence on possessions and "what is mine" will follow.

THE PROCESS OF SOCIALIZATION

Toilet training will be completed during the third year. This is based on the capacity to wait, that is, to time and to know where and when certain activities should take place. Space and time, therefore, become coordinated to simple body functions. This control contributes in its own way to the awareness of an "I," to regularity, and to the awareness of "what is mine." Children indicate the need for the identification of inanimate objects as well as people. There is a continuous conversation among the children as to ownership of material. It probably is important that the child have the experience of permanently owning some things which belong to him only, and as he wishes to believe, forever; simultaneously he finds that he has temporary ownership of things which also belong to others, but which he may have for an agreed-upon period of time. He can learn to share objects, therefore, when he does possess some without restriction and others only for intervals of time. These relationships with inanimate objects have as their forerunner a similar relationship to mother. The child sees mother as belonging exclusively to him; but he soon must learn to share her with other adults, with father, or with siblings. Frequently, there is another child-care person in his life: a maid, another relative, or a neighbor. Thus, he learns to differentiate between the permanent people in his life and those who may only be substitute or additional people, ones who are available for certain activities for a certain period of time. Human relationships, then, which are exclusive and shared, continuous and irregular, are reflected in the attitude toward possession of inanimate objects.

There is an obvious connection between the child's capacity for new motor strivings, his exploration of space, and his changing relationship with his mother. As he is now physically able to move away from her, is he also emotionally ready to do without her? Will he continue to equate physical separation with the feeling of loss of the mother? The answer to these questions will depend on the child's achievement of a stable, reliable relationship with his mother, which permits a stable mental representation of her so he can carry her image with him during those times when she is not visually available. Furthermore, it will depend upon his trust of mother's availability on his return. Will she be where he left her? Anticipation of her faithfulness will make it possible for him to be secure while he runs off, knowing that he, not the mother, has done so, that she has maintained a stable position in relation to him. There is a whole range of activity between the age of two and three which experiments with the task of being able to move away from mother and testing her permanency. Resolution does not occur suddenly.

During this age, separation takes place *with* the mother; only later does it occur *from* her. At this same time, the child may continuously return to mother after he has left her. He will touch her or sit on her lap for a moment only to move away again. Later, it may be enough to hear her voice or to look at her to re-establish the necessary contact and to "refuel," to use Margaret Mahler's term. Just as he takes his own possessions to a new environment, he also brings new-found objects back to the mother. He may pick up a stone or another child's toy or anything which strikes him as being "special" and bring it to her. Thus, the interchange of objects from one sphere of activity to another is part of the expansion of his functional world.

It is clear that the ability to separate, therefore, is a very im-

portant developmental step, and during this period it should occur
not by taking the child away from the mother, but instead with her
continuous assistance. Separation is a step toward independence
and, therefore, also toward a higher form of individuation. When
achieved, the child begins to observe mother on a new level of differentiation which will lead to sex differentiation. She is seen not
only as mother, but also as a woman; father then also becomes a
man, and the child, in turn, views himself as a boy or herself as a
girl. On this level of differentiation, the earlier pleasure in activity
becomes diminished with the appearance of new developmental conflicts and with the anticipation of dangers to his newly established
image of himself and others.

PSYCHIC DEVELOPMENT IN THINKING

Within this process, speech development and the sense of self become more differentiated, although continuing in the direction already outlined for the second year. What we have described for other
areas of psychic development is also to be found in the area of thinking, for which speech is an early expression. The initial thoughts of
the child are characterized by egocentricity; everything around him
is self-related and has no other existence. In the beginning, what is
outside and what is inside are not separated. Later, what the child
feels about himself and what he perceives becomes his position for
judgment of the external world. Slowly, he moves toward objectivity: He recognizes events outside himself as having their own
causality. The viewpoint of others now can be separated. There are
many steps which the child has to take in the precausal stage of development, and the third year of life gives ample opportunity to
observe them. He still gives evidence of "magical thinking" in which
he assigns power to others or to himself in which he is fearless, and
yet at the same time he needs reassurance. There is his prelogical,
intuitive explanation, his momentary and yet timeless experience of
events. At times he is concrete, and at other times, he is given to
unreal fantasies.

The child now makes attempts at identifying objects of the outer
world: What is a tree? What is the moon? Is this good? Is this bad?
Later on, the precausative relation of events is established: Why does
the tree grow? Why does the moon shine during the night? Why is
this good? Regularities in his life permit the anticipation of events,
and with it some causative connections can be made. We assume that

a child exposed to irregularities and continuous changes may suffer from the effect of disorganizing nurturing and from the inability to find explanatory statements about life from which he can develop causative thinking and judgment.

INCREASED VULNERABILITY

The two-year-old, with his growing awareness of his own self and his body image separated from the outside world, may show signs of increased vulnerability, which is based on a new awareness of his undue wishes and limited power coupled with an emerging sense of guilt. This differs from the vulnerability of those children who feel at a loss due to neglect. Striving for a better body image and sex identity, the boy speaks about the penis and perhaps implies a fear of losing it. The girl may express her fantasy about having a hidden penis or about having lost it. Ideas of power, of bigness, and of control of others or oneself are developed. Anticipation of punishment and feelings of guilt become related to sex differences. Fears harbored during the training phase may become carried over into this new awareness of genital function. This step toward body integrity with its wish for bigness so as to withstand injury will, at the time, lead to competitive feelings toward the parents and toward the peer group. Aggressive assertiveness, competitive measuring of strength, jealous harboring of possessions, and emerging friendships become a part of the child's life at the end of the third year.

At the same time, sex differentiation continues. The two-year-old begins to observe the differences between boys and girls, identifies between the two sexes, and now raises questions about them. With these steps, he harbors doubts as to the integrity of the body. He also finds explanations for sex differences on his own level of differentiation. The outbursts of his motor power and unlimited pleasure in his body function which occurred in the beginning of the third year are now reduced with the introduction of these new faculties. As the process of sex identity is more fully established, the significance of both parents reaches a new meaning. Imitation and identification with the same sex is now necessary for creating appropriate sex and social roles. The father now becomes "the man" and mother becomes "the woman," and the child has need of both models. Are they available to be imitated and identified with? What about the child who grows up in an environment which has only a male or only a female parent? How much does he have to learn about sex differences from his peers? These questions have relevance also to child-care programs; it is advisable to include male and female personnel when planning care for the two-year-old. Also, it is advisable to form coed groups of children rather than separating by sex.

To the principle of continuity of care and continuity of stimulation on an emotional and intellectual level, we must add the principle of differentiation. In so doing, we refer not only to the organism, but also to differential stimulation provided for by the environment.

The Two- to Three-Year-Old and the Group

It may be more accurate to view the child of this age as being *in* a group rather than as a *member of* a group. He still functions mostly out of his own emotions and interests and continues to do so in a group. At this age, it is not the group which decides what games will be played, what buildings will be erected with the blocks, or what family scenes will be re-enacted. It is the individual child. The group, therefore, should be small, so that individual attention can be given and the continuity of a one-to-one relationship can be maintained to some degree at least. Steps of progression are alternated with steps of regression, and the child-care person must be available for both in often rapidly alternating sequences.

One can begin to observe one child imitating another; later, there will be identification of one child with the other. The child exercises his right of possession and the feeling of "what is mine" and what belongs to others. Rivalry for the exclusive attention and care from the adult leads to frequent battles, which should contribute to the ability to share. Rivalry, first oriented to the human object, later includes inanimate objects. Other children become important either for the purpose of beginning a friendship or as objects of fear or anger. Even if group activities at this age level occur only twice weekly, children will look forward to them. On sight, they may spontaneously and enthusiastically rush to one another. They have no awareness of time sequence. For them, the experience at the moment is of prime importance.

SEPARATION FROM THE MOTHER

It is generally believed that the child has the capacity to separate from the mother for a longer period of time during the day after the age of three. It is posited that he then has a more secure image of mother within himself. But what can we expect between the ages of two and three? If possible, the mother should be present as the separation from her takes place; she should stay with him during his first experiences in a group away from home, so that the child may return to her at any time in order to reassure himself of her availability.

We know that under normal home conditions the mother leaves the child from time to time in order to shop or to go out in the evening. Most often, the child accepts such separations without panic. It is assumed that this acceptance is based on the child's feelings of security and on the knowledge that his mother regularly reappears in a known environment. So, after a brief expression of protest or fear, he can let her go. But a child should never be left alone at this age. He may still need protection, and the child himself recognizes this need for protection. He may get into situations that he cannot master alone, where he may feel abandoned if there is not an adult nearby. A major factor in this separation is the relationship which the child forms with the adult who is available to him during the mother's absence. As we have described before, the child needs the mother to achieve separation *from* her. Therefore, the shift from mother to another person should occur in her presence. The new person should become known to the child with the availability and participation of mother. The new adult should not appear for the first time to take over from her.

The impact of care in a group will depend on the role of the mother during the time she is available to the child, on the degree of her dependability, and how the child-care person can supplement or complement the mother's functions during her absence. If the new child-care person becomes more significant in the life of the child, problems may occur when he is returned to his mother. In other words, a new form of separation difficulty may arise when the child returns home. Such problems apply not only to group day care, but also to individual care undertaken by others than parents.

The place where extra parental care is instituted may be of importance. Is it in an environment which the child knows, as, for example, in his own home or with a neighbor who has been visited frequently? Is it a totally new setting where everything and everyone is new and strange to him? At this age, therefore, transition may require that the mother stay with the child in the new environment for a time or that the new child-care person should at first be brought into the home setting and by providing continuity help to facilitate the eventual change.

INITIATION OF ROUTINE

In the second year, the child has established a routine of his own body functions: feeding schedules, toilet training, etc. Now, at the age of two to three, he can learn to accept a program involving a group. These routines prepare this child to anticipate events and to bring about a sense of regularity, which he can internalize or against which he can measure his own needs and demands. Aiding the child in his acceptance of the shift from one program to another—from free-play to reading or to the rest period—is one of the essential functions of the adult at this time. Many factors assist the child in making a change. The adult must set up activities in such a way that interruptions are possible at a certain expected time, but still allow for the finishing of tasks so that achievement strivings are not interrupted. Thus, encouragement of the capacity to change from one activity to the other should be tempered by a recognition of the child's wish for completion and achievement.

At this age, there are many differences among children in their responses to routine, as in eating, for example. Appetite and the capacity to wait for a meal vary greatly. Many children need an in-between snack so that irritation based on hunger and lack of gratification can be avoided. Food fads and idiosyncracies are very common; variety and availability of choices become important. The same factors are true for sleeping routines. Some children still need a good deal of rest, while others awake early and go through the day without sleep. The so-called "rest period," therefore, should consider these individual differences. Let some children sleep; let others look at a book, listen to a record, or engage in some other quiet activity.

Under such circumstances, "rest" most often means a shift either from gross motor activity, such as running, or from group functions to being by oneself. The rest period is the time when the child should feel free from group stimulation, when he can enjoy those activities which come only from his own initiative and interest. It is not only the physical rest which is essential, but also the limitation of external stimulation. For some children, this becomes a period for regression into autoerotic activities, such as masturbation and thumbsucking. For others, it is a shift from motor activity to fantasy production, daydreaming, etc. Still others seek close physical contact with the teacher. Within normal limitations, each has its place and usefulness. When the daily program is a very long one, more than one cessation of group activity will be helpful.

MATERIAL AND EQUIPMENT

Children at this age require exposure to appropriate materials. As they build with blocks or work with crayons and paint, they are experimenting with space, weight, color, and form. At this period, this becomes a most intense learning experience. They are original, but they also imitate. Imitation and copying is a part of their production with materials just as it is in social interaction.

All in all, the child's emphasis is still on wish-fulfillment and on fears and fantasy rather than on reality. Fantasies are common, so are distortions of events according to the internal condition of the three-year-old. Fantasy and reality are in continuous interaction. Egocentricity is the basic position, but now there are beginning steps toward objectivity.

Summary

One must be prepared for a good deal of fluctuation in the child's function. At times he will still be the "baby" and demand total attention, a reflection of his early dependency needs. At other times, he will strive for self-assertion, achievement, and independence. A recognition of this range of progression and regression must be reflected in the program so that the teacher can respond to both. The teacher or caretaker will periodically be seen as another mother. Most of the time, however, the two-year-old will begin to accept the difference in roles and will see her as having somewhat different responsibilities and functions from his mother's.

Outbursts of aggression, temper tantrums, fighting, and destruction of material and buildings are a common occurrence. Aggression is not socialized and thereby balanced, and seemingly unprovoked attacks and fights can occur quite easily.

Recognition of individual differences by the adult is important in order to foster the child's awareness of his own self as being different from others. To the extent that the adult maintains the anonymity of the individual child in the group, he imposes limits on social differentiation. The more the group is seen as consisting of individuals in their own right, the more the child is able to find his own sense of self. Interaction in the group becomes very useful because the child can see the needs of others, observe other means of reaction, confront his fantasies with the fantasies of other children, and give his own explanations for his own actions while he hears those of others. Both imitation of others and identification with others in the group are factors leading to differentiation. Thus, the group cannot be so large that individual contacts, references, and personal statements cannot be made continuously by the adult. But, more than this, the adult must have a good deal of awareness of the ways that individual children develop. Because of these demands, most often our best teachers are assigned to the two-year-old group.

Group care provides an excellent opportunity to extend language, to expose the child to experimentation, and to engage him in activities which follow his natural curiosity. Through these learning experiences, it is possible to free the child from insistence on immediate gratification. The opportunity for intellectual stimulation, carefully coordinated with his emotional strivings, will lay the foundation for his later attitudes toward learning.

✺§ 5 §✺

Individualization of Child Care
and Its Relation to Environment

LOIS BARCLAY MURPHY

What the child experiences in his environment is affected by many characteristics of the child himself and also by ways in which the different aspects of the environment are organized by the caretakers. One child needs more scope for expansive motor activity, while another "wears out" manipulative toys rapidly. Noises disturb the sleep of one infant, while another sleeps better if the room is not absolutely quiet. One baby enjoys active cuddling and body play which is irritating to another. One infant masters new experiences easily, while another is slow to conquer his anxiety in strange situations. These and other patterns of responding to the environment may change with age. As specified in the previous chapters, there are certain typical needs and sources of pleasure or interest at each successive stage. Variations with age and differences among infants need to be viewed within our understanding of broad psychological meanings of the environment.

68

It is hoped that this chapter will help teachers and others working with children to observe, to think about, and constantly to become more perceptive about relations between the environment and the individual child's needs. Specific prescriptions are less important than awareness of the child's response to the particular pattern of background and immediate stimuli to which he is exposed; and they are less useful than the development of resourcefulness in meeting the needs of different children.

Infants and children grow up in very different environments around the world; each setting must provide the kind of material and personal stimulation, nutriment, and protection required for survival and functioning in the culture. In contemporary American culture, the prevalence of high-rise apartments in urban settings means that many infants and children grow up in homes that are congested or chaotic, tension-arousing, and all too often seriously threatening to the basic needs of growing children. Opportunities for motor exercise and discharge of tension are limited, and the basic foundations for sublimation and socialized channeling of motor and aggressive energies are lacking. At the same time, resources for sublimation and the capacity to modulate primitive sexual and aggressive drives are increasingly required as society moves away from the direct outlets of rural or primitive life. Children may have little continuity with a mother-figure when the working mother is the chief wage earner. Many children do not develop a sense of identity within a family and in the community.

In crowded urban settings, complex demands are made for flexibility, problem solving, adaptation to change, autonomy, and initiative, and capacity to cope with frustration along with the capacity to handle complex social relationships and the intimacies of family life. But the children do not have consistent help or resources to manage these complexities. Children are often exposed to multiple or conflicting standards with no help in resolving these conflicts. The earliest years are crucial in laying foundations for these capacities to deal with multiple aspects of the environment and feelings about them.

Equally fundamental is the need for certain elements in the environment to support sensory, motor, cognitive, language, and affective and social development basic to normal personality and mental development. The complex adaptational resources of the child are expressed in his adaptability, spontaneity, impulse-control, realism, warmth, and integrated social behavior (empathy, cooperation, leadership), or expressed in the opposites—resentment or constriction. These qualities depend in part on appropriate environmental conditions.

But assessment of the environment is a complex and hazardous task. The proof of the pudding is in the eating, and the evidence for the effects of any environment is surely the development of the children who are growing up in it. Many different factors can contribute to a specific behavior. For example, if the children in a given day-care or nursery school setting are tense, aggressive, and constantly involved in conflicts, is it because of current frustration in that setting or the result of tensions brought from home? Do they bump into each other too much in a too-small play area? Do they compete for too few toys? Are they reacting to an irritable teacher? If the children are passive, are they being handled autocratically? Are they undernourished? Depressed? Frightened? Bored? Do they need a kind of stimulation they don't have? Or if the children are spontaneous, alert, and cooperative, does the day-care environment get the credit for creating these qualities or, at least, for not inhibiting them? Or are they children whose vitality has been apparent in every setting?

Convincing evidence for the effects of an environment has to come from the careful study of comparison groups, a process that will take years. In the meantime, we have to plan environments as best we can, integrating scientific evidence regarding the needs of children with observation of their actual development in different environments.

Adaptational Capacities of the Child

Basic adaptational capacities which require support from the environment in the first two years have been spelled out in the previous chapters. In general, these can be stated as:

1. General level of well-being, growth, feeding, and elimination. The infant's response to the environment is reflected in the adequacy of his physical functioning and level of satisfaction of needs. Disturbances indicate the need for changes in the environment.

2. Perceptual and motor responsiveness to people and to objects in the environment. The adequacy of sensory stimulation (things to look at, listen to, explore with his hands) is reflected in the baby's alertness, interest, and increasing coordination of motor with perceptual responses.

3. Autonomy, selectivity, self-management, mastery, and coping resources. Even in young infants these begin to develop when the baby's likes and dislikes are respected and when he is encouraged in his efforts to manage his body and objects.

4. Social interaction. The capacity to evoke and to use communication, help, support, and soothing. These important foundations of good social communication are supported by the mother's or the caretaker's response to the baby's signals and her participation in and encouragement of the baby's spontaneous expressions.

5. Cooperativeness. Later learning, socialization, and adaptability begin as the infant accepts social patterning of physiological rhythms and is helped in handling aggression.

6. Management of frustration. The capacity to accept substitutes, to wait and to maintain interest and positive feeling despite delay or disappointment contribute to later "recovery capacity," or resilience. Its presence depends in part on how the environment from the first months helps the young child to cope with frustration.

7. Differentiation of self (from things and persons), between things, and between people. This process begins in the earliest experiences with things that do and do not stay with one's bodily self. If the environment lacks movable objects which are present at some times and not at others, this fixed monotony would be expected to interfere with basic aspects of development.

8. Self-feelings. Confidence, triumph, pride, etc., evolve from experiences of pleasure in active dealing with the environment—"making things happen"—and in successive experiences of achieving control of the body.

9. Goal-orientation. Curiosity as well as cognitive mastery of space relationships are stimulated by the availability of areas and objects to explore, manipulate, combine, and take apart on the initiative of the baby.

10. Increasing integration in play. Creativity and planning require materials for the child to use in developing his own ideas.

11. The development of a stable relationship. Dependence, imitation, identification, possessiveness (or belonging), and love are all part of the early relationship between mother and the developing child. Where there is no mother—or an inadequate one—continuity, closeness, and the quality of care that evokes "belonging" feelings have to be provided in the environment.

12. Help in mastering trauma. This can be provided by the environment—including help in mastering the separation problems involved in coming into a new environment.

Factors in Planning Care for Children

No plan for an outside environment (such as a day-care center) should be made without careful observation of a variety of different settings and discussion with the teachers as to the assets and problems afforded by those settings. No plan should be made without careful consideration of the needs of the specific children to be cared for in a given setting. And no setting should be made so inflexible that modifications are impossible as new needs arise. In making plans, each major aspect of the environment needs to be considered.

SPACE

Space should be considered in relation to the number of children involved, their needs for motor discharge and vigorous activity, their varying interests and needs for areas for quieter types of activity. The size and shape and the arrangement of closed and open areas are very important. Light, air, and height of windows not only are important for health, but also contribute to the sensory experience of the child. A physical area and its equipment can seem spacious or crowded, depending on its use. Two dozen vigorous four-year-olds who run, jump, and climb will need more space than the same number of five-year-olds, who can work well in small groups at tables, or the same number of two-year-olds, who are just beginning to develop motor skills. A large open area may be overwhelming to the two-year-old, who feels lost in the vastness. The same area broken by low room-dividers can give the small child a sense of cozy, intimate space, while permitting the teacher to oversee what goes on. On the other hand, open outdoor areas appeal to the child who loves to "zoom" across a long uninterrupted stretch of ground; another child, even in the same age group, will prefer being established in a safe sandbox or protected digging area.

Infants in hospitals are sometimes kept in cribs crowded into a small area. In this situation, the crying of one or two infants sets off crying in others. There is no opportunity for exercise on the floor which a three- to six-month-old baby enjoys. Too often the room is monotonous and bare, however scrupulously clean, and the nurses are dressed in identical uniforms. Such environments offer little stimulus to the basic processes of differentiation and mastery of the environment, as well as offering little sensory gratification.

OBJECTS AND EQUIPMENT

Also needed are objects and equipment in a wide range of sizes, colors, textures, shapes, and weights whose qualities and potential uses vary with the needs and interests of the infant and young child as these change with emerging functions. Two-year-olds, who do not yet understand "taking turns," need duplicate equipment; competition for wagons or other wheel toys will be less intense among older children who are able to share group property.

The requirement for variety and change within continuity is related to the need of the infant and young child (especially from six months of age on) for recurrent stimuli to observe and compare objects, a fundamental aspect of mental development. The infant in a totally monotonous environment has nothing to engage his interest or to encourage sustained attention and perceptual activity. At the same time, order is needed to help the child clarify his perception of objects in the environment and to help him organize them into his own "cognitive map." The infant may not be able to sort out a chaotic, confused, or crowded environment. Suggestions for appropriate objects and equipment will be made later in the chapter.

Structural aspects of the environment influence the comfort and efficiency of use of the various resources provided, and the child's internalization of pattern and style of functioning. Included here is the pattern of organized zones and unstructured areas; stimulation and respite, for integration requires both materials for stimulation and time for assimilation; conformity and self-determination; and patterns of eating and sleeping.

Children learn by response to social demands, by imitation and identification, as well as by exploration, discovery, trial-and-error, and manipulation on their own initiative.

PERSONS

In addition to their caretaking roles, persons possess stimulus qualities. Their time, energy, tempo, understanding of infants and young children, attentiveness, and ease of emotional responsiveness are aspects of the personal environment. Their continuity and consistency contribute to the child's experience of the mother-figure and support or interfere with the child's capacity to integrate different experiences.

Infants and toddlers have very specific needs in their relations with adults. While much of the following is written with mothers in mind, we are reminded of Chilman's plea in Chapter 9 that fathers not be overlooked. Primarily, young children depend upon continuity in a relationship which can be differentiated from other relationships. This is handled in different subcultures in different ways. The infant in the Israeli kibbutz has regular contact with its own parents only for a few hours a day. Yet this is also true for the children of the Queen of England or of all working mothers or of mothers who are busy with social activities or of well-to-do families in India. The babies in such settings usually have continuity with a second mother-figure, a nurse or ayah, who has responsibility for the child the rest of the time. This is a valued role. The authority of the nurse is respected by the parents and, ideally, the nurse's relation to the child is personal and stable yet definitely secondary to the relation with the parents.

The young child needs body contact appropriate to his cravings and tolerance. He responds to verbal communication. The "good" mother or nurse responds to the baby's vocalizations from the beginning, "talking to" him and helping the infant connect sounds with objects and actions and specific needs.

The sensitive adult responds to what the child initiates, valuing what he offers and building on his spontaneous activity, as well as on his communications. This includes offering a toy for which a child is reaching, responding by rocking or rhythmic activity when the infant initiates this, exchanging sounds, etc. In addition to his need for their service in physical care, the infant needs appropriate play with people, as well as with objects which evoke and hold his interest.

The mother-figure shares with, and evokes pleasurable responses from, the infant; she recognizes and tries to alleviate unpleasant experiences by providing comfort when the child is hurt. She tolerantly copes with crankiness, fatigue, and such irritable reaction to frustration as throwing things.

The mother-figure helps the infant and small child with his feelings. In the early months of life an infant needs direct comfort by being held, soothed, caressed, and reassured, and sometimes distracted with an appealing stimulus or even removed from the painful or overwhelming situation when necessary. Mothers usually experiment with different kinds of contact to find what reassures the individual baby. Gradually, the baby can understand comforting words when accompanied by soothing handling, and in time the words themselves become comforting. The good mother responds to and encourages spontaneous overtures from her child with humorous tolerance and

support. The growing child who has not been inhibited or overpro-
grammed may become mischievous, impish, and something of a
nuisance through his provocative teasing ways. While supporting
spontaneity, the mother-figure also protects the child from danger and
enforces necessary limits in a consistent way. Spontaneous, unplanned
interaction balanced with well-established routine care provides the
baby with opportunities to develop complex coping resources.

The mother also helps the toddler to "get used to" other people,
to master his fear of strangers and to begin to accept substitute caretakers. The child gradually develops confidence in his own ability to
select and to initiate interaction with the environment, to fend off
the environment when overstimulated, to evoke or provoke responses
when understimulated, and becomes more secure with new people.

Children with marked separation anxiety may be recognized in
certain instances by their own fear and crying or by tense and frozen
postures and expressions. They need the mother's presence for an
extended period of time while they gradually familiarize themselves
with the new environment and develop a relationship with the new
caretaker in a hospital or day-care center.

THE GENERAL ATMOSPHERE

Environment contains space, time patterns, things, and people—all
of which influence the child's sensory, cognitive, and motor development. At the same time, the environment offers important qualities
of attractiveness or unpleasantness, order or confusion, and qualities
of adult handling which influence the behavior of the children, the
tension level of the group, and the emotional investment of the child
in the environment.

These fairly elusive qualities have been implied in a report by
the author on two good day-care centers which provided well for
space, time, and teachers.

In both groups the children are for the most part warmly involved,
spontaneous, and also socialized and appropriately controlled. They
have developed the capacity to focus upon and listen to adults, to take
part in exchanges between adults and children, to pay sustained attention to picture books, puppet play, and verbal stimuli offered in
different ways. Development has been taking place in marked responsiveness to the environment, capacity for communication, cooperation,
impulse control in terms of capacity to wait, take turns, etc., and
other aspects of socialization of drives. Both groups are getting some

help in language. Perhaps most important of all, I have the impression that both are getting a foundation of gratification and interest in a group situation under the leadership of an interested teacher.

Such aspects of behavior depend not only on the material aspects of the environment, but also on the way in which these are used. A child may be served good food in such a mechanical, hasty, or pressured way that it does not taste good. The child may develop a sense of his own individuality through the choices he makes, the experience of selecting or rejecting, of taking a large or small helping. Whether decisions are arbitrary or freedom of choice is allowed becomes a crucial aspect of the experience of the child. The way in which food is served may contribute to rigidity and defensiveness or to ego strength. Similarly, a child may *learn* to pay attention or resent the fact that he *has to*; he can learn to focus eagerly on a picture, story, or task of deep interest. His feelings about the stimulation he is offered and his response to it will depend in part on the manner in which it is offered and his relation with the people who provide it.

Changing Demands

Developmental needs in each of the above facets of the environment will differ at different age levels. For example, the three-month-old infant needs protection from excessive stimulation. An older child may have resources to handle the same amount or kind of stimulation without help: He can move to a quieter spot, tell the adults what he needs, or protest verbally against uncomfortable experiences. We will now consider the environments and the development of stages of infants during their first three years of life.

THE ENVIRONMENT OF THE NEWBORN
AND VERY YOUNG INFANT

Even the newborn infant needs things to look at and makes some responses to stimuli in the environment during his waking periods, short though they may be. In the hospital, probably the figures of nurses moving about the room, the stimulation which they provide when taking care of him—particularly if they talk to him while doing so—is sufficient. After the first weeks, however, the baby needs colors and objects of varying complexity to attract and hold his attention and, as it were, to begin to teach him what eyes and ears are for.

Probably more important at first is the baby's need for tactile comfort and stimulation. In many cultures, swaddling provides a transition between the close contact he had in the womb and the very different situation he encounters in the outside world. Close wrapping in soft blankets is the usual solution in our culture, and most hospital baby nurses have their own ways of providing this. In this very early stage, being closely held is also soothing and relaxing to many babies.

Even in the first weeks individual differences appear. There are babies who waken at slight sounds, babies who want more vigorous rhythms while being held, or babies who like bright lights and those who turn away from them. There is no adequate way of knowing what an individual baby needs without carefully observing his responses to what is offered.

In the first six months, the caretaker's activities influence several levels. For one, she helps to establish smooth vegetative functioning and homeostatic balance. She selects food in terms of quantity, quality, and gratifying taste. She determines time of feeding, allowing autonomy in rhythm and termination of feeding. She cares for the infant's body, keeping him not too cool, not too hot, dry, and free from skin irritations. She provides protection from *overwhelming* external stimulation which is too exciting or interferes with sleep or causes much crying. She soothes the upset baby effectively. However, she sees that *adequate* sensory stimulation—visual, auditory, and tactual —is available in all areas. The nursing baby or the baby who is held while feeding fixates on the mother's face and eyes. Visual stimulation associated with gratification is the major stimulus for the "social smile," which evolves out of early partial smiles that are not sustained or under the baby's control as later integrated smiles come to be. Thus, the mother as a visual stimulus comes to be the foundation for basic social responsiveness, reinforced by the auditory, tactual, olfactory, and oral aspects of her stimulus value to the baby.

Other aspects of the mother as a visual object—her dress, hair, etc.—come to be seen by the baby as part of the whole mother and help to differentiate her from other persons. Babies also respond to other more complex visual stimuli, such as colorful pictures on the wall, mobiles with dangling figures, or useful and meaningful objects in their environments. The bottle is often the first nonpersonal object recognized by the baby. Babies have marked individual tastes for or against certain colors or qualities of objects. "Good" mothers and caretakers notice "what the baby likes" and extend the range gradually.

The soothing or stimulating sound of mother's voice is the first important sound in the environment which babies recognize. The baby needs response from a voice associated with gratifying experience to reinforce his own vocalizations and stimulate further differentiation and development of meanings. He begins the experiences which contribute to a relationship with a loved person. Mechanical soothers, such as repetitious tape recordings, which may be effective at first, lack the aspect of being a flexible response to the baby, as beginning when the baby cries and stopping when the baby is soothed. Thus, the element of interaction and meaningfulness in the exchange is lost. However, babies enjoy bells which tinkle or other sounds which are not too loud and which do not mask out important sounds of people.

Tactile stimulation is universally provided to the young by mammals and by human mothers in primitive groups. This is not necessarily directed to the baby. Mothers who carry babies on their backs or hips or in a sling in contact with the mother's body provide steady tactile stimulation while they continue about their work or other activity. Any of these conditions provide some rhythmic and kinesthetic stimulation as part of the contact between baby and the mother's moving body. In more advanced civilized cultures, the substitute for these forms of contact is periodic holding, rubbing, patting, rocking, or walking and rocking the baby in a cradle or carriage. The institutional baby is often in an environment where very little tactile stimulation is available, even in times of need. Mechanical aids may soothe, but their use is at the cost of the adequate development of the total complex relationship with a mother-figure needed for adequate social and emotional development later and for the baby's sense of identity, or "belonging."

The environment should provide *manipulative stimuli*. At first, these may be parts of the mother's body—her fingers or face—or, later, the immediate furniture in which the baby is carried or held and objects which stimulate reaching, grasping, throwing, and combining. These objects or toys may be in any shape, but they must be in dimensions which the infant can grasp. Legs, arms, heads, or other parts have to be small enough to fit into infant hands. The principle of the rattle, a small object which the baby can grasp and by inadvertent or deliberate movements evoke sounds, is a good one. The baby will be stimulated to more goal-directed activity if pleasurable consequences follow his efforts. Institutional babies tend to become overinterested in their own hands, presumably because other objects are lacking.

Family babies who are held, rocked, gently bounced, and played with in other ways experience passive exercise which contributes to their interest in self-initiated activity. The institutional baby is kept in a crib, perhaps because he is less trouble when he has more limited stimulus to motor activity. As a result, he is often delayed in gross motor development. An environment which provides varied motor exercise, stimulation, and reward is important to the flexible, versatile development of motility expected in our culture. Lack of motor skill handicaps the later development of the child and interferes with active coping capacities and skills in sports.

The baby in a family receives enthusiastic responses to his efforts to hold his head up, roll over, and to pull himself up to sit, stand, and then to walk. He is placed in a chair supported by a pillow; he is placed on the floor which stimulates rolling over or creeping; a toy is put within reaching distance. Perhaps the many different postural experiences of being held on laps, and shoulders, and being played with by tossing, bouncing, etc., in affectionately rewarding contexts contribute to the motor interest.

The mother or caretaker is a major environmental stimulus for the baby, as well as his protector and nurturer. She mediates the environment of the child and is part of it, providing a basis of security in repeated actions and events as well as spontaneous stimulation. Her capacity to balance care and respect for the baby's autonomy—meeting his needs and still allowing him to learn to adapt to and deal with the environment in his own way—will help him to develop his potentialities and his capacity to enjoy being himself. Development of both his cognitive capacities and his emotional resources depends on this balance.

THE ENVIRONMENT OF THE SIX- TO FIFTEEN-MONTH-OLD

At this age, all of the areas mentioned above are still important, but the baby's relation to his mother has become central, as he distinguishes her clearly from all other persons. Mother becomes more important as part of his expanding environment not only for safety and basic physical integration, but also for his developing capacity for companionship, imitation, and his identification of himself as a person who is in some way like mother. Thus, sustained time with the mother-figure and with familiar substitutes during necessary separations becomes a major factor in environmental handling. When necessary, he may need to "distance" from new stimuli while gradually getting used to them.

The infant is now beginning to connect sounds with words. His motor capacities are expanding; he is beginning to combine objects and to make many other connections. His needs are more complex: he needs more space, more chance to explore, and more objects to handle. The young child can use fully all of the opportunities for exploration which become available to him in a moderate-sized, middle-class home. At this age he can—and does—get into as many things as possible in the different rooms of the house and outdoors, constantly seeking out the unknown and unexplored at his own pace. Kitchen cupboards with their pots and pans, low bureau drawers, low shelves on tables and bookcases are all exciting. As fast as he becomes thoroughly familiar with the old objects and places, he pokes into new ones. It is probably crucial that the child be allowed to discover things for himself at his own pace rather than being exposed to new places and opportunities too rapidly or too slowly.

A photographed record of the behavior of a fourteen-month-old girl provides an example of normal exploratory activities of children in the second year of life. The following is a list of her activities in a single afternoon.*

She tries to put on lipstick, undo her shoelaces, and turn on the radio. She feels the kitty's fur, hugs the kitty, imitates the kitty, offers the mother cat a cookie and watches her eat, and plays with the cat's tail. She turns the pages of a mail-order catalog and looks at the pictures by herself. She plays with a toy duck, with an electric cord and plug, with the kitchen pans (putting one pan in another, etc.), and puts the lids on pots. She bathes teddy, climbs up the steps to get a toy, reaches to a dog to pat him, wraps up a doll in a towel and carries it about. Finally, she peeks through a gap in stairs to see what she can see under the stairs.

By implication, one can see the range of activities a young child needs to have available in order to support development. A host of learnings follow from these explorations. From getting under, on top of, and into things arise concepts of things, size and space relation-

* From unpublished photographic records of the author.

ships, possibilities of combining, understanding of textures, weights, what is destructible, permissible and not permissible, and so on.

THE ENVIRONMENT OF THE ONE-YEAR-OLD

The second year of life is as critical for mental health as the first because of the rapid development of crucial new functions, such as walking, talking, and self-feeding, which bring changes in the child's relationships to his environment. It is probably because of all these more or less simultaneous new capacities and the changing opportunities and awareness which they bring that the child is so sensitive to separation from his mother, so shy, so resistant, so hard to manage, and so easily disturbed (Bowlby, 1954; Murphy, 1964).

Such problems as early speech difficulties, serious withdrawal, aggressiveness, or extreme tantrums must be understood in terms of simultaneous pressures and strains in this year. Toilet-training worries may be increased by anxiety over separation from the mother, loss of her attention because of the arrival of a new baby, or even her preoccupation with another pregnancy. They may coincide with moving to a new home or trauma caused if the mother is hospitalized for illness or required to care for a hospitalized older sibling. If the child himself is hospitalized for an operation, accident, or illness, his body pain is further increased by anxiety at separation from home and mother. Some of these severe reactions may lead to permanent development difficulties, emotional disturbance, or retardation if therapeutic treatment is not made available promptly.

Around eighteen months of age, most babies have become toddlers. Their range has widened. Outdoors they like to pick up, feel, and inspect grass, leaves, twigs, sticks, stones, snow, and icicles. They like to play in water and sand, throw and then chase a soft ball, throw bean bags or other objects which have a little weight, pull packing materials apart, "mess with" all kinds of textures, pull pull-toys, and push their own walkers or carriages. Indoors, they enjoy poking and peering into closets or other new unexplored places. Active toddlers at this stage may be exhilarated by climbing steps, chairs, tables, mastering new ways of getting up and down, into, and onto different kinds of furniture. They like to bounce on the bed, slide off backward, and experiment with other body sensations and encounters with objects.

All these experiences bring questions about new words, so that concepts and ideas develop parallel with and out of the child's experiences and the richness of his environment. It is at this stage that the effects of a constricted, narrow environment and restricted activity begin to be most obvious. If there is insufficient newness, the child may compulsively and repetitiously ride a scooter around and around or he may give up and sit sucking his thumb or banging his head or repetitiously push one toy back and forth.

Picture books, especially with pictures of objects, animals, or birds actually seen in or around the house, hold the child's attention for longer and longer periods. He is now apt to enjoy a "What's that?" game with mother or other adult who will look at pictures with him.

The normal child also listens a great deal and is interested when his mother or caretaker tells him the "word for" all the objects he touches, plays with, or experiments with. If he is a "verbal" child, he may constantly ask "What's that?" and in this way increase his vocabulary when the adult responds in a satisfying way. The young child also learns more about words and voices and expression through little songs and word games such as "This little pig went to market," lullabies, and the like. All of these mother–baby games contribute to the range of verbal and conceptual resources of the child. When the mother is too busy, too tired, too depressed, too hostile, too dull, or otherwise too unavailable to engage in such activities the child does not have the stimulus he needs for development at this stage.

The child now begins to be curious about where things come from and where they go. The process of flushing the toilet or emptying the bathtub or sink may be fascinating. The child's eagerness leads him and his parents into a gradually expanding environment. Trips to the zoo, the supermarket, the park, a lake, or just riding in the car are exciting to children at this age and for the next year or two. Later the child can explore alone, but at this age these trips have to occur in the company of a parent or parent equivalent. Without the support of the trusted familiar person, the child may get panicked by too much newness. Panic is particularly apt to occur when the child is exposed to sudden loud sounds, such as the blast of a boat or a train whistle, the rush of steam from a train exhaust, or the screech of a nearby siren. In such situations, sensitive children may cringe, scream, or cling desperately to the mother. Different children are sensitive to different types of stimulation—what is frightening to one may be a source of delight to another. In the latter part of the first year and in the second year the caretaker can begin to explain, in a simple way, what the source of the pain or discomfort was and what will help it, and to assist the child to differentiate between real and unreal dangers. "The steam from the big train won't hurt us when we stand here"; "thunder is a big noise but it doesn't hurt us. You can make a big 'boom,' too." This is a period of rapid passive learning, during which the child takes in more than he can respond to verbally.

Children under two need protected, selective exposure to the widening environment in which they are so interested. Typically, a mother will say, "I have to chase him all day long—there's no telling what he will get into!" Considering the wealth of experience of the middle-class child who is just under two years old, and its enormous stimulus value for his language and communication as he accumulates new things to talk about and ask for, the experience of the institutional child of this age is at best meager. He is usually overrestricted and protected; there is little chance for him to have the "run of the place" as a well-cared-for middle-class counterpart does, at least in certain rooms of the house.

At home, the family style of managing the environment for the child in the second year of life has much to do with the degree of anxiety and conflict subsequently developed by toileting, breaking, or touching things. Some families make the house "baby-proof" during this stage before impulse-control is well established: Breakables are simply kept out of reach. Some mothers keep a potty-chair in a convenient location in the living area so the child can learn to "go" on his own initiative. Minimal interference with the drive to autonomy characteristic of this stage of expanding motor skill occurs when such techniques are used and there is maximum opportunity for gratifying experiences in exploration and use of environment. Group care can support the emerging autonomy of the toddler by the use of techniques similar to these, provided a sufficiently high ratio of adults to children is available for supervision, companionship, and stimulation.

In either setting, training needs to be both positive and negative: Not to play with or near the stove is a negative example. How to play with balls or toys is positive. Wherever he is, the child needs supervised freedom, since he does not understand dangers. He also needs appreciative response to his rapidly developing and differentiated feelings: response to his delight, pride, affection, sympathy; support when he is anxious; understanding of his anger and protests.

THE ENVIRONMENT OF THE TWO-YEAR-OLD

The activities and interests of the two-year-old and his uses of the environment have been extensively described by Woodcock (1952). As Peter Neubauer commented in Chapter 4, all developments in the last half of the second year are continuing to proceed toward greater integration and complexity. Concretely, this means that the well-developed two-year-old can do more, say more, listen more, observe more, be more independent, and use a wider range of resources. He may romp with his pets and enjoy fitting into the play of older preschool children. He may learn to ride a tricycle, go down a slide (with some help), swing in a low swing, sing the words of songs with verses, and listen to stories; or perhaps he is in the process of developing these activities. He adds new parts of speech—pronouns, verbs, adjectives—and his sentences begin to be more complex. He is interested in cars, busses, trains—everything with wheels. He wants a "two-gun holster." He may be proud of his little red wagon and like to carry things in it to help his dad and mother.

Doubtless because of this increasing versatility and adaptability, growing skills and capacity to communicate, it was usual in the late 1920s and 1930s to enroll two-year-old children in nursery school. But the results were usually far from good when the children were handled in groups of twenty to twenty-five with only one teacher and an assistant, as was too often the case. Highly competitive, devoid of social skills or the capacity to cooperate with a peer leader, the two-year-old's aggressive attacks outran the capacity of the teacher to maintain peace or foster control. Children in such groups often were not happy and many were anxious when separated from their mothers. As a result, by the mid-1940s many private and university nursery schools limited their enrollment to children three years old and older. More recently, experiments have been tried with smaller groups, more teachers in proportion to children, and more gradual induction of the children. Mothers are encouraged to stay for the first days or weeks until their children are at home in the new situation. These changes, plus a more maternal type of handling, have shown that proper adaptation of the environment to the needs of the two-year-old results in a good experience.

If he has had extensive opportunity to put things into, onto, and under other objects, the child's conceptions of space, sizes, weights (bigger, smaller, heavier, etc.) have been growing, and he is ready for more complex combinations, organizations, and patterns. Long before his drawing skill has reached a level where his observations can be recognizably represented on paper, the two-year-old can utilize blocks and toys to reconstruct and to clarify experiences, events, wishes, and fears. In this way, children learn to manipulate concepts, develop new ideas, and learn to contain (or begin to sublimate) drives and feelings. Typical two-year-old conflicts over toileting, separation from mother, or being displaced by a new baby are worked out, as different solutions are tried. Happy events such as "daddy-comes-home-from-work" are reproduced. In this way, the young child enlarges his inner world of image, his capacity to cope with outer events and the feelings they evoke, and his increasingly complex grasp of everyday relationships and experiences. All of this, as well as his increasing motor mastery and capacity to communicate, are steps toward the phase Gesell has referred to as the serene three-year-old. At three, he has become at home in his world.

Once again, we can turn to a record of the activities of a two-year-old boy between breakfast and lunch.*

He crawls under the coffee table, then up on a chair, then on the kitchen table. Sits on the observer's lap for book reading, then into the rocking chair, and out again over the arm. Lifts up typewriter cover and investigates keys, goes into desk drawer for pencil and paper, followed by a "drawing" session. Then into the pan cupboard, taking out a supply of pans and lids to play with. He stands on knees on sofa arm, falls on sofa, slides to floor and repeats this several times. Crawled into bathtub and tried to turn on the water, pulled the cord to open and close the front window drapes several times, and lined up his blocks, making a "train."

Then we take a walk outside. He stops to pick up sticks, rocks, leaves; home again, he pulls carton of pop bottles off shelf. Takes out bottles and puts them back in the carton, places a stuffed animal in his high chair and feeds it some candy, tears open a letter of advertisement which came in the mail. Opens door to the clothes chute and drops a few blocks down. Then onto a chair by the table and puts a finger in the meringue of a pie before getting caught and turns to open a drawer where the flashlight is kept. Spends considerable time trying to turn it on.

This period is marked by integration and further differentiation. If the resources available in group care are too limited, the child lacks opportunity for the more complex integrations on three important levels: on the *cognitive level*, he fails to orient to and clarify the environment through opportunities to reconstruct it; on the *affective*

* Record kept by a mother and given to the author.

level, he is unable to clarify feelings and resolve conflicts; finally, on the *motor level*, he is unable to achieve body mastery, lacking a wide range of opportunities for varied motor activity. In such cases we are apt to find restless, jittery children who are constantly accumulating tensions from unadjusted experience, unresolved conflicts, and unexpressed feelings.

Many traditional nursery school procedures contribute to the expansion of a sense of self in the two- to three-year-old child. The child's name or picture selected by the child on his "coat cubby" or "toy cubby" stimulates the child to develop a feeling that "this is *my* place, where I keep *my* things."

Mirrors in bathroom or cloakroom (even the one-way mirror for observation of the playroom) are used playfully by the teacher and the children to help the children identify each other and themselves in the mirror and to identify their own characteristics in an accepting way. Name games, such as "Who-is-it," "I like," "I choose," "What do you see?" and the like, help the child to differentiate his place, his name, and his preferences from those of others. The teacher helps this self-identification process by respecting and appreciating what the child builds, draws, makes, and says. "That is a nice story," she observes. Or, "You made a fine tall tower." In all these ways, the child's awareness of himself is stimulated. He finds out what he can do with his body, what he likes, what he can plan, and he thinks of himself as a respected trusted person who is growing up, one who likes to learn.

Children differ in the speed and order in which they acquire basic skills for self-care, participation in a group (nursery school or day care), for meeting the demands of adults for emotional control, sharing, cooperating with mental tests and physical examinations, and for coping with the opportunities, challenges, threats, and stresses met with in the environment. Experiences of mastering skills and tasks continue to support pride and other positive self-feelings.

The period of two to three years old is normally a phase of development of awareness of one's sex—whether boy or girl, the activities typical for each sex, and of differences between self and others, whether grown-ups or babies, big sisters or brothers.

This is also a period of rapid expansion of feelings. The two-year-old may scream in anger, terror, or jealousy. He may hug, kiss, or squeeze in outbursts of affection. In the day-care center, many of these feelings will emerge or erupt. Learning to recognize these feelings is one step toward controlling them.

Feelings and self-awareness come together as the child begins to play out many roles, adapting his toys with the help of his imagination. In this way he begins to prepare for constructive, creative use of his environment and solutions of his problems at later stages.

SUMMARY OF DEVELOPMENT STAGES

Translating development into detailed and minute achievements—so fine that only the well-trained observer or eagle-eyed mother will note them—always carries certain risks. There is the ever present danger that the sequences will be taken so seriously and applied so literally that one fails to look for the individual child or to make allowances for special talents, latencies, or disabilities. The following charts, which summarize development at the three chronological phases we have been discussing, are compiled more as a guide to the potentials which will emerge. They may serve as a nudge to the caretaker or counselor to see that opportunities for experiences leading to such achievements are provided.

Adaptations for Individual Needs

The adequacy of the environment is always relative to the needs for support of the particular emergent functions at any given time. The environment needed by different individual children is functionally related to the entire pattern of needs of each individual child. For instance, a slowly maturing eight-month-old baby who has just learned to sit up may use a playpen for a considerable period of time to support his next efforts in motor coordination, pulling himself up to standing, etc.; he may also use his playpen as a safe place to play with a variety of toys which arouse his interest. However, another eight-month-old baby whose motor development has followed a faster time schedule may be seriously frustrated and inhibited by extended confinement within a playpen; actively crawling or beginning to walk, this child needs a wider area to explore and opportunities to develop his expanding motility.

PERIODICITY IN SPECIAL NEEDS

Different features of the environment may be relevant under different conditions of well-being. A baby who is not well is fretful and easily

Development in the First Year

Body and Self
- Adjusts position in crib.
- Adapts posture on the lap for comfort.
- Turns to facilitate vision, hearing.
- Reaches for, touches, manipulates, throws.
- Practices motor skills; sits, pivots, rolls, pulls self up.
- Creeps.
- Stands, steps with support.
- Develops body image, identifies body parts.

Impersonal Objects
- Shows cathexis of environment, attentive looking.
- Orients to space and objects by vision; visual exploration and familiarization.
- Recognizes objects, discriminates, selects.
- Explores by hand, feeling, tracing, experimenting with objects.
- Uses motor exploration, discovery.
- Develops concept of object constancy.
- Throws away and retrieves, loses, finds, searches.
- Expresses aggression to objects through hands and body; controls aggression.

Persons
- Develops selective attention to persons.
- Sustains attention to mother, visual pursuit.
- Smiles socially.
- Receives and shows pleasure in mother.
- Evokes response by active, affective expression, vocalizes to get play, comfort, help.
- Differentiates mother.
- Shows anxiety at strangers.
- Differentiates responses to different persons.
- Shows separation anxiety.
- Masters separation anxiety.

Affect
- Differentiates cry.
- Frowns.
- Smiles.
- Laughs.
- Shows delight.
- Differentiates expressive vocalization.

Language
- Vocalizes.
- Develops syllables.
- Associates "ba" with bottle, etc.
- Engages in reciprocal baby talk.

Development from Twelve to Twenty-Four Months

Mastery of motor and language skill and ways of using these in the environment are basic for this stage and contribute to blossoming autonomy. Sequences vary with individual children. There are also wide differences in appetite, motor interest, affective intensity, shyness, resistance, preoccupations, language development. The following items illustrate some of the varieties of behavior which may be seen at this stage.

Body and Self
Fights diaper change.

Develops smoother locomotion.

Begins to run, climb.

Learns to avoid bumps.

Begins to feed self, then wipe face with napkin.

Plays at brushing hair.

Pulls off shoes, socks; tries to put on shirt, sweater, hat.

Bounces on sofa, slides off.

Shows off tricks.

Tries to walk backward.

Learns to rock in rocking chair.

Impersonal Objects
Has transitional object: "teddy," "blanket."

Plays contentedly with toys for thirty minutes or more.

Experiments with things that make noises, sounds.

Extends range of exploring, empties kitchen cupboards, pokes into shelves and drawers, pulls out pots and pans; puts small things into bigger things.

Tears paper, magazines.

Gets on top of or under coffee tables, desks, beds, climbs on kitchen table.

Pulls wagon, carries toys and "loot" from one place to another.

Persons
Explores mother's hair, earrings, glasses.

May be shy and curious, yet interested at the same time; turns partly away, etc.

May stare at strangers solemnly.

Plays "Peek-a-boo."

Runs to be picked up, cuddled; grabs mother's or father's leg in hug.

Enjoys rough-housing, tossing games, being thrown on the bed, etc.

Inhibits impulse in response to "No!"

Teases, pretending to do the forbidden.

Affect
Develops triumph, delight, pride in achievement, skills, and in making things happen.

May protest, cry in sharp anger or rage when frustrated.

Delights in newness, discovery.

Has many expressions, much affection.

Manipulates situation by emotional display.

May still have intense separation anxiety, followed by angry withdrawal at mother's return.

Language
Responds to verbal signals.

Uses verbal play.

Uses words.

Names.

Expresses wants.

Follows verbal cues.

May increase vocabulary rapidly.

May ask "What's that?" frequently.

Responds to picture book game with mother's asking or showing.

Uses words or phrases plus gestures to summon adults, and wants to communicate.

Development from Twelve to Twenty-Four Months (continued)

Body and Self	Impersonal Objects	Persons	Affect	Language
Develops acute sense of autonomy: "Do it *myself!*" Tries to bathe self, uses wash cloth.	Rides and steers kiddy-car.	Pats, hugs dog, cat.	Is affectionate, likes hugs, kisses, cuddling; begins to give love.	Listens to simple stories.
Blows bubbles under water.	Loves to splash in water and explore sensations of water contact.	Punches, slaps, knocks down intruding younger children.	May show humor.	Imitates animal sounds and car noises.
Becomes self-assertive, selective.	Digs, fills pails, pots, or bottles with sand, seeds, pebbles. Dumps out sand, pebbles.	Shows interest in persons.	Resents pressure, constriction, training.	Hums, may sing.
Knows own body parts.	Plays on toy xylophone.	May cry or withdraw from strangers if parents are absent but accepts stranger if parents are present.	Has intense positive and negative affects.	Understands far more words and ideas than he can express.
Is pleased with image in mirror.	Piles and knocks down blocks.	Imitates mother, dresses up, copies postures.	Has low thresholds for anxiety.	
Body sensitivity increases, abdomen more sensitive.	"Helps" mother sweep, dust.	May imitate going to the bathroom if not trained.	Is vulnerable and cumulative trauma is possible through simultaneous stresses.	
Tries two-legged hop, somersaults.	Leafs through mail-order catalogs.	Demands adherence to routine.		
Begins to clean up own mess.	Arranges graduated rings.	Controls others, gives orders.		
At times may insist on privacy.	Talks with toy telephone.	Tests, opposes, resists adults when coerced.		
Sense of self has become intense, through mastery, opposition, assertion, exercise	Returns ball thrown.	Increasingly differentiates,		
	Becomes possessive, makes a house or special place for own toys.			

of choice, protest, selective cooperation.

Struggles to master obstacles, hard tasks.

Makes selections, has preferences.

Gives doll or teddy-bear rides.

Carries several objects at one time.

Likes to open and close doors.

Combines toys in complex play.

Wants variety, enjoys outings.

Watches TV.

Learns to master many aspects of the environment through observation, exploring, trial-and-error, testing, problem solving.

has wide range of adult-child interaction.

Development from Twenty-Four to Thirty-Six Months

Body and Self	Impersonal Objects	Persons	Affect	Language
Expands motor interests.	May still cling to transitional objects.	Shows mother, father achievements.	Is less raucous.	Has concepts still general, undifferentiated; calls other children's caretakers "mother."
Is short-stepped; gait constrained.	Is more choosy, has favorite toys.	Explores clothes, jewelry of adults.	Modulates beaming smiles; whimpers or whines.	
Shows off new clothes, shoes.	Still touches and explores objects.	Runs errands for mother (gets mop, etc.).	Wants goodnight kiss.	Sings songs.
Begins to master slide, swing.	Has great interest in faucets, light switches, door knobs, keys, latches, and toys that turn and move.	Enjoys roughhouse with father, piggy-back rides, marching games.	Has periods of upheaval, temper lability, sudden heartbreak preceding new integration.	Uses phrases, simple sentences.
Marches, claps to music.				Counts: "one," "two."
Tries to dress self, work zippers, snaps; may be very persistent.	Hammers pegboards energetically.	Likes to investigate his peers; pokes, pats, hits.	Shows increasing humor at surprises, harmless accidents, animal actions, incongruities, tricks, mistakes; burlesques adults.	Enjoys rhymes, chants.
Pulls at, tugs clothes to get undressed.	Fits puzzles, takes apart, puts parts together.	Stares, watches others play.		Understands and uses abstract words: "high," "far," "heavy," "later."
Experiments with motor patterns.	Likes little things.	Engages in solitary and parallel play.	May be tender or aggressive in turn to smaller babies.	Understands and uses texture words: "soft."
Tries to turn and twirl or walk on tiptoe.		Joins group fleetingly.		Talks about events.
May use both hands at once; fingers still work together.	Likes means-ends activity— moving stool or box to climb to higher objects; explores heights.	Associates persons with their accustomed places, roles; is surprised to see them in different places.		Is animistic.
Balances between independence and interaction with others.	Identifies places where things and people belong.	Is gradually able to let		

Needs and seeks variety.

Resists suggestions at times, accepts at other times.

Acts on choices; performs preparatory steps to carry out plan.

Plays out own daily routines, his intimate experiences.

Contrasts his situation with other children.

Clears the table.

Draws, scribbles with crayons.

Plays with dolls increasingly.

Creates dramatic play with simple plots.

Lays blocks in a row; works at problems of bridging.

Has difficulty in achieving a circle (organization limited).

Likes to watch distant objects, planes flying overhead, birds.

mother leave without distress.

Recognizes songs and tunes.

Knows names of neighbors and where they live.

Uses verbal associations with pictures; "reads" aloud to self.

disturbed by noises and may need a degree of quiet which was not necessary previously. A baby who is suffering from the irritability and distress of painful teething will need more individual care, help in achieving some degree of comfort, and distraction from his pain than a baby in a high state of well-being, who is eagerly responding to new motor capabilities or to the new capacity to create noises by shaking rattles or other toys in his crib.

A baby who is well settled into a familiar environment, one who has developed the capacity to follow his mother or caretaker visually at some distance and to maintain auditory orientation to the sounds she makes, can tolerate greater physical distance from her than a baby who feels insecure in a new environment or one who is not able to maintain orientation at a distance.

Special adaptations in handling the child may be required to deal with periods of blocked development, marked anxiety, extreme retreat, or cessation of development in speech or motility which had already begun. Sometimes children as young as one to three years old may need help in resolution of conflicts through play therapy.

Evidences of marked or low thresholds for anxiety, infantile depression, flattened affect, and so forth need to be taken more seriously than has generally been characteristic in the care of infants and very young children. All too often the passive child who is "easy to handle" is overlooked because the rambunctious child demands attention.

UNFAVORABLE BACKGROUNDS

Children from extremely ambitious lower-class families are sometimes under pressure for conformity, extreme politeness, cleanliness, etc., to the point where they are excessively compliant or inhibited, dependent on adult direction, or imitative to the point of seeming artificial. Such children can be helped by specific encouragement or concrete directives to explore, to try out new experiences and activities. They can be told, for instance, "It is all right to play with the messy clay here—we have time to clean it up," implying that in different places different rules may hold.

Observation of preschool children from the "stable working-class group" in contrast to those from the "disorganized lower-class" shows that these groups differ widely (Pavenstedt, 1965). Children who grow up in extreme slum conditions or with no consistent care, routine, order in the home, or place for their own possessions (if they have any) may have a total disregard for or unawareness of structures and patterns of group behavior and play. They may lack curiosity or warm interest in the environment; they do not know how to use the materials available and may be vague about themselves as well. They may be fluid and evasive in defense against the threat of new situations rather than flexible, and they may be isolated without being actively autonomous or resourceful. They may not "bother" the teacher because they expect little or no response. They may be quiet in a passive apathetic way or active in a scattered way. They may have little or no capacity for sustained attention, or they may be fearfully conforming.

Children from the unfavorable backgrounds described above need much more individual attention from the teacher—more direction and help in developing the fundamental capacities to orient themselves to new situations, to use varied materials, to participate in routines, to become aware of their own potentialities, and to cooperate with and respond to what adults can give them. The teacher may need to demonstrate what a crayon, pencil, or chalk will do; what can be done with clay and other plastics or with blocks and toys. Perhaps the child needs help in learning to manage wheel toys, etc. More important, the children may need a gradual approach to close contact and step-by-step help in responding to adult companionship, suggestions, affection, and play. The kinds of things a "good" mother does with a year-old baby may be helpful for these children at a much older age. The child may need to be held on the lap or be allowed to sit close. As the teacher encircles him with an arm, they can chat or look at books together.

The child who has been deprived of intimacy with a warm adult may especially need "time alone with one grown-up"—ten or fifteen minutes—as frequently as possible. These moments can contribute to the child's feeling of being cherished, being thought about individually, and being able to respond emotionally in a way the group situation does not permit. The adult should focus on special preferences, interests, and needs of the child, playing the particular games, singing the particular songs, reading the particular books, helping with the particular part of dressing, etc., which is important to that child.

This use of personal adult-with-child time in the second year can include the Mother Goose rhymes, songs, rocking-chair activity, clapping games where the mother claps with the child, or touching games, as "Peas Porridge Hot" or "This Little Pig Goes to Market," where the mother touches the child's hands or toes. These games not only add to an awareness of self, but also are intended to reinforce the child's positive feeling about the environment, about the grown-up world, and about himself, thus fostering identification and an interest in growing up through the feeling that grown-ups are nice and it would feel good to be one some time.

Such personal care and love may not be possible for some children to accept at first. Very distrustful children may need support from a distance by an intuitive, cautious, interested adult whom the child slowly comes to accept as safe, and only then responds to. With such children, the grown-up may best start by quietly imitating the child in an unobtrusive way or otherwise starting where the child is, then gradually extending the activity.

HELP IN COPING WITH FRUSTRATION, DISAPPOINTMENT, AND FAILURE

Children can learn to accept or find substitutes, adapt their plans, change the situation, get help, evoke desired responses from others, and in other related ways cope with frustrations, as well as to persist in efforts to master obstacles. The mother-figure can help by offering or suggesting substitutes, while encouraging the child's own coping efforts. The most deprived children in our research sample had very few resources for coping with difficulties, while the children of good backgrounds had many coping ideas and positive attitudes toward coping with difficulties (Murphy, 1962).

Children can also be helped to develop acceptable ways of discharging tension: "Run and shout outdoors not indoors." An important step in communication is learning to ask or to tell instead of screaming or crying for what is wanted or not wanted. Children can be stimulated to use fantasy constructively: "Let's *play* supermarket since it is raining today and we can't *go* to the supermarket."

Children need understanding of their volatile emotional reactions from the adults in their environment. These feelings run a wide range: angry, frightened, or suspicious feelings, desire for closeness, feelings of gladness in sharing, doubts, conflicts and guilty feelings, inhibitions and anxieties. Even two-year-olds can express basic feelings clearly: "I love you," "I'm scared," "I don't want," etc. Feelings about conflicts, disappointments, and disturbances at home may be displaced in the nursery school situation.

Consultation is needed sometimes from a child psychiatrist or analyst, who can help to interpret a child's troubled feelings to the teacher or social worker and help her to support, provide release, or control as needed. The teacher cannot be a therapist. But the experience in the group can be therapeutic in the sense that it can help the child to recognize and get along better with his feelings and to take further steps toward emotional maturity and integration of feelings with understanding.

HELP IN PARTICIPATING WITH OTHER CHILDREN

Children who have been grossly deprived may feel strange with middle-class people who speak differently, dress differently, and in various ways act differently. A process of acculturation may be needed, its length depending on how isolated the child's community has been from middle-class life. Various techniques can be used to lure the child into participation. Marching songs, circle games, and songs involving clapping or rhythmic actions in unison can contribute to the children's sense of group membership. If the demands are very simple and within reach of all the children, even two-year-olds can participate in simple rituals such as lighting candles or saying greetings. Conversation around the table at "juice times" and mealtimes, talking about the events in nursery school, the food itself, or other shared experiences can involve all the children.

The preschool years are also a period during which early foundations of sympathy, empathy, or concern for others are laid down (Murphy, 1937). In lower-class children, such feelings may be more highly developed but they need support from the empathy of teachers. Some children are timid and hesitant or overboisterous and aggressive in the group situation. They need help to learn the simplest acts, to become accustomed to talking, etc. The adult may also be useful in bringing two children together to help each other, for example, to construct a house or carry a board together. Children have to learn to respect the needs, wishes and feelings of others. Taking turns is one way of doing this, although it takes intense children a long time to learn how to wait for another to finish.

The mother-figure or teacher will do well to ask such questions as the following in assessing the kind and amount of help needed by a child:

Does the child need stimulation of interest, receptiveness, relationship, responsiveness, warmth, activity, exploration, discovery, making choices, etc.?

Does he need stimulation of speech, communication?

Does he need stimulation for active participation in simple play with adults or others?

Does he need special support for initiative, problem solving, self-help, etc.?

What kinds of need satisfaction or restitution of emotional supplies does he need?

What contribution has his past training—being taught certain kinds of activities or certain ways to solve problems—made to his learning?

Supervising the Teacher and Assistants in the Child-care Setting

At its best, supervision is not autocratic and didactic, but rather guides the awareness of the adult who is working with the children, gives positive support to effective work, and raises questions about methods which do not seem to be helpful to the child. It is oriented toward the development of the teacher, toward increasing her self-confidence, self-respect, resourcefulness, perceptiveness, spontaneity, and warmth with the children. Directives which are not understood or accepted can do more harm than good and can lead to literal or inappropriate applications or to tense resentful feelings which will be reflected in behavior with children. Teachers can be stimulated to a broader awareness of the child's needs in the environment by observing children in different day-care and nursery school settings and discussing them with the director or with visiting educators.

There are many questions about how to help the cognitively and emotionally deprived child which cannot yet be answered. We need the observations and records of trial efforts of many different supervisors, teachers, child-care workers, and other professionals in contact with groups of children who are receiving care for the first time. Discussions can deal with broad questions as well as with concerns about individual episodes and children. For example:

What do we mean by stimulating the culturally deprived? What kinds of stimulation are needed in this group? How much? Offered by whom? When? What criteria can be used in evaluating the results?

What if it "doesn't take" with 25 per cent of the children? What is going on within the children when they daydream and don't "take in" cognitive stimulation?

Do some children need relief from anxious preoccupations before they can respond to other cognitive stimulation? Can children be helped with anxieties about the "Bogey Man"? About mother's illness? Father's absence? A new baby? A teacher's departure? A community disaster, such as a fire or tornado?

Do some need support for cognitive interests they already have? How does one reconcile "beginning where they are now" with additional opportunity?

How do we know when children are becoming surfeited with too much or do not have the right kind of stimulation?

If some children are behaving in "undesirable" ways, how can we understand why they need to behave this way? Is it a necessary defense—although temporary—against threats which they cannot cope with in any other way?

No one has all the answers. The needs, conditions, and individual differences among children from different styles of family or neighborhood life are bound to vary in different settings. The supervisor as well as the teacher has much to learn. In a cooperative relationship each can learn from the other.

At the same time, the untrained teacher usually needs a few basic guidelines aimed toward the protection of the child. She needs techniques in learning how to keep an eye on a whole group at once, how to get children to eat, and a host of other skills. As problems arise, the worker can be helped to think out loud about possible solutions, considering them with the supervisor.

Translating Goals into Environmental Terms

The lore of the nursery, handed on from mother to mother, and the "bag of tricks" of the nursery school teacher are seldom written down. When persons trained in other specialties are faced with making practical application of such phrases as "sensory stimulation" or "selective differentiation of the environment," they may not have the slightest idea what to do with the very young child to make such rarefied goals come to life.

For such persons—people trained in elementary or secondary education, psychology, sociology, and other disciplines—some of these simple essentials are spelled out below. Such readers will also wish to consult good textbooks in early childhood education and the inexpensive pamphlets published by the Children's Bureau of the Department of Health, Education, and Welfare.

A. *Equipment and experiences.*
   1. For body-building, developing coordination, etc.
      Indoors: Steps; large block-constructions; circle games with marching and running; stretch–roll–crawl exercises; scrubbing, cleaning, and sweeping; indoor climbing equipment.
      Outdoors: Wheel toys, tricycles, wagons, etc.; large building equipment, big blocks, boards, boxes, places to dig, and tools for digging; climbing opportunities: steps, jungle gym ladders, ramps, saw-horses, large sewer pipes for tunnels, low trees.
   2. Materials to stimulate tactual discrimination and knowledge: toys, cloth and other materials, pencils, clay, blocks, fit-together toys, water, sand; seeds, beans, lentils; pine needles, cones, leaves, rocks, logs; Montessori-type equipment which stimulates awareness of size and which can be assembled inexpensively.

      If no water is available for play, a wooden or metal tub or small plastic pool can be provided for indoor or outdoor use.

      Plastic material such as dough, finger paints, sand, water, etc., can be used expressively and creatively. These so-called "unstructured" materials contribute to integration by evoking fantasy and expression of ideas. Blocks of different sizes, materials, colors, and shapes can stimulate awareness of comparative sizes and structural relationships and construction of more complex objects than can be managed with sand or mud.

      Both soft, cuddly toys and plastic materials are often omitted from nurseries on the grounds that they are hard to keep clean or to clean up after. This is only one example of serious psychological deprivation for the sake of perfectionistic cleanliness.

      Visual experience is an aspect of tactual experience for sighted children, but they also need to be stimulated to observe, watch, and put their observations into words. Arrangements on the walls and in cupboards should be orderly and foster recognition and choice.

      Auditory experiences are also important. Sounds need to be experienced and talked about: bells, simple musical instruments, pots and pans, blocks or toys falling, rain, wind. The child develops understanding of concepts and language through sharing and communicating his experiences. Sounds are made by things—bells, etc. Sounds are also made by people talking softly or loudly, yelling, whispering, laughing, crying, singing, clapping hands, stomping on the floor.

B. *Mental development can be fostered.*

1. All the above stimulate the child's development of basic concepts, such as "under" and "over"; "big" and "little"; "soft" and "hard"; "together" and "apart"; "alike" and "different"; "heavy" and "light"; "slow" and "fast"; and many others. But the child needs stimulation for more complex ideas and understandings, such as "road" and its uses; "bridge," "house," "store," "garage," "airplane," "auto," "train," and concepts of going places.

   Capacities to organize, relate, and integrate details are stimulated by the use of toys, puzzles, and building materials. Stories and pictures should be both heard and told. Trips to observe buildings and workmen expand the child's knowledge of the world.

2. Conversation about experiences is more than asking and answering questions. True discussion includes sharing feelings of surprise, interest, pleasure, and discomfort, and helping the child to put into words what is going on. The ability to pay attention, to become interested in objects and how they work, in events and what brings them about, grows out of such shared experience with an adult who pays attention to and is interested in the child's experience.

   Children who have been neglected or inadequately cared for by deaf, ill, too busy, tired, retarded, or withdrawn mothers need special help in communication. This comes most naturally when the teacher or helper talks to the child about whatever is being done, giving names to objects and activities. Then she responds to the child's expressions of feelings, wishes, or explanations of his activity.

   Children can also extend their ability through singing in unison and talking about what they sang about. The teacher can stimulate expression of wishes and interests by asking for choices. Every good teacher is in constant contact with her children, ready to respond to both verbal and nonverbal communications, to help the child feel that she is interested in what he is doing, his thoughts and feelings, and that what he says is important.

   Eating times are good periods for sharing conversation and for other warm interaction which will reinforce the child's response to what is given to him and encourage communication and expressiveness. Satisfying eating experiences play a major role in stimulating positive feelings about the environment and about relations with people. Greater alertness and arousal, including greater responsiveness to other stimulation, follows.

3. Curiosity and cognitive stimulation require a variety of experiences. The regular introduction of new objects, new pictures, new books, new stories, and new songs which are selected in relation to the interest and the experiences of the children contributes to cognitive stimulation. Children can make up simple songs or enjoy those concocted by the caretaker. With infants and children under three, very simple rhythmic repetitions of a tuneful phrase or sentence makes learning new words fun. So does conversation about observed inanimate and animate objects—how an inchworm walks as contrasted with an ant or a caterpillar or a spider or a turtle. Respect for the child's discoveries and response to what he wants to express supports his capacity to communicate and also to think about his observations. The teacher can ask questions about the everyday experiences of the child, ask him to describe what he has noticed, help him to see more clearly by the use of small magnifying glasses which make a snowflake or a bug clearer. Her interest will encourage the small child to ask questions and the teacher can help him to put his observations together.

When a child observes something interesting, the teacher can ask him to tell the other children about it, perhaps at juice or lunchtime. As she asks other children to compare their own observations, she encourages them to recognize the value of their individual experience.

4. Imagination, plans, and the future. Play at "pretend" games can be stimulated by the teacher. Through word games, she can stimulate imagination and help a child to recall the past and plan the future. These activities are important in the integration of experience and development of understanding. For example, "Let's play that Mary is the mother and Joe is the daddy and they are just waking up in the morning. What will you do?" If the children are hesitant and totally unresponsive to her verbal suggestions, the teacher can, herself, enter the "pretend" game. After the children have participated by following the teacher's lead, they will develop their own imaginative activities. Observations on trips in the neighborhood can contribute new ideas: "We saw the mail man today. Billy, you can be the mail man and show us what he does."

New experiences stimulate a very realistic type of imaginative activity and provide the material for more elaboration by the child later.

Planning together what to do after nap time helps the children to be aware of sequences, then time, and is an impetus to use imagination realistically.

C. Social development

1. Children need stimulation to achieve a group feeling, and to develop the capacity to help each other and work together. They can make a house together, carry long boards together to make a road or fort, make a sand tunnel together, or push each other in a swing. These and similar activities involve the collaboration of two children.

   Children can help button each other's coats, hunt for lost mittens, clean a sink together, and do many other things if the teacher is interested in helping the children in a flexible way to learn to cooperate. It is important not to overdo this or let it get mechanical, self-righteous, or false. Several children can make a picture book together, each child contributing a picture for one page. They can develop group feeling from sitting together to hear stories, from group singing or listening, marching or clapping, or dancing to music.

2. Certain activities contribute to self-reliance and autonomy.* Among them:

   Dressing oneself when possible.

   Washing and cleaning oneself as well as objects in the nursery school (paint jars and juice cups, the plastic apron used while finger painting, etc.).

   Preparing simple foods (mixing, cutting, molding dough for cookies; shredding lettuce; decorating cookies, cupcakes, etc.).

   Table setting and serving; carrying the basket of cookies around and holding it for each child to help himself; pouring milk.

   Putting away toys and other equipment. Such experiences can develop responsibility and also stimulate clearer awareness of order and space. What will fit? What belongs

---

* "Basic education" as developed in India is directed toward helping the child contribute actively to the fundamental needs of life. By its principles, stimulation and support is given to increasing self-sufficiency and self-respect as the child matures.

with what? Is there enough room for this? Finding answers to such questions helps to clarify the child's concepts and ability to organize.

Helping teacher by bringing objects on request, etc.

Feeding the rabbits, birds, fish or other pets.

Summary

Nurses, caretakers, and parents may be observed at any point along a range from utterly matter-of-fact routine handling of babies to actively exploiting and overstimulating them by excessive tickling, bouncing, throwing, etc., to the point where the baby no longer enjoys these activities but is upset, exhausted, angry, or frightened. At both of these extremes the baby is treated essentially as a *thing*. The infant's feelings are not recognized, and the later consequences of constant early disorganization are not understood. Crying, even screaming, is not perceived as an expression of distress or disturbance but simply as a baby's way of letting off steam.

By contrast with both of these extremes, good care of infants and young children is alert to the likes and dislikes of each baby, what each one can take and tolerate, what helps each one to develop interest in the outside world and in people, and regards each as an individual human being.

REFERENCES

Bowlby, J. Psychopathological Processes Set in Train by Early Mother-Child Separation. In M. J. E. Senn (Ed.), *Problems of Infancy and Childhood.* New York: Josiah Macy, Jr., Foundation, 1954, pp. 38–87.

Murphy, L. B. *Social Behavior and Child Personality. An Exploratory Study of Some Roots of Sympathy.* New York: Columbia University Press, 1937, pp. ix, 344.

———. Some Aspects of the First Relationship. *International Journal of Psycho-Analysis,* 45: 31–44, 1964.

———, et al. *Widening World of Childhood. Paths toward Mastery.* New York: Basic Books, 1962, p. 399.

Pavenstedt, E. A Comparison of the Child Rearing Environment of Upper-Lower and Very Low-Lower Class Families. *American Journal of Orthopsychiatry,* 35: 89–98, 1965.

Woodcock, L. *Life and Ways of the Two-Year-Old.* New York: Basic Books, 1952.

PART II

Translating Child Care Goals into Procedural Terms

It is one thing to say that babies differ in their needs and another to identify and arrange the resultant variables so that they lead into a plan for action. The two psychologists who have contributed to this section, Lois Barclay Murphy and Jacob L. Gewirtz, reflect quite different theoretical orientations.

Dr. Murphy suspends the child in his environment and proceeds to examine both so meticulously that we can almost see the play of light and shadow as if cast by hidden spotlights on a theater marquee. In the resulting illumination, a rationale for selecting a child's experiences emerges in everyday nursery terms and activities. Dr. Gewirtz chooses to conceptualize the environment in terms of the stimuli which have a discernible impact on the behavior of the infant. In his terms, there is no "deprivation," "enrichment," or "tender loving care" except as these aspects of the caretaking environment elicit (or fail to produce) a response which is, on the one hand, valued and reinforced or, on the other, overlooked by the caretaker.

Both authors direct their comments to specific means by which caretaking can produce patterns of behavior in children which are functionally adaptive in our society.

6

Assessment of Infants and Young Children

LOIS BARCLAY MURPHY

Assessment of infants and young children for the purpose of guidance, care, and prevention of interferences to growth requires a different orientation from the more customary assessment in a medical setting. There, assessment has been typically oriented toward classification of pathology or deviation from standardized norms. But growing children characteristically show different kinds of transient symptoms at different developmental phases. While these may sometimes be precursors of later illness, symptoms in and of themselves cannot be sufficient to guide the handling and care of the child. Moreover, individual differences in growth rate and growth patterns during infancy and the early years make rigid standards and fine discriminations in mental level much less useful than they are at later ages.

What is needed is an assessment which would simultaneously

keep several factors in focus: (1) the child's over-all developmental status and degree of freedom from defect or damage; (2) the child's individual growth pattern in relation to his needs and to his guidance and care, whatever the setting; and (3) the types of stress to which he is predisposed by the foregoing factors in combination with his setting, his ways of coping with stress, and his means of mastering problems created by his individual patterns of behavior and by over- or under-stimulation from the environment.

It is obvious that in this approach, assessment would be oriented not primarily toward norms, but rather toward the recognition of the tremendous individual differences in babies and young children, in their rates of growth, patterns of development, individual interests, and needs. We are seeking a comprehensive picture, at a given time, of the child's functioning in terms of the environmental setting of his life and of his pattern of vulnerabilities and strengths as these have evolved from the prenatal period on.

The Immediate Aims of Assessment

Assessment of the developmental status of a young child may be undertaken on various levels and for many reasons. For example, it may be timed in order to evaluate a child's readiness for a major environmental change, such as entering a day-care center, nursery school, Sunday school, or kindergarten. It may precede the proposed absence of parents for a vacation, hospitalization of the mother, travel, or moving to a new home. A study may be helpful before the arrival of another child in the family, proposed operative procedures, such as a tonsillectomy, or any opportunity which would test the child's potentialities.

Evaluation of the infant may be oriented somewhat differently than evaluation of the young child. Infant evaluation would include (1) the *assessment of normality*, as in a clinical evaluation of the infant (Escalona and Moriarty, 1961) or as it is done in planning for adoption or foster-care placement; (2) the *assessment of potential reaction to separation* from the first caretaker, mother or mother-substitute (Yarrow, 1961); (3) the *assessment of development* in a given institutional setting (Provence and Lipton, 1963); or (4) *assessment of individual tendencies* likely to influence the course of development. In these assessments, the vulnerability of the infant in relation to his strengths and to his specific needs from the environment are considered. Also, the infant's interests, selective responses to the environment, capacities, coping patterns, and assets which need support and appropriate resources in the environment are studied in detail. Detailed analysis of developmental difficulty or failure may be undertaken to provide understanding and a basis for assisting the child to cope with his difficulties. This strategy is most clearly seen in cases of crippled, blind, deaf, or obviously brain-damaged children who, with or without the help of mechanical aids or prosthetics, are helped to make maximal use of their capabilities. In the good school or hospital, these children are helped to compensate for their diagnosed defects, to develop skills of many kinds, and to enjoy play and work with other children.

Obvious, easily visible disease, damage, or defects can be recognized at least to a certain extent by lay people as well as by professional workers. Mothers or other persons in contact with the child will usually seek help to clarify the degree and source of the problem and to remedy the difficulty as far as possible. But mild motor or sensory defects in coordination, hearing, vision, etc., are often not recognized until a child enters school. In the meantime, during his first five or six years, the child has developed his own combinations of defensive maneuvers, withdrawal or hyperactivity, positive coping efforts combined with habits of avoiding situations which he cannot manage adequately. He may be managing well or poorly; he may have missed experiences needed for adequate development and may thus appear retarded.

Often the "normal" child is assumed to be free from gross difficulties and receives little or no help with lesser although sometimes multiple handicaps. His difficulties may gradually become cumulative, interacting with his frustrated feelings, the annoyance or pressure from parents, and the usual conflicts and rivalries in the family. Hence, it is of the utmost importance to diagnose even mild degrees of hearing loss or defect, visual difficulties, motor difficulties, visual-motor coordination, problems in control, etc., during the earliest years so that adequate compensation can be provided sufficiently early and the child can be given the specific kinds of help needed for active mastery of the demands of the environment.

For instance, whenever a child shows extreme hesitation to orient himself in new situations, one needs to know if the child has specific difficulties which make orientation hard for him. Hesitation or slow orientation may be felt as withdrawal or unresponsiveness by other children or by adults not aware of the myopia, hearing loss, or whatever interferes with the child's grasp of a situation. Moreover, a wide variety of primary conditions—developmental imbalances, sensitivities, and ambivalent reactions to stimulation—interact with the child's capacity to employ his resources, to adapt himself to the environment, and selectively to adapt the environment to himself. All outcomes of these interactions are affected as well by the modulating or exacerbating influences of the infant's interaction with his mother and other salient persons in the environment.

We would do well then to check every zone in evaluating the adequacy of, or deficiencies in, the equipment of the child. By definition, we expect deviations from the optimum as well as from the average. Roger Williams (1956) documents the wide range of deviations from the norm within normal samples. Because we are concerned with the functional consequences of such variations, we have intensively studied a sample of "normal" children growing up in relatively stable, yet normally stressed, working-class and business-class families.* Among these we found one or more infantile disturbances of smooth functioning in at least half of the babies: vegetative difficulties (colic, elimination difficulties, sleep problems, etc.), autonomic lability, high sensitivity or reactivity to stimulation, proneness to infectious illnesses, and developmental imbalances, or imbalances of input-output exchange with the environment. The more extreme degrees of these ordinary variations in functioning and the outcomes of interaction of several of these were often found in association with infantile irritability and unhappy mood level, and with some tendency toward persistent hostile or depressed undertones through later stages of development (Murphy and Moriarty, forthcoming).

SUMMARY

A survey of potentially positive and negative factors in the child, in the environment, or in their interaction may provide a basis for selection of experiences which will compensate for limitations and promote positive development. Certain children seem to be particularly

* Data on the infants are discussed in connection with their later development in Murphy and Moriarty (forthcoming); see also Gardner and Moriarty (1968), Escalona and Heider (1959), and Heider (1966).

vulnerable to developmental damage from such factors. When done carefully, the assessment can lead to a prescription of help needed to further the child's development, whether he is in a day-care center, nursery school, hospital, other institution, or at home.

The Concept of Vulnerability

We are now in the process of recognizing certain environments as a predisposing factor in the vulnerability of children. The situation as defined by Drillien (1964) in Scotland may be characteristic of some communities in this country as well. He reports that 75 per cent of premature infants of very low socioeconomic status *and* with "inadequate" mothers were found to have problems at the preschool stage. The percentage of problems was less when mothering was "adequate." Such findings suggest the desirability of careful assessment of the factors potentially affecting development, especially in infants and young children, from any one, or combination of, so-called "high-risk" categories. "High risk" implies proneness to severe difficulties and can characterize communities, families, mothers, or infants.

Among high-risk communities we would pay special attention to the *disorganized* lower socioeconomic class. It should be recognized that material deprivation does not necessarily imply emotional deprivation; nor does deprivation necessarily imply disturbance. In fact, in the United States there has not yet been adequate study of the strengths in *stable* lower socioeconomic groups. Instead, attention has been focused on the low drive to achievement, lack of preparation for school work, and widespread health problems. In the process of correcting these deficits, it is important to learn more about, and to protect, the positive coping resources which have also been characteristic of many of the people in healthier low socioeconomic groups.

As it now stands, however, disadvantaged children—that is, children from the lowest socioeconomic groups—may be expected to show different and more difficulties than children from higher groups. The difficulties are directly and indirectly related to several factors. General stimulation deficit, monotony, chaos or confusion in the home and community may occur. There may be disturbed emotional relationships and/or mental illness in the family (Srole et al.,

1962), especially depression in mothers. Greenacre (1952) finds a predisposition to anxiety; major control or integrative difficulties may be due to prematurity and other pregnancy or delivery stress (Pasamanick and Knobloch, 1956). Lauretta Bender cites poor vegetative functioning, motor integration, and other problems in infancy related to various combinations of the above. We have seen inadequate autonomy of cognitive and other basic ego functions resulting from a chronic state of distress and vegetative disturbance.

Among high-risk mothers we would note especially those with sensory defects, deficiencies of strength, energy, or physical resources as well as apathy, depression, extreme passivity, excessive lability, and marked irritability or hostility (Murphy and Moriarty, forthcoming). We can assume that the care of the infant is likely to be inadequate in certain respects, and in some cases, the relationship between the infant and mother will be disturbed. Recently various agencies and legislatures have had to take a closer look at the sheer risk of physical damage to the infant or young child by disturbed or frantic parents. The term "battered child," with its unhappy connotations, has come into wide use. Therefore, assessment of children of high-risk groups or mothers needs to review the early history and its consequences, and the detailed difficulties and needs of these children.

High-risk children include the genetically handicapped and others vulnerable to stress related to specific lacks. Pasamanick and his collaborators (1955) and other investigators of retardation (Hunt, 1961) have clarified the fact that in an enormous number of "mildly retarded" children, the retardation is associated with deprived home and social conditions. The real question becomes why some children succumb to such damaging conditions while others withstand them. This requires us to think in terms of a borderline or "vulnerable" group of children whose development may be distorted by the *interaction* of different combinations of constitutional and environmental factors and by the cumulative sequels of these interactions.

A few investigators such as Sheldon have commented on the special vulnerability of children within the normal range who have, however, certain deviant patterns of body build and constitutional equipment, such as extremely ectomorphic boys. Investigators studying growth (e.g., Stolz, 1951) have pointed out the vulnerability of children with deviantly rapid or slow growth rates who are, nevertheless, still within the normal range. We have slowly acquired the basis, then, for thinking more clearly about vulnerability in the child without gross abnormalities. An inventory of significant areas is contained in Appendix A.

The Scope of Assessment

The scope of assessment will vary depending on the aims and uses to which it will be put. For example, a relatively limited assessment may be focused on ruling out or diagnosing major defects, disease, injury, or developmental disturbance. This is one aim in assessing the suitability of a child for a given group experience. By contrast, a more comprehensive demand may be made, as in research, for a developmental profile of the child's maturity in different lines of development at behavioral levels (Freud, 1965; Doll, 1932, 1953) and physiological levels (wrist X-rays, pediatric measurements, etc.). Such a profile needs to consider the relation of the child's developmental patterns to expectations in a given subculture group, including the expectations in the day-care center and, by implication, the relation of the child's pattern to that of others in the group. Some cultural variations in expectations are explored below.

A more pointed evaluation of developmental hazards and resources will be offered by an inventory of the child's vulnerabilities and strengths, and an analysis of the interaction of these with each other and the environment, the way in which the child uses these vulnerabilities and strengths, and the resulting adaptational style or self-image of the child.

Assessment of a severely disturbed child who has been causing anxiety to parents and others, in addition to showing evidence of being grossly unhappy or blocked in development, requires all of the interdisciplinary resources which can be mobilized. A pediatrician, psychiatrist, psychologist, psychiatric social worker, neuropsychologist, and other examiners as needed should be involved. Together, they may reach an understanding of what is wrong in the child's experience, what is contributed from his own intrinsic handicaps, and what environmental disturbances have interfered with his adaptation efforts.

When it is generally agreed a child is functioning very well, accepts substitutes and change easily, and is able to use the environment in satisfying ways, minimal formal examination data will be needed to provide a baseline record of the child to which later changes may be compared. The basic height, weight, adequacy of nutrition, activity level, balance of developmental achievement, ways of using drives, and maturity of drive development, style of relating, and selective interests in the environment can be noted with relatively little investment of professional time. It should be possible to evaluate the child's health and general level of functioning with a relatively quick examination by a public health nurse or other person, who in addition to basic professional training, receives some special training for the assessment process.

Nonnormative or individualized assessment is concerned with an evaluation of a child's development in relation to what should be expected of him, given his equipment—vulnerabilities and strengths—in a specified subculture and family with its unique supports, demands, deprivations, and stress. A level and pattern of cognitive functioning, verbal communications, etc., which would be accepted for a child in a working-class family might be inadequate for a child in an intellectual family. The degree of independence achieved by two- to three-year-olds in a rural setting, which has permitted great autonomy and freedom for motor explorations, cannot be expected of a metropolitan city child brought up in an apartment and whose opportunities for autonomy are drastically reduced. Control of urination commonly developed in young infants in Nigeria, where babies are carried on the mother's back under parts of her clothing, cannot be expected of the infant in American culture, whose toilet training often does not begin until walking is well established and "the child is old enough to understand."

Moreover, different subcultures, even within a rather limited geographical area, may provide widely different patterns of stimulation, demands, support, and stress for the infant or young child. Opportunities for play with a wide range of materials are often far greater in middle-class families than in rural and some working-class families. Thus, failure to achieve the norm assumed to be desirable may reflect primarily the opportunities of and demands on the child rather than intrapsychic difficulties or conflicts.

Each of these subcultural patterns is likely to contribute to typical patterns of strength and weakness. For instance, traditional child-rearing patterns in India contribute to a high level of frustration tolerance but a lack of active drive to solve problems in new ways. In Nigeria and other parts of Africa, some local examiners feel that acquired retardation results from prolonged confinement to the mother's back; in orphanages in Iran and elsewhere, excessive confinement to cribs during the first two years of life has the same effect.

This type of retardation may be reversible when stimulation is offered during the next few years (Dennis and Najarian, 1957). Note again that there is inadequate definition of patterns in different studies of socioeconomic groups. While studies by Drillien (1964), Pasamanick and Knobloch (1956), and Srole et al. (1962) make a coherent picture, precise delineation of subgroups is needed.

ASPECTS OF THE FORMAL EXAMINATION

The strangeness of the examination and the examiner can create a source of error in assessment of infants and young children. Strange objects, instruments, and furnishings contribute to the orientation problem of infants, especially sensitive and differentiated infants and those who already have orientation difficulties. Reactive babies will not be the same in a doctor's office or research laboratory as they are at home. Many babies behave differently with father or siblings than with mother. Such variability is an important aspect of the appraisal.

The mother or familiar caretaker should always be present and hold the baby at least during the first part of the study. She may be encouraged to help the baby in her own way to "get used to" the new situation. The mother's report on aspects of the child's behavior in the study situation which are similar to his behavior at home is an important part of the record. Deviations from typical behavior and the conditions under which it occurs offer clues to the child's sensitivities and areas of stress, as well as his way of handling them. Allowing the mother and baby to play or allowing the mother to feed, change, and clean the baby provides opportunities for observation of the mother's ways of supporting and comforting the child and the child's ability to use support from the mother, provided the mother herself is not too inhibited by the examination situation.

During the extremely rapid developments of the first two years, any behavior of the infant should be considered in the context of what he is going through. He may be simultaneously teething, learning to creep, becoming aware of strangers, and developing impulses to throw and to retrieve. Each of these may evoke painful, frustrating, or anxious feelings and the combination may be more than he can manage alone. Marked withdrawal in a previously well-functioning baby is rather frequently noted at the eight- to ten-month-old stage, when all of these hazards confront the infant at one time. If the support of the familiar caretaker or mother is withdrawn at such a time, the chance of a traumatic outcome or interruption in development is greatly increased.

Failure to evaluate the current physical state of the infant is another major source of error. Fatigue, hunger, illness or aftereffects of illness, sleepiness, or other conditions affecting the baby's level of arousal may contribute to atypical reactivity—either hyper- or hypo-activity and responsiveness—compared with his functioning when comfortable and awake. If the baby has had painful inoculations, he may cry fearfully and be inhibited at the sight of a doctor in a white coat. Such a response may be positive evidence of alert awareness of the environment. The mother may speak about aspects of the situation which the baby associates with previous painful or frightening experiences.

Failure to respond, avoidance, turning away, or other forms of withdrawal cannot be treated routinely as failure in a test. Such responses reveal the infant's way of handling a strange situation as a whole or of handling a specific stimulus within the situation. It may be part of his strategy to gain time, to size up the new place or person, to make his own "cognitive map." Conversely, a high level of reactivity does not necessarily imply a high level of differentiation or integration. A very reactive baby may be all impulse, later prone to collide with the environment at the cost of bumps to himself and damage to the environment. Thus, the degree of purposefulness in activity needs to be considered from the beginning. Vague as a month-old baby's movements may seem, they can often be understood as reaching toward or pushing away, when the total situation is taken into account; they can often be the first steps in a profoundly important sequence of individual learning processes.

Wide scatter in mental functioning suggests disturbed development and can indicate zones where special help is needed in order to improve the child's skills, as well as the need for special resources to encourage exercise of individual interests and skills. A child's repeated failure to respond to any of a range of stimuli ordinarily included as part of an infant's or young child's experience may be a clue to current or imminent developmental difficulty. Potential indicators would be failure to respond to sound, to focus on visual stimulus, to explore visually or by touch, to make postural adjustments when being lifted, to smile at adults, to express delight at stimulating objects, to reach for objects, to practice motor skills such as rolling over, to use a playpen actively such as in pulling up or moving around, to play with toys, to bang or throw or try to evoke an adult's attention, and to seek comfort if made anxious by the approach of a stranger. In case the opportunity for such responses to be elicited does not occur spontaneously, one can purposefully handle the child in such a way that it will become apparent if understimulation or an inhibited response to overstimulation is contributing. If the infant continues to fail to respond, full professional assessment should be made to find the sources of difficulty.

INFORMAL OBSERVATIONS: ROLE OF MOTHER AND HOME VISITORS

Even the most complete standard examination in a doctor's office cannot provide important data on the child's behavior at home, both when maximally at ease and when threatened by home stress. Direct observation or current home reports will be needed to provide a comprehensive view of how the child uses his capacities, the ways in which his vulnerabilities and special needs interfere with his development, and aspects of the environment to which he responds positively and negatively.

The mother is often the most valuable source of information about the recent behavior of the baby. Her informal observations, paired with more systematic and formal records of professional observers, provide an important basis for tentative evaluations of an infant's resilience, persistence, sensitivity, and other variables basic to his adaptational style and capacity.

At successive developmental stages, it is important to have information gleaned in the midst of ongoing vicissitudes of life in his home environment, as well as the infant's responses in more or less standardized situations. Such data might well be elicited by asking: What experiences or circumstances are gratifying, frustrating, and disturbing? To what is the child indifferent? How does he respond to and deal with frustrating or satiating or disturbing experiences? How does the baby try to reach, prolong, or increase satisfying stimuli? If he is the kind of baby who "knows what he wants and when he wants it" or who is "easily insulted" or who "refuses to be held in a position he dislikes," how does the mother or caretaker respond to his decisiveness? If he becomes frustrated easily, how does the caretaker help him to develop more tolerance? The mother's response to such typical questions can be compared to the child's actual behavior during examinations or while under differing conditions or care.

REPEATED ASSESSMENTS

In order to provide for the optimal development of the individual child, assessment should define major aspects of the constitutional make-up of the child, weaknesses with which he may need help, strengths that can be fostered, and special interests which need support. When seen in these terms, assessment should not be a process which is completed at one phase; rather, it should include periodic reviews of the child's development, based on observations by caretakers and by the mother, as well as on periodic examinations oriented toward the particular questions relevant to the child's developmental stage and any critical phase that might accompany it. Responsibility for integrating and pursuing all the assessment findings from time to time may rest with the pediatrician, consulting psychologist, or professionally trained administrator.

In the process of recurring or continuing assessment, it is important to watch for evidences of the quality and level of differentiation and integration taking place in the individual child, and to modify the quantity and quality of care in relation to retardation or imbalances in development which may be reflecting caretaking defects in terms of the needs of the individual baby.

In particular, those doing the assessment need to be alert to the difference between babies who can make maximum use of crumbs of experience, or an available range of stimulus material which can be manipulated. There are babies who can stimulate the environment and evoke what they need, as contrasted with those who need stimulation or who withdraw excessively from unsatisfying experiences.

Individual differences in caretakers should be evaluated in relation to the needs of individual children. The personality style, tempo, stimulating qualities, and caretaking resources must be matched with the pattern of needs of the individual child.

Individual Differences and Their Relation to Assessment

Whatever the purpose of assessment, the evaluation of developmental status and progress of the infant and young child must be carried out in a context of awareness of the enormous range of normal individual differences in any sample of the population. A mother or continuous observer may note that a particular child "can do everything," "eats and sleeps well," "is interested in everything," "gets along with everybody," "is happy alone part of the time or with others part of the time," "knows what he wants and insists on getting it," "stands up for himself," "is satisfied with something else if he can't get what he wants." Or the mother or observer may note that the child is shy or hesitant, easily upset or anxious when mother leaves, cries easily, is frightened of strangers, does not get along with other children, isn't interested in much of anything, or "you have to buy his smiles."

Such leads are very important in establishing the picture of a given child's resourcefulness, independence, readiness to get along in a group, general level of well-being, and so on. One infant pattern within the normal range observable by the mother is that of the fussy baby. *Chronic*, as opposed to *occasional*, fussiness is unpleasant for the adult, but very often bespeaks the capacity of the child to be openly expressive about discomfort. The problem is to ascertain to what extent the discomfort arises from unpleasurable reaction to *external* influences—such as heat, cold, wetness, textures of materials surrounding the baby, uncomfortable postures, or inability to see or to hear—or to *internal* sources of discomfort and stress, such as gastrointestinal difficulty. Restlessness may also be seen when a sensitive baby is moved from his familiar setting to a new and strange one, when he is put into an unfamiliar crib or carriage, or when changes are made in furnishings, drapery, lights, or other background aspects of the surroundings. Sometimes fussiness or restlessness is due to discomforts which can be modified, and with a little assistance the baby can be helped to manage better. Perhaps he simply should be allowed freedom to wiggle or push to a different part of the crib. However, when a baby is, of necessity, exposed to a disturbingly strange environment, such simple changes in the setting may not be possible. The chief source of comfort would then be the reassuring, soothing response of the mother or caretaker through direct contact, such as patting, caressing, rocking, talking to the baby, arousing his interest in a preferred type of stimulus, such as light, a musical toy, or a fuzzy animal. His age may determine just what suits best.

Perhaps most important of all are the wide differences in emotional responsiveness and "sending power" which are so important in evoking the attention of adults and which contribute to a mutual sense of attunement. Mothers, and other adults as well, may feel rejected by an unresponsive, unsmiling baby; they may feel that their attention is not welcome or that it is useless to attempt to stimulate the child. Actually, unresponsiveness may be due to a wide variety of aspects of endowment or functioning of the baby. At the most extreme and pathological end, some degree of blindness or deafness or other difficulty in receiving stimulation may be involved. At the opposite extreme, an oversensitive baby may protect himself from the danger of being exposed to excessive stimulation by not responding positively to stimulation which is provided. There is some evidence that infants may either develop raised thresholds in order to reduce the impact of stimulation or simply show a type of withdrawal. However, it may be that the baby has highly selective preferences for certain kinds of stimulation which are not available and will become responsive only when these are provided. Between the extremes of the baby with some sensory defect and the baby who is oversensitive, we find normal babies who are relatively unresponsive except to a high degree of stimulation or to stimulation of certain kinds. For instance, some infants who do not respond to the small amount of visual, auditory, or tactual stimuli available in their ordinary surroundings may become much more eager and gay when handled vigorously with energetic bouncing, tossing, or tickling—a type of stimulation which might be distressing to another baby.

Highly sensitive and perceptive babies may sometimes remain passive longer than infants with a strong motor drive. Such passivity or a tendency to be preoccupied with receptive experiences may not be pathological at all, but simply reflect a natural need for a baby sensitive to many modalities of stimulation to have time for the clarification and differentiation of the rich experience which he is absorbing. Some of the infants who take in the environment in multidimensional and extremely refined terms can be seen to use in creative ways at later stages what they have assimilated. This is in contrast to the more gradual or step-by-step intake of other babies who are more vigorous physically and whose development of large muscle, and perhaps also of small muscle, coordination proceeds at a more rapid pace. Differences in muscle tone, sphincter control, and eye-hand coordination affect the child's rate of achievement and zest in mastery of the basic tasks of self-feeding and control of elimination. Along with these fairly obvious differences, quite normal infants and young children vary in alertness, pace of maturation, and sensitivity in different sensory areas. They range widely in their capacities to use their senses in orienting to the environment, to reach out for enough stimulation, and to protect themselves from excessive or unpleasant stimulation.

These, and many other specific characteristics interact with each other and with the environment to produce a particular style of adaptation in infancy, modified as the child matures and new potentialities emerge. It should be borne in mind also that—as Moss (1965) puts it—the infant at home "shapes" the mother or caretaker to respond appropriately to him by his smiles and by his distress. Mothers probably imitate their babies more than babies imitate mothers in their exchanges.

Modifications within the child will occur as new capacities emerge. A child who is easily frustrated and who cries or whines a great deal in the first two years may become much happier after locomotor and speech skills provide him with other ways of extracting what he desires—that is, after he is able to go and get or to ask for what he wants. The complexity of the interactions of these individually varying capacities contributes to the dynamically changing patterns of the child's personality. Although some children are very consistent from one stage to another, many others do a dramatic "turnabout." In some cases, the apparently soft, passive baby boy develops an unanticipated drive after acquired motor skills arouse new possibilities of exploring the environment. A baby who does "nothing but look and watch" sometimes becomes vigorously responsive and expressive, apparently after becoming sufficiently familiarized with the world. Consequently, we cannot judge the child's functioning solely in terms of his behavior. In order to judge whether specific treatment or changes in the environment are needed or whether it is reasonable to expect further progress with new emergent capacities, we need evidence about the kinds of stimulation the child is receiving, as well as data on his capacities. At the preschool stage, knowledge of the child's fantasy will sometimes help to forecast behavior changes.

In almost any traditional institution caring for babies from the neonatal stage to the age of two or three years, one can see an astonishing variety of responses to the environment. For example, among the babies from six to twelve months of age, there will be some pathetic infants who have hardly achieved a three- or four-month level of development: spindly, undersized and underweight, totally lacking in alert and eager responsiveness of the sort which is so delightful in the normal four- to six-month-old baby. These tiny human beings behave as if life held nothing good for them and no hope or expectation of goodness. They may stare, but there is no light in their eyes and not a hint of a smile. Babies like these, who seem to find nothing to live for, may die before they have achieved the capacity to move around in the environment and discover something in it for themselves.

In the very same nursery one may find babies at the same age who have managed to achieve something nearer normal size and weight and who show more capacity to evoke what they need from the environment. If they are in glass cubicles, they will reach out and try to bang on the cubicle to attract attention. If they are in a playpen, they will stick their arms through the spokes in the playpen to obtain a touch. Still, they do not smile and in the highly aseptic and conscientiously routinized hospital smiles rarely occur. Not all baby hospitals are like this, of course, and the proportion of children who manage to thrive is related to the level of understanding of needs of individual babies, the quality of relationship, and the response which caretakers give to the overtures from the babies themselves, along with the amount of affection, loving care, and play which they are able to provide.

In a nursery with a larger proportion of caretakers to babies—one caretaker for every three or four babies instead of one for eight to a dozen—much better health and much more responsiveness in the children may be found. Still, differences among individuals are very great. Certain babies will withdraw as far as possible from any stranger, while others will watch curiously, or, if they are able to move around, will reach out and approach the stranger, ready to make a contact. Some of the babies are making progress in speech, while others have developed very little. Some rock repetitiously in a playpen when they are not actively being cared for by an adult. Even in a hospital where there is a great deal of loving attention, the variety of materials made available to the babies may not be sufficient to sustain spontaneous exploration, manipulation, and active, persistent interest. If only rattles and blocks are available, for example, the materials do not differentiate or recognize the variations in interest of babies of different ages and abilities as would the contents, say, of a woman's handbag or a kitchen drawer.

Whether we are talking about very depriving group care for babies or about some of the better examples, we still find that there is a need for a far more systematic and sensitive assessment of the needs of individual babies as a basis for planning the care, the environment, the materials, and the opportunities which would meet the needs of the specific baby and make possible a more adequate realization of the potentialities of each one. For every baby there is a level of both quality and quantity of stimulation which evokes a response that leads to interaction with adults or other children and thus to integrative development, communication, and active experiencing and mastery of the environment. The level must be ascertained for each baby if we are to protect him from personality disturbances.

IMPLICATIONS OF VARYING PATTERNS

Bright and very bright children usually can do things earlier than a more average child. Thus, a well-developed bright three-year-old (IQ 130) may function at a four-year-old level in sensorimotor tasks, visual discrimination, speech, etc. But if this same child is only three years old in emotional experience, he may be under considerable pressure if he is expected to be as mature emotionally as he is in motor and verbal skills. Differences in emotional maturity may be as great as cognitive differences. Thus, emotional, intellectual, and motor levels need to be studied separately. Inferences from one area to another can be misleading, since not many children are advanced in all areas to the same extent.

All children need help in balancing their weaknesses, and they need time for the maturation of those functions which are slower than others. A mildly retarded child (IQ 70) may be behind the average three-year-old, more nearly approximating the two-year-old's behavior in verbal or motor skills. But this child has lived three years, and if he has been handled well he may have more composure or more social skill than the normal two-year-old who is at a similar verbal level. Some mildly retarded children have considerable social warmth and adaptability, a positive value which needs to be considered in planning for the child.

Children show a wide variety of patterns of relative strengths and weaknesses. Convenient distinctions can be made between those who are better at verbal activities than at performance, and vice versa. The child who is skilled in manipulation, making things, solving puzzles, handling his body, and in motor activities generally, may need more attention and help in the areas of speech, communication, playing with other children, preparation for reading, etc. Beyond these broad differences, a given child may have a lack in one specific area in which he needs help: handling a zipper, tying his shoelaces, using scissors. In another dimension, he may need help in understanding time and the words used to express this concept, in expressing feelings of fear or anger, in tolerating postponement, frustration, or interruption, finding substitutes when something is used up or not available, and in choosing between alternatives.

No available test adequately assesses the ordinary everyday strengths and weaknesses of children, their skills, and their coping resources. Only through living with the child and watching where he has trouble can it be discovered what specific help he needs. Help in using materials, in getting along with children, and in handling his disappointments may be as important as help in observation, learning vocabulary, or mastering a tricycle. Some children take much longer than others to develop any of these skills. Some simply need more time and practice on their own, while others need to have the task broken down into steps or explanations of what will help.

Just as important as the basic capacities of the child are the individual ways in which he uses his resources—sometimes referred to as "integrative functions" or "ego functions." Here, we include the child's openness to the environment, to new experience, and his investment in the world; his responsiveness to people and sending power; his selectivity, decisiveness, and autonomy in using the environment; his flexibility and capacity to accept or to reject in different situations; his restructuring capacity and capacity to impose his own structure on the environment; his control of drives, sublimation, and use of aggression for problem solving versus destruction; and his social participation and use of erotic drives for warmth as compared with seductiveness or extreme exhibitionism. As listed, these functions could be applied to any age; yet their beginnings can be seen as early as the first six months of life. Evaluation must take into account the appropriate level and balance of these resources at the age level of the child being studied, and the feedback his behavior elicits from adults.

Similarly, even minor defects, damage, or weaknesses can threaten the development of the child's ego function. Such defects might include undiagnosed nearsightedness, which interferes with the important early orientation processes of the child in his environment; hearing difficulties resulting from repeated ear infections or congenital nerve loss; height-weight imbalances or other skeletal imbalances, or mild deviations such as in structure of the feet (for example, a very long narrow foot in a heavy child). Any of these may contribute to locomotor difficulties which in turn interfere with the development of play and mastery of the environment generally. Extended illnesses which have involved long confinement to crib or playpen or extensive bandaging, such as that used with severe infantile eczema, will interfere with both locomotor development and the autonomy which it should have been stimulating. Marked skin sensitivity, which makes many kinds of contact in the environment uncomfortable for the child, may result either in his becoming appropriately selective in his responses to the environment or in a general tendency to retreat from contact experiences. If he chooses the latter, reduction of direct contact and manipulatory experiences may then underlie defects in the child's mastery of the environment, so that the child seems less resourceful and shows less understanding than other children who have had a wider and freer experience and have become more knowing.

Only recently have effects of low levels of brain damage begun to be understood. While much more research is needed, research by Pasamanick and Knobloch (1956) and others noted above indicate that some or all of a wide range of adaptational difficulties ("behavior problems") and learning difficulties are to be found in children with histories of prenatal and birth difficulties. At the extreme end of the continuum we have Lauretta Bender's report of integrative difficulties from earliest infancy in every zone among schizophrenic children; and there is Rimland's (1964) marshaling of evidence for organic deficit in extremely autistic children. It seems fair to assume, pending further research, that we can think of a continuum of central-nervous-system adequacy; and between the optimum at one end and extreme deficit at the other end, there are gradations—probably not occurring in a normal distribution curve—which to varying degrees affect the adaptational capacities of the infant and child. Depending on their nature and scope, such mild deficits may interfere with perceptual, motor, or affective control, or combinations of these. Lowered thresholds for anxiety or anger may leave the child vulnerable to deprivation and frustration. Long before he enters school, the child with a mild deficit is generally exposed to greater frustration by his difficulties in self-help and in motor skills typical for his age group. Thus, he may be a frustrated and "difficult" child even when—or because—a great deal of care is provided in the family.

DIFFICULTIES AND SOURCES OF ERROR

It can be seen from the preceding discussion of individuality that there are many pitfalls in any kind of assessment. While correlations between infancy test scores and later scores are limited as reported in longitudinal studies of mental development (Bayley, 1949), it has been demonstrated that infants selected as falling within the normal range proved to be normal at the latency stage (Moriarty, 1966, p. 190). However, there may have been "false negatives," that is, Escalona may have rejected infants from the normal group who functioned normally later (Escalona and Moriarty, 1961). If so, these were not identified, since no follow-up study of the rejected infants has been done. While Gesell's eighty biographies (1939) include children who were slow as infants and later average or superior, as well as cases of the opposite, his groups do not include defective children. A study in Hawaii (Bierman et al., 1964) shows that a team consisting of a pediatrician, a psychologist, and a social worker can provide a more accurate prediction of later functioning than an examination conducted by any one of these persons alone.

All these studies focus on the infant himself, as he is seen in terms of his developmental accomplishments or skills. In view of what we are learning about the infant's need for optimal stimulation and his very early defensive reactions to narrowed or to excessive stimulation, it seems clear that all evaluations and predictions of developmental achievements should be made in relation to the interaction between the infant and his environment (see Chapter 5). Similarly, other constitutional characteristics which would tend to accelerate or to delay the integration of early perceptual, manipulative, and motor achievements would need to be taken into account. Finally, illnesses or any other events or experiences contributing to restriction of the environment or of the infant's capacity to respond to the environment, and any traumatic experiences, such as abrupt changes of physical setting or caretaker, must be considered as well.

Mild delays of development occurring under negative conditions (constitutional, health, or environmental factors whose effect may be temporary) are of less significance than delays for which causal factors cannot be identified readily. It seems probable, however, that certain general or pervasive characteristics of the organism will prove to have greater consistency from infancy to later stages. These might include such qualities as smoothness of coordination, tempo, alacrity, amount of vocalization, sensitivity, reactivity, lability, tendencies toward stiffening and rigidity versus flexible adaptability, acting on the environment, equanimity versus predisposition to anxiety, persistence in problem solving. Even so, we expect to find shifts in behavior characteristics as the stressful, supportive, stimulating, or depriving aspects of the environment modify the early patterns. We find that certain babies who develop well and reflect a high level of comfort in infancy have little need to develop techniques for coping with frustration and in later childhood become easily discouraged, even embittered, when gratification does not come so effortlessly. So we cannot think of "optimum environment" as equivalent to "maximum serenity." Rather, it appears that good development in the long run involves the presence of enough challenge, frustration and difficulty to evoke the child's resourcefulness and to prepare him for the likelihood that life will present him with problems that must be solved by his own efforts.

In line with this, we do not find the best development coming about when mothers are infinitely attentive, anticipating every need before the infant has a chance to become aware of it, and providing utterly dependable gratification. Too much, as well as too little, attention, perceptiveness, and need-gratifying care interfere with the most adequate development of the infant's own resources. Either extreme "spoils" the baby. Thus, we have to gauge carefully what actually is "too much" or "too little" for the individual infant. There are no shortcuts to "knowing the baby," what it wants, needs, can and cannot "take."

DEVELOPMENTAL VICISSITUDES AND EVENTS

Beyond the evaluation of the ongoing setting for the infant's or the child's experience as it may have stimulated his coping resources or threatened his integration, an assessment is needed of consequences of ongoing significant events presenting special challenges or potentially contributing to traumatic effects. Examples would include prolonged or anxious separations from loved persons or places (whether by hospitalization, moving, illness, or death); body assaults, such as the baby's own illnesses, accidents, operations; or chronic stressful conditions, such as severe infantile eczema. These should be described in detail in relation to the frustration, challenge, stress, or handicaps they generate in relation to possible secondary gains and expectations of subsequent regression or rebound effects. Records at the time such potentially disturbing experiences occur would greatly facilitate accurate later evaluation of difficulties should they arise or subsequent individual adaptational patterns which need to be understood.

As part of assessment, the location of "critical periods" in the development of specific functions in the infant should be attempted. Specific kinds and amounts of stimulation which promote development vary with the developmental stage of the subject, his previous experience, and the range of stimulation to which he makes positive responses. Ongoing assessment should also evaluate the extent to which change might be disturbing to an infant or toddler. Change itself may not be as important as the timing, how comprehensive and extreme it is, the way in which change is handled with the child, and the extent to which the child's familiar attachments, habits, and needs are given consideration.

SELF-IMAGE

We also want to evaluate the child's self-image and self-feeling, including those aspects of functioning and his relations to the environment which contribute to the maintenance of healthy narcissism, pleasure in being himself, or sense of well-being, and beyond this a feeling of self-worth, respect, pride, and confidence. The first of these can be seen in infancy, while the additional aspects of self-feeling are differentiated and elaborated as the child matures. By the age of two or three, pride and self-respect become very obvious in the healthy well-functioning and respected child. If such positive feelings about self are lacking, it would be important to explore what feelings of rejection, shame, and anxiety, or what conflicts are already undermining the child's good feeling about himself. One part of this would be a careful study of the infant or child's interaction with significant adults and other children in the family, including the relation of their personality style, tempo, and ways of interacting with the baby to his response and level of self-feeling.

In addition, an assessment of environmental support and stress would include the physical care of the baby and his response to it and the emotional tone and atmosphere of the environment, whether there is a great deal of tension conflict, angry fighting or a physical attack of a nature which is frightening or depressing to the baby, and whether the day-by-day living patterns are chaotic or in other ways make it difficult for a baby to develop clear orientations and images of his world, and trust in his world and himself (Erikson, 1950).

DEVELOPMENTAL CHANGES IN DEFENSE MECHANISMS

Assessment of outcomes of all the interacting, preceding factors at successive stages would need to include an account of current patterns of regression and the extent to which this has been positively used and has led to resilience; depression and how severe and what developmental losses this has entailed; useful versus excessive self-protective retreats from the environment; and fixation of certain drive-focused patterns of functioning. Also, destructive or asocial reactions, retaliation, and the like should be noted along with resistance to socialization of aggression and factors contributing to this.

Disintegrative tendencies, reflected in qualitative or quantitative loss of cognitive functioning, of motor control, or affective depth, and the circumstances under which any combination of these takes place are important clues to what is stressful to the child.

Defense mechanisms used by the child most typically should be noted along with their effects. For instance, displacement can be useful if it is not too extreme and if it does not interfere excessively with the development of reality testing; also projection, when not extreme, can be a useful defense. Temporary denial is needed at times of extreme distress or pain, but it will contribute to a pathological development if it is too prolonged or too extreme.

It is also necessary to evaluate the child's capacity for mobilization of autonomous efforts and his capacity for compensation—using substitutes, evoking restitution, and using help of others in dealing with stress. Particularly important is the child's balance between use of his own resources and the help of the adult.

ENVIRONMENTAL AND AFFECTIVE FACTORS IN COGNITIVE DEVELOPMENT

Assuming freedom from genetic determinants of retardation, brain damage, disease, and the like, our hypothesis is that cognitive development depends on a healthy, eager investment in and response to the environment. A potentially stimulating environment provides for the elements of pleasure in the baby's or young child's interaction (gratification, response to what "the baby likes," the child's spontaneous interests); of mastery or achievement within the infant's or child's capacity; and of differentiation or actual differences which stimulate the baby to sort out the new from the old, the pleasant from the unpleasant, the dark from the light, the smooth versus the rough, and a host of other shades of reality.

Conditions must be such that these effects are facilitated. While spelled out more fully in Chapter 5, we might mention here the following requirements:

Opportunity for choice among a variety of possibilities, allowing the child to express his interests. Opportunities for change and new choices as challenges are successively mastered. Opportunities for experimentation with objects instead of pressure to handle them in stereotyped ways.

Conditions for integration that depend on time to assimilate, the length of time varying with the tempo of different children. The presence of objects which have the potentiality of being combined or being used in ways that produce different results—make noises, move, make interesting effects, etc.

Stimuli for curiosity as it is supported by the impulse and opportunity to search for new, interesting objects, later to take apart and discover parts and insides. Searching depends on availability of partly hidden objects or objects which have disappeared, and space to explore which contains unfamiliar objects.

Rewards for memory, remembering and finding (finding a treasured object where he remembered seeing it).

A sustained gratifying relationship with a caretaker that provides for him an example of interest, positive response, and enthusiasm for discovery; support for his spontaneous responses and choices, preferences and discoveries; rewards for active manipulation, making things happen, trying things out; responses to his vocalizations by "playing-back" and using his own syllables in meaningful, simple words with gratifying associations; and playful interaction, combined with words, in such activities as "Pat-a-cake," "Peek-a-boo," "Hide and seek" (Where is mommy?).

Expressions of approval, pleasure, and pride in the child's achievements and products.

The Outcomes of Assessment

After a picture of the child has evolved from formal sources of assessment and from less formal observations, answers to the following questions can become a guide to action.

What kinds of stimulation can this child at this age best use? In what quantities? In what time patterns?

How much protection does the infant or child need from what kinds of stimulation or conditions? What degree of intensity has a positive value for him? What extent or duration of stimulation is optimal—neither excessive and overwhelming nor too little to arouse interest and response?

What degree of structure, order and space, setting of time sequences, limits, etc., are helpful?

What degree of freedom can the individual baby use? Under what conditions? With what opportunities?

What kinds of special assistance, management, or therapeutic help does this young child need?

Restitution and support may be needed for the child deprived in one or more areas. If mildly apathetic, he may need emotional stimulation—carefully dosed—by special attention from a warm adult. He may need general improvement in the objects and sources of gratification available to him: sensory, sensorimotor, motor, speech and communication, play, social and other forms of stimulation selectively offered in terms of the readiness of the child. He may need individual attention for a specified length of time daily in order to achieve various goals. The mother or caretaker may wish simply to provide companionship or control or to evoke imitation or identification or a response. She may wish to teach or train in self-care (feeding, toileting, dressing) or in speech and communicative skills. She may seek to support or assist in play, work, chores, responsibility or contact with other children. Or she may wish to interpret, explain, give insight, resolve, or release feelings which the child has not been able to manage.

Restitution may be planned in specific areas. A child who is malnourished needs carefully selected protein, vitamin, or mineral supplements. A child deprived of adequate stimulation may need experiences with music (record players, instruments, singing); with color materials (finger paints, and paint with brushes); with motor stimuli (rocking toys, push toys, swings, slides, climbing apparatus); with cognitive stimulation (as provided by questions, trips, surprises, puzzles, stories, picture books, bright wall posters). The child may need help with speech stimulation (expression of needs, experiences, naming and asking) or with rest and sleep and other routine needs. A child may need protection: Sensitive children may need a time for semi-isolation and protection from overstimulation; poorly coordinated children may need protection from injury; allergic children and others have special food needs; easily fatigued, excitable children and those who have recently been ill need more rest and more time away from the group. Children prone to upper respiratory infections need more care regarding wind, temperature extremes, and drafts. In quite a different vein of thought, a child may need to be protected from overanxiety or from guilt and fear which can result, for example, from such events as breakage or destruction of objects, toileting accidents, anger at siblings, and so on.

The foregoing suggestions are not offered as a comprehensive list, but as illustrative of the many areas which will have to be considered.

APPLICATION TO DAY CARE

One outcome of careful assessment of large numbers of infants and young children will be the development of a variety of patterns of care from which programs could be selected after the needs and potential of each infant or child have been evaluated. How and to what extent an infant or young child's needs can or cannot be fulfilled in group care, how large a group can be tolerated by the child and for what length of time, in what kind of setting, with what kind and number of staff—these are questions which can be answered only with the help of relevant assessment.

One child may have the capacity to use group experience with the average amount of support from teacher and aides; another will need a one-to-one adult-child relationship; still another will respond to special equipment and handling such as given to atypical children in settings like the Boston Children's Center.

Assessment of potential reaction to separation from the primary caretaker (mother or mother-substitute) requires an assessment of the infant himself in terms of his relationship to the mother-figure and to substitute figures, his response to strangers and to strange places. Some children can immediately accept a separation, but not many middle-class, urban children are ready before the age of three (cf., film, "This is Robert"). Most four-year-olds and some three-year-olds are ready for group experience. But many two-year-olds and some three-year-olds still need extended orientation and support from the teacher as well as the presence of the mother for some time (Murphy, 1956; and film, "Patterns of Beginning"). Some children cannot tolerate separation until they have matured further or have recovered from trauma or vulnerability connected with earlier experiences. Counterindicators are intense fear of a stranger, acute separation anxiety, or marked sensitivity which would make the child vulnerable to overstimulation or to being too easily disturbed by noise in a group.

The length of day can be tailored to the child's ability to tolerate the group. Some can manage a whole day, from 7 A.M. or 8 A.M. to 5 P.M. Others can manage only three-quarters of the day, say, from

9 A.M. to 3 P.M. Still others thrive on a half-day, from 8:30 or 9 A.M. to 12 or 12:30.

To be considered also are the social capacities of the child with respect to his responsiveness to social stimulation, capacity to evoke response, his ability to cooperate, and the extent to which he can identify with others. In terms of self-functioning, the caretaker should consider the child's enjoyment and capacity for pleasure and the range of experiences enjoyed, the extent of his autonomous drives leading to self-care and initiative, and the level and sources of his anxiety.

OBSERVATION IN THE GROUP CARE SETTING

As the nursery school or day-care center becomes acquainted with the child, guidance can be formulated in terms of strengths and weaknesses in the child's functioning. Here the pattern of vulnerabilities and resources for adaptation underlying the infant's or child's developmental pattern should be seen. A complete vulnerability inventory is contained in Appendix A. Certain factors have particular relevance to the day-care setting, however, and some of these will be expanded at this time.

A young child will make more rapid progress if he is encouraged in what *he* wants to do or tries to do, if it is within his range and is acceptable to his mother or caretaker. Stimulation to the development of new, needed skills will be most effective after the child has developed confidence in the skills he already is working on. The sensitive caretaker is always confronted with the old dilemma of encouraging the child where he is able versus pushing him to acquire competence where he is not.

It is worthwhile for the teacher, nurse, or observer to spot carefully where each child stands: what he can and cannot do, i.e., his present areas of competence; what ordinary everyday problems he can and cannot solve; what he tries to do but still needs encouragement to support his persistent effort; what he needs some help with until his skill and his confidence improves; what he needs to master first before he can do something clearly beyond his present capacity.

The teacher or caretaker can also observe problems with which the child needs help or restitution. Such problems might include difficulty in separation; in sleep, energy level, fatigability, or other areas of physiological functioning; limited vocabulary; limited range of pleasurable experiences; tendency to become frustrated easily; lack of flexibility; lack of clarity about self; lack of control of impulses, emotional inhibition, unexpressiveness; inability to explore; inability to play; puzzlement or lack of familiarity with objects or routines and fearfulness related to these.

Children differ widely in the pace of motor development. Some learn to walk by the age of nine months and others not until seventeen or eighteen months. The amount of experience the child has had in getting around, learning to avoid bumps, steering himself through his environment, exploring his environment, and developing capacities to crawl under, over, etc., varies greatly. Thus, the amount of protection and need for opportunities for exploration varies. The kind of support in motor development that is naturally offered by members of a responsive family should be recognized in the day-care setting.

Visual and auditory functioning should be assessed especially in children who are hesitant or slow in orienting. About 25 per cent of our elementary school children need glasses; some of these were observed to have orientation difficulties in very early childhood. Visual difficulty can be an important factor in a child's capacity for adjustment in new situations, especially situations as complex as a group setting.

Similarly, mild hearing defects, which might not be noticed in the closeness of the family situation, are fairly common at the stage where children are having upper-respiratory infections involving ears, nose, and throat. Difficulties in auditory aspects of communication and orientation to the environment, by affecting speech and verbal development, will affect cognitive and social development generally.

Some children do not have adequate experiences of communication. This would include the child who has been left alone a great deal or who has been protectively kept in a playpen or a crib or other isolating device too long, the child who has been cared for by a nurse or mother who is hard of hearing or who has been left alone simply because of mother's fatigue, depression, illness, or lack of energy due to other reasons. Such a child may need more sustained one-to-one experience in active communication in order to provide the opportunities for development of passive speech, and the motivation for communication.

Problems of impulse control are apt to be triggered by explosive feelings of anger or fear in situations of frustration, attack by other children or other situations beyond the child's capacity. Inadequate expression of feelings and direction of impulses is apt to accompany poor development of communication, since children who cannot *talk* about their feelings are under greater tension and are more prone to explosive discharge, whether in affect storms or sudden bursts of aggressive or frantic behavior. In one study (Murphy and Moriarty, forthcoming), a combination of high drives and high sensitivity or reactivity with low development balance (e.g., poor "adaptive" functioning on the Gesell Infant Test combined with high social level) was seen in children with speech difficulties. This suggests that preschool children with speech difficulties associated with high tension from such a combination of variables need help in directing drives, solving problems, "letting off steam," and avoiding overstimulation.

Similarly, high autonomic reactivity, minimal brain damage, visual difficulties, or difficulties in motor coordination contribute both to problems of control and to frustration, which lead to mounting tension and increased difficulties in control. Where combinations of these factors are present, the child may need help in preventing the piling up of frustrations and in expressing his feelings and communicating his needs.

Closely related to vulnerabilities are the types of stress to which individual children are susceptible. What types of potential stress should the caretaker or teacher be aware of? How can she help the infant or young child deal with it? Is the child frightened by animals, noises, thunder, vacuum cleaners, fire engines, rough play or aggression from children, angry adults, or other violence? Is the child frightened or anxious about swinging too high, removing clothes, body inspection, nurses or doctors, toilets or toileting, running water, new foods, crowded space, small space or open space, demands from adults for verbal response, demands for group participation in new activities, demands for difficult motor activity, or the like? What is the child's way of dealing with stress? Does he handle this by attacking or changing the environment: getting rid of the threatening object? By protest: screaming, crying, protesting verbally? By escaping: retreating to a safe spot? By getting support: seeking physical contact with a protective person, asking for reassurance? By trying to understand: anxiously asking questions, watching in order to understand what is going on? By comforting, protecting himself: sucking his thumb, grabbing his penis, etc.? By delaying action until he has made a plan? By blaming, criticizing? Other?

What are the consequences of the child's way of dealing with stress? Does it give him leeway to get accustomed to new situations and new demands (is he watching a great deal)? Or does it prevent him from getting oriented, getting used to new situations (as when he turns his back on the whole situation)?

What kinds of help can he tolerate and use? Some children respond to being picked up and held soothingly but not to being told what to do. Some respond to indirect stimulation as from music. Others understand reassurance in words. The wrong kind of help for the individual child amounts to pressure and may fixate his pattern unnecessarily and prevent flexible progress.

USE OF ASSESSMENT IN WORK WITH PARENTS

While the findings from assessment should be freely and invitingly shared with parents, it is important for this to occur in such a way as to support the parents' own growth and autonomy. To some extent, the discussion of findings may help them recognize the potential importance of aspects of the baby's behavior and responses that they may have regarded as inconsequential. It would be desirable for those doing the assessment of the child to be available for group discussions with parents in which questions of general interest could be discussed. The awarenesses of parents and professional people can be exchanged. Such discussions can help both parents and child-care workers understand some of their own problems in response to a child. For example, a fussy and irritable baby often gives the caretaker the feeling that he is rejecting what she is trying to do. If the caretaker can understand some of the baby's intrinsic difficulties in adjustment, she can not only be more tolerant of the baby's fretfulness, but also help to mitigate some of its causes.

Discussion of the findings of assessment can help to clarify the balance of freedom and control suitable for different children. Extremely well-functioning, well-coordinated, and well-oriented babies who are able to pace the stimulation of the environment to an appropriate dose of exploration and mastery may be allowed a great deal of freedom. By contrast, irritable, overreactive babies and children who have difficulties in orientation or in impulse control and who do not adapt the environment to their pace of intake and mastery may need much more organized, selective, and controlled handling. Through discussion of such nuances, the parents can become aware of the many ways in which they can tailor their responses more appropriately to their own baby.

REFERENCES

Bayley, N. Consistency and Variability in the Growth of Intelligence from Birth to the Eighteenth Year. *Journal of Genetic Psychology*, 75: 165, 1949.

Bender, L. Personal communication.

Bierman, J. M., A. Connor, M. Vaage, and M. P. Honzik. Pediatrician's Assessments of the Intelligence of Two-Year-Olds and Their Mental Test Scores. *Pediatrics*, 34: 680–690, 1964.

Dennis, W., and P. Najarian. Infant Development under Environmental Handicap. *Psychological Monographs*, 71 (7, Whole No. 436), 1957.

Doll, E. A. *Mental Deficiency Due to Birth Injuries*. New York: Macmillan, 1932.

————. *The Measurement of Social Competence; A Manual for the Vineland Social Maturity Scale*. Minneapolis: Educational Publishers, *Educational Test Bureau*, 1953.

Drillien, C. M. *The Growth and Development of the Prematurely Born Infant*. Baltimore: Williams & Wilkins, 1964.

Erikson, E. *Childhood and Society*. New York: Norton, 1950 (Revised edition, 1964).

Escalona, S. K., and G. Heider. *Prediction and Outcome*. New York: Basic Books, 1959.

————, and A. E. Moriarty. Prediction of School-age Intelligence from Infant Tests. *Child Development*, 32: 597–605, 1961.

Freud, A. *Normality and Pathology in Childhood*. New York: International Universities Press, 1965.

Gesell, A., et al. *Biographies of Child Development*. New York: Hoeber, 1939.

Greenacre, P. *Trauma, Growth and Personality*. New York: Norton, 1952.

Heider, G. M. Vulnerability in Infants and Young Children: A Pilot Study. *Genetic Psychology Monographs*, 73: 1–216, 1966.

Hunt, J. McV. *Intelligence and Experience*. New York: Ronald, 1961.

Moriarty, A. E. *Constancy and IQ Change: A Clinical View of Relationships between Tested Intelligence and Personality*. Springfield, Ill.: Charles C Thomas, 1966.

Moss, H. A. Methodological Issues in Studying Mother-Infant Interactions. *American Journal of Orthopsychiatry*, 35: 482–486, 1965.

Murphy, L. B. *Personality in Young Children*. New York: Basic Books, 1956.

————, and associates. *Widening World of Childhood*. New York: Basic Books, 1962.

————, and A. E. Moriarty. *Development and Adaptation*. San Francisco: Jossey-Bass, Inc. (Forthcoming.)

Pasamanick, B., and H. Knobloch. Socio-economic Status and Some Precursors of Neuropsychiatric Disorder. *American Journal of Orthopsychiatry*, 26: 594–601, 1956.

————, and M. Lilienfeld. Association of Maternal and Fetal Factors with Development of Mental Deficiency. *Journal of the American Medical Association*, 159: 155–160, 1955.

"Patterns of Beginning." Film produced by Dr. L. Joseph Stone, Department of Child Study, Vassar College, Poughkeepsie, New York.

Provence, S., and R. C. Lipton. *Infants in Institutions*. New York: International Universities Press, 1962.

Rimland, B. *Infantile Autism*. New York: Appleton-Century-Crofts, 1964.

Sheldon, W. Personal communication.

Srole, Leo, et al. *Mental Health in the Metropolis*. New York: McGraw-Hill, 1962.

Stolz, H. R. *Somatic Development of Adolescent Boys*. New York: Macmillan, 1951.

"This is Robert." Produced by Dr. L. Joseph Stone, Department of Child Study, Vassar College, Poughkeepsie, New York.

Williams, R. *Biological Individuality.* New York: Wiley, 1956.

Yarrow, L. J. Maternal Deprivation: Toward an Empirical and Conceptual Reevaluation. *Psychological Bulletin*, 58: 459–490, 1961.

⋞ 7 ⋟

The Role of Stimulation in Models for Child Development

JACOB L. GEWIRTZ

The purpose of this analysis of the implications of environmental stimulation for the behavioral development of young children is two-fold. Our first aim is to examine the utility of such conceptions as environmental "wealth" and "deficiency." These conceptions emphasize the availability of stimuli to the developing child, but they do not take account of whether the available stimuli can be functional for the child's behaviors, that is, whether such stimuli evoke behavior or are involved in learning by the child. Hence, the potential impact of concepts concerning only stimulus provision may be limited.

In this examination we consider some of the ways in which the stimulus-deficiency conceptions of "privation" and "deprivation" for

The writer wishes to thank Linda Brandt, Laura Rosenthal, Deborah Singer, and Karen Stingle for their discriminating editorial assistance with this and the succeeding chapter.

139

the child in early life have been used, whether standard learning concepts for the systematic impact on behavior patterns of recurring environmental conditions potentially offer a more adequate basis than we have at present for understanding the developmental patterns at issue, and the directions in which these concepts might be extended to improve that understanding. Thus, it is seen how many behavior outcomes of deficiency conditions of stimulation may depend on whether stimuli in their various roles are provided in effective temporal relationships with behavior. An "asymptotic" learning model is then offered as an alternative to the deficiency conceptions considered. It emphasizes the possibility for desired behaviors of the child to be brought to maximal levels through the differential provision of stimuli in effective learning contingencies.

The second aim of our analysis is to consider the meaning of the term "environment" and to provide a basis, in terms of our current knowledge, for devising an articulate technology to enhance children's behavioral development via differential stimulation in both deficient and privileged settings. In the next chapter, it will be seen that the concept "environment" has very limited meaning other than as a summary statement for stimulus effects on the specific behavior classes that are of interest; similarly, the term "behavior" has limited meaning except in terms of its functional relationship to the controlling stimuli comprising the environment. Emphasis is therefore placed on the requirements for a detailed specification of the behaviors to be fostered, as well as, in parallel detail, on the environmental conditions that could expedite behavior changes.

Limitations of Current Concepts for Environment and Child Behavior

Let us begin our analysis by asking the meaning of such terms as "satisfaction," "joy," "happiness," or the term "love." There are no universal definitions nor consensually defined indices of these terms. We know that these words are used and valued in everyday discourse; but what happens when these terms are used to describe behavior outcomes in child development? As employed, these terms tend to be highly abstract, often far removed from the level of a child's behavior. Because these romantic terms have "surplus" meaning and hence are used variably even in professional work, they cannot bring to empirical analyses the precision required. Further, in approaching and defining a new problem area, even less abstract terms, such as "smiling," "laughter," or "vocalization," may not be sufficiently detailed to permit a differentiated analysis of behavior. For instance, there are undoubtedly many different aspects of crying or smiling that can be meaningfully isolated from the response system that was previously considered homogeneous (Gewirtz, 1965).*

In research on the outcomes of child-rearing conditions on child behavior patterns, global variables have been devised to summarize either environmental stimuli or child behaviors, but not both aspects of the interaction equation at the same time. As is seen in Chapter 8, it is the details of these sequential interaction contingencies that provide the concepts comprising the extant theories of the impact on the child of his experiences with his environment. Hence, the discrepancy between the level of abstraction of the global summary variables representing one side of the required equation and the level implied in the concepts of the theories must inevitably limit advances in both theory and empirical research.

Apart from this issue, a number of theoretical concepts have been inefficiently employed in reported research. Variable and loose terminology has often inadvertently highlighted particular aspects of the parent-child interaction process and its outcomes, while understating others. Although the function of theory is to emphasize different aspects of a problem, it has often not been the theories per se that have been the bases for these differential emphases, but rather

---

* It is also important to consider the possibility that "expressive" behaviors (e.g., smiles, laughter) are conditioned early in a child's development. For example, the expressive value of the smile may well reflect earlier conditioning. If the discriminable appearance of a face (the conditioned stimulus) is followed systematically by activities such as lifting or tickling (unconditioned stimuli) which produce smiling or laughing, or if smiles to the face are followed by consequences which are reinforcing to the child, subsequent appearances of the face may come to evoke the smile response. By similar procedures, other expressive behaviors of the child may become conditioned early in life, under either the classical or the instrumental conditioning paradigm. These conditioned expressive behaviors, in particular smiles or laughs, are thought by some to be expressions of the infant's "joy" or "satisfaction," and hence to index the "wholesomeness" of a child-rearing setting. However, these expressive behaviors may reflect simply that the particular environment provides stimuli which exhibit conditioned control over these responses, and hence that the environment has provided those stimuli with the expressive behaviors in timing relationships sufficient to effect conditioning. Therefore, for approaches using such indices of wholesomeness, the adequacy of a child-rearing setting is seen to involve the same considerations as will be emphasized in the present analysis: that is, provision of stimuli in effective timing relationships with socially valued behaviors to constitute favorable conditioning opportunities.

the loose form in which key concepts have been defined and used in these theories. Two such key concepts that will be examined here are "environment" and "drive."

CONCEPTS OF "ENVIRONMENTAL WEALTH" AND "STIMULATION"

The concepts of "environmental wealth" and "stimulation" have been employed more intuitively than precisely in child-development analyses. There is no a priori meaning for such concepts as "environmental wealth," in the sense of a dimension extending from poor or deficient to rich or abundant. Indeed, there is no generally accepted meaning of the concepts "environment" and "stimulation." Non-behavioral criteria for these concepts (as well as for "wholesome" environments) are essentially meaningless for an approach to understanding child development. As will be shown, these concepts must be based on functional criteria, specifically the control of behavior systems by stimuli, to be useful in an analysis of the impact of the cumulative experience of the child on his action systems. Without such a specification, the concepts for environment and stimulation are more suitable to literary ventures than to approaches that lead to behavior analyses and technologies.

"DRIVE" CONCEPTS

The ambiguity of theoretical concepts and some of the direct consequences of their loose usage in theoretical and empirical analyses can also be illustrated by the issues arising when *drive* terms (used here interchangeably with the terms "need" and "motive") are introduced to aid in ordering relevant research realms. The drive concept contains surplus meaning in that the operations it implies are generally inexplicit, numerous, often incompatible, and may not represent clear alternatives of one another. Moreover, such flexible concepts can present difficulties even when used in more specific ways, e.g., as intervening-variable abstractions (i.e., calculational devices) or to refer to a hypothetical state or process at a "reduced" level of analysis. This is because those concepts, once advanced, could encompass or explain each new turn of events with the help of some ad hoc assumptions that need not be consistent across successive confrontations with sets of new data.

The drive concept has also been advanced gratuitously to account for the "seeking" of stimulation characterizing a substantial portion of early human adaptive behavior; to "explain," without the invocation of an independent drive index, the basis of stimulus functioning. Thus, a novel stimulus has been said to function to reinforce a response upon which it is contingent because the organism has a drive *for* that stimulus! Another example of an inconsistent and loose usage of the drive concept can be found in analyses of early social learning, particularly those analyses which blur the distinction between momentary performance (or drive) effects of differences in setting conditions and long-term acquisition (or habit) effects (Gewirtz, 1967a, 1967b). These analyses have been misleading in the general area of infant stimulation, learning, and development and the more specific area of caretaking interaction between environment and child. The often-used concept "learned drive," which many no longer see as involving a contradiction in terms, can serve to illustrate this confused state of affairs.

Eventually, an all-encompassing drive concept will fall away under pressure from the obvious utility of various explicit, narrowly defined indices that accrue as subcategories. The term "drive" will then function more than it has up to now, as a chapter heading ordering a large number of diverse phenomena at a level of abstraction similar to that of the term "learning."

The drive concept has also been used in a particular long-term context to order chronic "deficiency" conditions of stimulation and their outcomes. Because this variant of the concept has been employed widely, we shall now consider it in detail.

The "Deficiency" Model

The drive concept appears in a particular long-term context where terms like "affect hunger," "emotional starvation," "privation," and "deprivation" have been employed to provide the conceptual bases for ordering changes in the strengths of child behaviors through extensive time ranges. These behaviors are maintained by particular social responses from adults. The social stimulus commodites "sought" (i.e., those maintaining the behaviors) include "attention" and "affection." Put in its most general form for the long-term case, the deficiency conceptions "privation" and "deprivation" seem to involve the assumption that if young children receive an "inadequate" supply of "essential" stimuli from their caretaking environments, they subsequently show atypical adaptive behavior patterns of responsiveness to social and nonsocial stimuli. These atypical patterns are thought to include developmental arrest, depression, and apathy in young children. In older children, there is often no apparent requirement for the earlier "deficient" stimulus commodities (e.g., attention, affection, stimulation). For example, Levy (1937) has written of a "lack of emotional response," a "shallowness of affect." At other times, the pattern is thought to include insatiable or indiscriminate requirements for these stimuli, as well as a limited capacity for social relationships and attachments.*

Emphasis on a drive notion, particularly on a deficiency-hunger drive concept, to order long-term conditions of stimulus provision is misleading. The hunger-drive concept carries irrelevant meaning derived from its usage in contexts which are, in their essential properties, quite different from those to which the overlapping terms "primary affect hunger," "emotional starvation," and "maternal deprivation" have been applied. For instance, one version of the model used appears to assume that stimuli are indispensable for infant development, very much as food and water are indispensable for survival. This usage can be illustrated with Levy's (1937) classical statement:

> Affect hunger is . . . an emotional hunger for maternal love and those other feelings of protection and care implied in the mother-child relationship . . . a state of privation due primarily to a lack of maternal affection, with a resulting need, as for food in a state of starvation (pp. 643–644).

The deficiency model thus seems to be considered an analogue of the homeostatic hunger-drive model which has been applied in other contexts to order the organism's periodically recurring requirements for the indispensable stimuli of food and water. However, this latter model, which orders relationships between the time that food is available and the time that food maintains behavior in a test, holds for phenomena taking place through a short time range of hours or at most a few days (not months or years).

Moreover, a key implication of the homeostatic deficiency-hunger model is reversibility (i.e., complete satiability [recovery] after periodic short-term deprivations with behavior indices returning to their

---

* This literature is surveyed in greater detail in a later section of this chapter. At that time, an analysis of the possible mechanisms involved using standard learning concepts is attempted, as extensions of earlier analyses by the writer (Gewirtz, 1961a, 1961b, 1967a, 1967b).

normal base levels after each satiation occasion). There is no implication of residual effects that can cumulate over time to be manifested later in systematic behavior changes with regard to the events for which the child was earlier deprived. The use of this deficiency model tends to be accompanied by an emphasis on relatively few salient behavior indices. This seems due in part to an underlying assumption apparently involved in the deficiency model, that indices like those provided by the rate of food-oriented behaviors, which rise periodically, will return routinely to their initial level after the periodic deficiency state has been assuaged. The emphasis on few indices may stem from the fact that the model implicitly deals with behavioral changes not as molar responses per se, but rather as symptoms indicating a physiological process at a different level of conceptual analysis, and one that is the key to the total survival of the organism.

In the same vein, another implication of the deficiency model is that it is unnecessary to attend closely to either environmental stimuli or behaviors required by a differentiated analysis in learning terms. Even while the deficiency model is being set up in a sense as a "straw man" in our analysis, the argument here is that this model focuses on what appear to be *minimal* conditions of development. It considers neither the range nor the potential upper limit of behavioral development. It also plays down the systematic changes in behavior and the concepts required for ordering the cumulative effects of recurring conditions (contingencies) of the environment.

Some long-term physiological stress effects of chronic food-deprivation operations have been identified (Keys et al., 1950). For example, total food deprivation in human adults may result in fatigue, weakness, sleepiness, irritability, depression, and a deterioration of coordination, performance, and concentration, as well as a disappearance of the "feeling of hunger" after three or four days. In addition, prolonged semistarvation may result in poor social adjustment, including symptoms of emotional disturbance and a deterioration of moral standards. Some of these chronic food-deprivation effects may bear a slight similarity to chronic "emotional-hunger" effects as listed by Levy (1937). However, these outcomes do not make the simpler hunger model useful for explaining long-term effects. The effects of chronic semistarvation were neither emphasized nor even specifically identified at the time that the emotional-starvation model was first advanced, and they are not ordinarily grouped with the more common hunger phenomena which involve short-term cycles of deprivation and recovery (via satiation). "Appetites" (preferences) for particular foods have been thought to be one outcome of the pattern of the repeated consumption of those foods under periodic deprivation-satiation regimes involving a level of receipt of appetitive stimuli through lengthy time segments, and hence may also be considered relevant to the issue. However, food preferences do not facilitate use of the short-term periodic hunger model to explain long-term phenomena either, for it has been usual to explain acquired appetites by a learning conception. Hence, it is seen that neither long-term partial or complete food deprivation nor acquired appetites justify use of the analogy of the homeostatic hunger model as the basis for cumulative long-term effects like those said to result from chronic conditions of stimulus availability as are indexed by terms like "emotional starvation," "affect hunger," and "stimulus privation."

Thus, in the context of the assumption of short-term effectiveness behind the use of the motivational concept "hunger," it is neither warranted nor potentially useful (and it can even be misleading) to attempt to order long-term functional relationships between the availability of any stimuli (even food) and effects in behaviors relevant to those stimuli by assuming a hunger for that stimulus class, with the particular network of empirical relationships implied in the hunger concept. These effects are ordered more efficiently at present by learning concepts, which have evolved precisely to account for systematic behavior changes effected by recurring environmental conditions operating through long time spans. It may of course be necessary to extend learning conceptions or to devise new ones to order the long-term phenomena at issue, but those concepts (even as revised) should be the most efficient ones for that purpose. This can be illustrated by some extensions to standard learning conceptions that are proposed in a later section of this paper. In addition, it can be most productive to separate short-term deprivation-satiation operations for social stimuli and their effects on behavior from conditions thought to operate through longer time spans with cumulative, not-readily-reversible effects on disparate behavior systems (Gewirtz, 1967a and 1967b).

While our conceptual analysis readily suggests that the long-term deficiency-hunger model is inadequate and even misleading, it has still other weaknesses. Its existence and implicit acceptance by many has seemed to preclude their search for the very conditions in the environment which actually or potentially control socially valued behaviors or behaviors in need of modification. Thus, this model has limited an understanding of the processes at issue, but it has also muddled the engineering context for implementing socially desirable changes in behavior. Some illustrations of this are presented in the next section. Fortunately, many in the field appear to be attending increasingly to the functional relationships at issue rather than to the conceptual model itself. This is so, we would assume, partly because of the apparent logical flaws which make the model a difficult one to use, and partly because of the increasingly differentiated literature that has been appearing in recent years on the possible modes of environmental impact on behavior.

SOME POSSIBLE CONSEQUENCES OF ADHERING TO A DEFICIENCY HUNGER MODEL

A child must learn to distinguish between multiple caretaking environments, concurrent or sequential, by making responses appropriate to each. For example, one caretaker may feed a child only after he begins to cry; another may feed that same child only after some other vocalization. If the child learns to discriminate between the two caretakers and responds appropriately to each, the first caretaker may think the child fussy and negative; the second may consider him highly responsive, vocal, and positive. More difficult discriminations are required of the child when the contingency patterns of relief caretakers are superimposed on those of the regular caretakers, and when the regular caretakers change their own behavior patterns in an unsystematic manner. As we shall see, the situation is analogous where one of the subject's environments is a therapy setting.

There are several paradoxes that stem from the control of a child's behavior systems by multiple environments. We shall concern ourselves here primarily with the consequences for a child of a major change in caretaking setting. We have seen that a child's response may attain reinforcement in one functional environment controlling his behavior and not in another (e.g., in the environmental setting he has just left more than in the one which he has just entered). When the child leaves a group care setting for placement in a foster or adoptive home, any response maintained in his earlier environment may well be emitted. His new well-meaning caretaker will probably be warm, flexible in her behavior patterns, and accepting of the child. She may demonstrate her acceptance by responding to him "on his own terms" when he exhibits the responses he learned in his previous environment. In this way, the earlier response may be maintained and the child's transition may be a smooth one. If this child has been attended to for a high rate of crying or for other attention-seeking behaviors, the new "mother," caseworker or therapist, under the deficiency-hunger model which has typified much of the thinking on maternal deprivation found in the literature, may view these responses as reflecting the child's strong "need" for attention and love resulting from his formerly *insufficient* supply of these commodities. She, too, may continue to attend to his attention-getting behavior in an attempt to make up for what she incorrectly interprets as a history of receiving a deficient supply of attention and love. Paradoxically, then, these very responses that were being maintained by attention in the former setting now are again maintained by attention in the new setting, if it operates under the logic of the deficiency-hunger model. The behaviors may be maintained at the same rate as in the earlier setting, or perhaps at a higher rate, which the new caretaker may in turn interpret as indicating that the earlier "privation" is even greater than she originally estimated and requires additional time and effort to satisfy or reverse.

A shift in environmental conditions can lead to yet another paradox. In her attempt to give her charge sufficient love and attention to make up for his supposedly deficient history, the new caretaker may bring out and maintain new behavior patterns of his which can lead to either positive or negative outcomes. One positive outcome in the new setting may be a behavior pattern of the child that is more social or "mature" (and hence more consensually valued) than that in his former setting. This is the case, for example, when the behaviors exhibited are more like those of children of his same age (whereas, before, the child's behaviors were more like those of younger children), and/or when his behaviors are oriented more toward autonomy and achievement than they were previously. In addition, the child's behaviors may now be maintained by stimuli provided by caretaker behaviors which indicate that subsequent initiations of all types are more likely to be reinforced (as when the child receives approval from a particular person instead of mere attention from anyone).

When parents, caretakers, therapists, etc., succeed in effecting a change in the child's behavior to a more socially-valued pattern, they may conclude they have made the child more "secure," for they note that he no longer appears to need so much attention and love. That is, he exhibits behavior to attain attention and love less frequently. On this basis, the presumed "hunger" for attention and love, due to an assumed paucity of these stimuli in the earlier environment, is thought to be at least partially satisfied. It has been argued (Gewirtz, 1961b) that such decreases in behaviors maintained by attention may be due entirely to one or more basic conditions operating in the new setting that are different from conditions in the former setting: the same response is maintained but on a reinforcement schedule that requires fewer responses; different reinforcing stimuli are mainly or solely available; the reinforcing stimuli that are available are provided contingent only upon more socially valued (e.g., "mature") behaviors; attention stimuli remain available, but the behaviors they maintain come under close discriminative stimulus control; and a variety of similar possibilities. Therefore, it is parsimonious to consider these behavior indices and changes in a child's demands under a learning model and not under a deficiency-hunger model. A learning model can explain such outcomes in the changed setting as due to new learning by the child effected by new reinforcement contingencies and/or as due to adjustments in the child's behavior systems required by simple changes in the conditions of stimulus provision.

New contingency patterns can also lead to negative outcomes. For example, it is possible that inept caretakers may limit the opportunity for the child to exhibit one or more of his learned responses by not reinforcing or by punishing them, thus limiting the possibility for the emission and learning of novel responses in the setting. The child may then become unresponsive to environmental events or manifest other types of problem patterns. Furthermore, a sudden change to a higher rate of stimulation in the new setting (whether or not the stimuli are provided contingent upon behavior) can produce simultaneous abrupt changes in many related behaviors. (These disruptive changes may be independent of the previous rate of stimulus provision, whether it was high or low, or whether the stimuli were provided on a contingent or noncontingent basis.) Paradoxically, this disorganization or increase in the rate of responses maintained by attention, due entirely to the conditions of a child's transfer to a new setting, may also serve under the deficiency-hunger model to indicate that an "inadequate" supply of these stimuli was received by that child in the earlier setting.

These paradoxical situations arising from the operation of concurrent and/or sequential environments can be understood by examining the moment-to-moment conditions maintaining a child's behaviors in each environment (Gewirtz, 1965, 1967a). Such diagnoses can be validated by manipulating the stimuli assumed to be maintaining the behavior in question, and thus seeing if the behaviors are in fact modified.

An Alternative to the Deficiency Model

A possible alternative to the deficiency model may be termed the *asymptotic model*. This model assumes that the child is relatively robust from the point of view of his behavior systems and that there is a wide range of stimulation conditions from inefficient (or poor) to efficient (or best) which differentially affect behavioral development. The hypothetical maximal, or asymptotic, level for each specified behavior outcome would have to be estimated for each individual. As we shall see in Chapter 8, there is little purpose in attending in detail to stimulation without simultaneously attending to behaviors that can be affected by the stimuli provided.

Developmental norms provide one framework for discussing the range of levels to which responses may be brought. It is critical for several points to be kept in mind when such norms (e.g., those collected by Gesell and Amatruda, 1947) are used to evaluate a particular pattern of development. The conditions under which the normative data have been collected affect and hence limit the norms themselves. For example, the developmental norms that are often used have been collected in routine settings from children who are *not* reared under conditions that can facilitate behavioral development, that is, "contingent-caretaking" conditions (Gewirtz and Etzel, 1967). The norms for most behavior systems would probably reflect far higher stages of development for each chronological age level had they been collected under facilitative contingent-caretaking conditions. Therefore, it is important to remember that the widely used developmental norms do not provide upper limits for most behavioral systems that can be fostered through a program of focused caretaking. They are the norms for what are often unrepresentative samples and have been collected under conditions that are likely to be different from those typical of institutions and many family settings.

The asymptotic approach is important in directing the attention of researchers and engineers to the possibility of establishing patterns of stimulus conditions within a wide range corresponding to the wide range of levels to which diverse socially valued behavior systems might be raised (for example, up to the asymptote for a behavior).

Thus, instead of focusing on the "lower limit" of child rearing, in which "sufficient" stimuli (undefined as to identity or quantity required) are provided to children periodically or when "needed," the asymptotic approach emphasizes that potentially there are a great variety of ways to direct aspects of the environment in order to facilitate the changing capacities of the developing child. So, while the deficiency model emphasizes little more than periodic dispensations of stimuli into the child's immediate area, without requiring that particular behaviors of the child be taken into account when these grossly specified stimuli are provided, the alternative approach should encompass as many as possible of the extant behavior concepts which have evolved from experimental paradigms in highly controlled settings. These concepts have been applied heavily to myriad problems not unlike the ones that concern us in the present analysis. Moreover, an essential if implicit assumption of the present analysis is that there are few alternative concepts that could provide a basis for the required analysis.

LEARNING CONCEPTIONS AND THE ASYMPTOTIC MODEL

The major class of articulate approaches currently available for evaluating the systematic impact of recurring environmental contingencies on behaviors are *conditioning theories*. The asymptotic model is compatible with, and involves strong assumptions stemming from, these theories. Learning concepts have evolved to accomplish just this purpose of describing and providing bases for understanding the basic process of systematic and enduring behavioral changes effected by recurring environmental conditions. In recent years these concepts have shown their utility for ordering a great variety of complex behavior phenomena in both social and nonsocial contexts. They thus seem well suited to the analysis of the conditions of care-taker-child interaction, whether or not their extension will ultimately be required for this purpose. Indeed, we have argued that a great variety of systematically ordered change phenomena can be approached as instances of "learning," since that term is but a class heading under which instances of systematic performance changes effected by recurring environmental contingencies can be grouped. Thus, however broadly the concept of behavior change is conceived in connection with the research problems to which it is applied and whatever the levels of analysis employed, such systematic changes reflect instances of learning under almost all theoretical approaches.

These approaches may differ, however, in the definitions and flavor of their concepts for encompassing these learnings and their outcomes.

The approach outlined here can organize and index changes in a child's behavior patterns (his sequential acquisitions and development). Most theorists who deal with child-development phenomena, as well as with procedures for implementing valued behavior outcomes, ultimately describe the conditions that must be provided to facilitate child behaviors. These descriptions must be made at the level of stimulus, response, and interaction. (See Chapters 2–6, and 8 for further documentation.) Thus, a level of analysis like that used in learning approaches is the only one appropriate for many "environmental enrichment" purposes. Therefore, our purpose in Chapter 8 will be to outline the concept classes or mechanisms that reflect environmental control and its acquisition for the developing child in sufficient detail, in order to maximize their utility.

Before leaving this point it should be noted again that the first question for those concerned with improving environmental stimulation for infants and children involves a detailed specification of the behaviors we wish to foster, for it is only in this way that experiential conditions can be devised to bring out these behaviors.

The ultimate test of any theory is its utility in organizing an area. Under this consideration, the learning approach to caretaker-child interaction has been a useful one, as a large variety of recent research can attest. Its strengths and weaknesses are not unlike those typically found when the body of basic research findings in ethology or in the area of perception are generalized to environment-child interaction settings and the behavior of children. The strength of the approach stems from its underpinning in basic learning and performance principles derived from animal and human research and, in recent years, from increasing research on child learning. A learning-theory approach may have power for other reasons too, in that the level of analysis employed is commensurate with the phenomena investigated. It has the twofold advantage of attending to every overt act of the child and of directly approaching the diversity and actions of the environment as the primary determinants of behavioral development. A variety of behavioral contexts, including interaction, can be organized under the principles of these learning approaches. The learning approach shares its major limitations with similar approaches that are also beginning to organize events in natural settings. That is, the assumptions of *any* approach remain to be put to the test in the complex everyday context of the child's social settings where they may be qualified in many ways by conditions there.

As seen in this chapter and the next, learning concepts, which involve a network of simple relationships, offer a ready means of identifying and testing many functional elements of the environment that impinge on the organism. These elements are the evoking, discriminative, and reinforcing stimuli of a learning analysis. Such an analysis facilitates the identification or isolation of the relatively few events (and event combinations) out of the myriad possibilities comprising the "total" environment that can function as stimuli for an organism. These are the events that can have a systematic impact on the organism's behavioral development. Hence, a learning analysis not only attends to the types and frequencies of environmental events offered to children but also takes into account the details of the interchanges between the stimulus events provided and children's behaviors. Thus, in attending to the interaction between two persons, such an analysis must focus on more than just the "amount" of commerce between them. The behaviors leading to consequences that are important for each of the interactors must be isolated for emphasis. These consequences are the "discriminative" and the "reinforcing" stimuli of an operational learning analysis which employs the conception of S-R chaining.

COMPATIBILITY OF THE ASYMPTOTIC MODEL

It must be noted, however, that sufficiently detailed alternative approaches should be entirely compatible with the micro-analytic approach outlined here. Moreover, insofar as the relationships identified within each approach are valid, the constructs of any macro-approach should, in principle, coordinate at all points with the constructs of the micro-approach. Thus, the "quality" of the attachment or relationship between caretaker or parent and child should correlate directly with the different classes of stimuli that the behaviors of the adult provide in relation to classes of the child's behavior. An example is a situation in which an adult has a "sensitive" relationship that fosters a child's growth, appropriate to his developing abilities. That is, the adult provides patterns of stimulation that change in correlation with the ever changing capacities of the child. Specifically, this means, in our terms, that the stimuli provided by the adult are continuously coordinated with the behavior of the child. By dispensing appropriate stimuli contingent upon each behavior occurrence, the caretaker can cue and strengthen (reinforce) such behavior. "Sensitive" can also imply that the sequential contingencies proceed in an orderly fashion, with the cue and the reinforcing stimuli incorporated in optimal timing relationships into the stream of the child's behavior.

Models for Deficiency Conditions of Stimulation and Their Outcomes

In the preceding consideration of long-term deficiency conditions and outcomes for human development, we were concerned with the adequacy of the long-term hunger-deficiency model for ordering those phenomena; we considered the literature only insofar as it would illustrate and provide a context for the conceptual analysis advanced. Let us now backtrack to survey more thoroughly the literature on deficiency conditions in humans. For the purposes of this analysis, it is convenient to present the material under two major subheadings: one focusing upon the phenomena of *privation*, and the other on the phenomena of *deprivation*. We shall also consider the deficiency pattern fostered by caretakers where child behavior patterns can evolve in such a way as to be labeled "retarded" or "backward." This occasion to survey some of the existing literature will also permit us to speculate, in greater detail than was done when the asymptotic model was advanced, about conditioning mechanisms that may provide the bases for portions of those long-term deficiency phenomena. This task is most appropriate in a context where we have argued that learning concepts (earlier considered in abstract form as the asymptotic model) have evolved specifically to order the behavior outcomes of recurring environmental conditions.

In recent years, due primarily to the work of Levy (1937), Bakwin (1942, 1949), Bowlby (1940, 1951), Goldfarb (1945a, 1945b, 1955), Ribble (1943, 1944), and Spitz (1945, 1946a, 1946b, 1949, 1954), privation-deprivation concepts have occupied a central role in formulations attempting to establish that deficiency conditions in early childhood are antecedents to aberrations in later behavior patterns of the children. One facet of the joint concept, *privation*, involves the *absence or an inadequate supply of "essential"* stimuli to the child in the caretaking setting for lengthy periods in early life; the second aspect, *deprivation*, involves the *removal of important stimuli* from the child's setting, as in separation. These deficiencies in supply may lead to patterns of limited and atypical responsiveness to nonsocial stimuli and to atypical patterns of adaptive and social behaviors. These behavior patterns may also include limitations in inhibitory tendencies and guilt reactions, as well as hyperactivity, unmanageability, and difficulty in concentration. In younger children, the patterns may include developmental and intellectual arrest, depression, and apathy; and in older children, impaired social maturity may be involved, with either no requirement or apparently insatiable and sometimes indiscriminate ones for the formerly deficient commodities (e.g., "attention," "affection"), and a limited capacity for interpersonal relationships (attachments). This outcome has sometimes been termed "superficial affectivity."

Reports from diverse sources seem to agree that a general deficiency syndrome can occur in the presence of apparently adequate physical care. When examining this literature, however, it is not a simple matter to evaluate either the nature of the assumptions advanced or the reliability of the observations reported. For one thing, as we have seen in part, the operational meaning of the concept itself or implications of the theoretical formulations from which it is derived are never stated explicitly. Moreover, no single level of conceptual analysis appears to characterize the area. Thus, we are unclear about issues like the identities of the required or indispensable stimulus commodities, the definition of an adequate supply of them, or the importance of a relationship with a caretaking person. Further, reports of the behavioral effects of the assumed deficiency conditions tend to contain much ambiguous material, while the assumed deficient conditions are generally described in ways that are far less precise than are the detailed descriptions of the behavior outcomes. Moreover, it is not always clear which set of antecedent deficiency conditions results in a particular deviant behavior pattern.

For the typical child, functional stimuli are thought to be available from the beginning of life, although not necessarily in great abundance. Functional stimuli are those stimuli that are discriminable to the child and are provided in effective temporal relationships to his behavior. Stimuli may be made more discriminable by implementing a setting condition (Gewirtz, 1967a) (for example, food deprivation for an appetitive stimulus, darkening a room for a light stimulus) or by limiting the occurrence of irrelevant stimuli competing with or masking the relevant stimulus. It is thought that, for the average child, many unconditioned emotional response complexes become habituated, and that the child becomes

responsive to his environment which contains conditioned discriminative and reinforcing social stimuli that are functional for his behavior.
In this context, there are several paradigms which can adequately
account for the consequences of too little stimulation or the removal
of the maintaining environment. One paradigm involves the dimension of the *availability of stimuli* which can support the early behavior
and learning of the child; another involves the dimension of *change
in behavior setting* from one which supported the earlier and basic
learnings of the child. These paradigms and others are presented in
detail with supporting data by Gewirtz (1961a, 1961b). In addition,
a useful analysis and summary of the "maternal deprivation" literature can be found in Yarrow (1961).

PRIVATION PHENOMENA

The adverse behavior outcomes classified under this label appear to
be due to the limited availability of stimuli, typically from earliest
life onward. As compared with the number and variety of these
stimuli found in the usual family environment, the child's environment provides a paucity of stimuli, whether functional stimuli generally or particular types of functional stimuli (e.g., social ones), at
the very time when early adaptive and social learnings by the child
ordinarily occur. The few functional stimuli available are insufficient
to support these learnings. In these cases, abundant stimuli may be
available, but these may not be functional due to an absence of appropriate setting or context conditions or an otherwise inept mode of
provision. Further, because the child has only a limited opportunity to
become habituated to eliciting stimuli for startle and avoidance behavior complexes, he may remain responsive to such stimuli for
longer periods. The privation of specifically social cue stimuli is conceived to occur when abundant functional stimuli are provided without discriminable social cues. The child developing in this way can
habituate many emotional behavior complexes and become generally
responsive to nonsocial stimuli but not to discriminative and reinforcing stimuli available from people. Thus, he can become "autistic."

At a more macro-analytic level, the outcomes of "institutionalization" and "multiple mothering" have been grouped by some under
the heading of "privation." Both conditions may involve discontinuity of a "maternal figure," and sometimes also "impersonal" care.
Distortions of maternal care in a family setting that involves "rejection," "inconsistent" care, or "overprotection" by the mother have

sometimes been thought to represent privation conditions (Yarrow, 1961). In the terms of the present analysis, the first two instances can be said to involve the limited availability of functional stimuli in early life, as well as the lack of a homogeneous set of cue stimuli provided by one particular person who accounts for most of the child's care—a "mother-figure." Aberrations in child care in the family can involve the additional factor of withholding cue and reinforcing stimuli important for the child and possibly also involve the provision of aversive stimuli (rejection), inconsistent discriminative and reinforcing stimuli, or conditions, often termed "infantilization" or "overprotection," where age-appropriate behaviors are prevented from entering the child's repertoire. This last set of phenomena might be more fruitfully classified elsewhere than under privation.

DEPRIVATION PHENOMENA

The adverse behavior patterns relevant to this general case appear to be due to the removal of stimuli as in a shift in the functional environment. This involves an abrupt and continuing change from an earlier maintenance pattern of availability of functional cue and reinforcing stimuli to the child *after* these stimuli have acquired important meaning for him mainly through learning. The shift may involve a stop in the provision of most or all stimuli from the source from which they were freely available earlier, or it may involve only the removal of the setting-context conditions that have enhanced the efficacy of key stimuli. It may also entail the availability of the essential stimulus aspects of the maintaining environment, but from a new and very different source than before. An example is a child's *separation* from an object-person to whom he is strongly attached (his parent or main caretaker). Another but less frequent case is that of the sudden *rejection* of a child by a person to whom he is strongly attached. In these cases, neither the relevant discriminative stimuli that have defined reinforcing occasions for the child nor the reinforcers themselves are available any longer, and responses employed with reference to those stimuli are no longer appropriate. On any single occasion, this situation may result in the child's exhibiting behavior patterns like those usually found in the initial stages of experimental extinction: an initial increase in frequency of the response as compared to an earlier period under reinforcement, as well as irrelevant emotional responses, which further interrupt the earlier response patterns. Moreover, these responses preclude the occurrence of behaviors alternative to the ones interfered with, thereby making any new adjustment learning in the setting extremely difficult. Thus, the serious behavior outcomes of deprivation may often involve, or result from, a continuing condition of "frustration" brought on by an extreme and lasting change in the controlling environment. The effect on the key behavior systems of the child precludes a reasonable adjustment to the new behavior setting. The mechanisms of behavior change due to shifts in the maintaining environment are considered in detail in Chapter 8.

THE UNINTENTIONAL SHAPING OF "BACKWARD" BEHAVIOR PATTERNS

One problem that arises frequently is due to the conclusions drawn by parent-caretakers about children who have had deficient reinforcement histories caused by neglect, malice, or incompetence. From what they take to be behavior limitations in the children or from information supplied by some diagnostic procedure, the caretakers may conclude that the children are afflicted with some organismic anomaly (brain impairment or injury) or simply that they are retarded. In point of fact, the children's "backward" behavior patterns are often the result of adverse reinforcement histories due to a paucity of stimuli during the early formative period (privation); or the patterns may involve only the consistent absence of coordination between some stimulus classes provided (which might otherwise have been ample in number and type) and some child response classes (Gewirtz, 1961b).

This process wherein caretakers define their charges as "backward" may feed on itself like a self-fulfilling prophecy, as they may then continue to offer a restricted stimulus diet to these children, on the assumption that "backward" children cannot benefit from the stimulation. Alternatively, as Bijou (1963) has pointed out, under the rationale that such a deficient child "needs" more than the usual amount of attention because he is "handicapped," the parent-caretakers may differentially reinforce the child's dependent behaviors, both instrumental and emotional, and, at the same time under their humane rationale, may systematically extinguish or punish independent activities of the child, precluding his acquiring effective, resourceful, and mature behavior patterns and insuring that he will remain helpless and infantile. Clearly this type of caretaking process quickly vindicates itself in terms of its outcomes: these children, who might otherwise have functioned rather well, come to need the stifling "help" that has been imposed on them by their well-intentioned caretakers (Gewirtz and Etzel, 1967). Thus, often because of the attitudes of their parents and caretakers more than because of their presumed or actual afflictions, these children develop in a stilted way, passive in environments in which active responsive children could develop fully.

Required Extensions to the Simple Learning Model

At its present stage of development, the simple conditioning model we have used extensively to analyze the impact of environment on behavior is incomplete. It does not as yet articulately handle several issues concerned with ways in which differential experience with stimuli can systematically affect behavior outcomes. It appears that we shall have to extend our learning concepts or devise new ones in at least two important areas: (1) to encompass some of the phenomena implied in the use of deprivation and privation concepts through *long* time segments; and (2) to deal generally with the possible effects of cumulative experience with stimuli. This latter issue is particularly important at the present time, when much effort is being devoted to the design and implementation of caretaking and teaching environments for "bringing out the capabilities" of young children. Hence, in addition to the purely scientific pressure on us to maximize the scope and utility of our concepts, we also have the correlated aim through the use of improved concepts of designing improved settings to provide children with experiences for wholesome development.

As will be detailed in Chapter 8, the standard learning concepts emphasize the possibility that various environmental events with minimal unconditioned stimulus value may acquire discriminative (cue) stimulus value because of their systematic relationships with functioning stimuli, in particular, reinforcing stimuli. Under the classical or respondent conditioning paradigm, an event may acquire discriminative value for a conditioned response when it systematically precedes the unconditioned stimulus. (This pairing relationship is often termed "reinforcement.") Under the instrumental or operant conditioning paradigm (and the concept of S-R chaining), an event which systematically precedes a response reinforced by some contingent stimulus can become a discriminative stimulus for that response. Under both paradigms, reinforcing conditions function to give value for behavior to previously neutral stimuli.

Some experiential conditions which do not readily fit the standard conditioning models and which appear to account for learnings in important sectors of early life include *dimensional* learning and the learning of *background levels and contexts* for the operation of stimuli. These learnings may be based to a great extent simply on the "registration" by the young organism of events from many classes, falling at diverse points along numerous dimensions.

ROLE OF STIMULUS REGISTRATION IN
EARLY DIMENSIONAL LEARNING

The issue of stimulus registration and its role in early dimensional learning arises in connection with the role of reinforcement and the necessity of an open-ended approach with regard to the postulation of its operating mode in a particular context. It appears that much of early dimensional, categorical, and contextual learnings may occur on the basis of the child's exposure to stimuli from a large variety of classes, levels, and combinations, regardless of whether or not the child is reinforced for responses to such stimuli. It is readily assumed when overt responses are followed by reinforcing consequences that these occasions constitute dimensional-learning trials. However, the point being emphasized here is the likelihood that a considerable portion of the occasions for dimensional learning may occur without reinforcement, as conceptualized under either operant or classical conditioning paradigms. That is, it is our contention that dimensional learning is also dependent upon the discrimination-learning trials in which responses are *not* followed by reinforcement. The assumption is that, as in the general discrimination-learning case, the child learns to identify not only the discriminative occasions for reinforcement ("S^D") but, at the same time, the discriminative occasions for non-reinforcement ("S delta"). On this basis, it is thought that a child comes to discriminate between stimuli varying along salient dimensions (e.g., height, area, brightness) and that his responding to sets of stimuli in terms of such dimensions constitutes dimensional learning. Moreover, it is assumed that the efficiency with which the child comes to discriminate these salient differences is a direct function of the "positive" ("S^D") and "negative" ("S delta") discriminative instances he has experienced, in terms of their number and range, the proportion of each set, and like factors.

Further, insofar as a child has the capacity to discriminate more and more subtle differences among stimuli along increasing numbers of dimensions and within growing numbers of classes, it is assumed that his behavior systems can come increasingly under subtle discriminative and reinforcing stimulus control. In this context, the types of experiences a child has with the stimuli in his environment can affect his learnings. That is, if responses to particular stimuli are generally reinforced but responses to other stimuli falling at distant positions along similarity dimensions from those particular stimuli are not, it is likely that dimensional learning (i.e., discrimination, the absence of generalization) will occur with reference to those particular stimuli. If, however, the child's responses to all members of a set of stimuli are reinforced whether or not they all appear to fall along a stimulus dimension, it is likely that generalization (the absence of discrimination) will result and that class learning, the inverse of dimensional learning, will occur.

It is a truism that early dimensional learning, insofar as the discriminability of cue and reinforcing stimuli is at issue, will be an important factor in whether, when, and how rapidly subsequent learning will occur. If the dimensional-learning process is thus based to a substantial extent on the simple opportunities of exposure to stimuli, it becomes important to engineer improved environments in which the child is systematically exposed to increasing numbers of diverse environmental events. For example, these environments may be designed increasingly to provide stimulus instances that fall close to each other along salient (simple and compound) stimulus dimensions and that therefore require increasingly fine discriminations by the child.

It seems especially appropriate at the present time to design experiments to test the differential effects of diverse stimulus events on dimensional learning of infants and children. One can test the difference between learning based solely upon the provision of stimuli according to some learning paradigm (involving reinforcement of some overt response) and dimensional learning based entirely upon passive experience with stimuli (insured only by the monitoring of registration or attention responses to them). Indeed, the design of such a project must ask specifically what types of experiences with standard stimuli that vary along selected dimensions will lead to the most efficient dimensional learnings. Not only are we questioning the differential role of registration of stimuli versus reinforced responses to them, but we are also raising the possibility that acquiring responses to stimuli is differentially important for dimensional learning, depending on the particular learning paradigm involved in the acquisition. In addition, the possibility exists that dimensional learning occurs differentially as a function of the particular overt responses made to stimulus instances.

LEARNING OF BACKGROUND CONTEXTS FOR STIMULATION

Another set of experiences that appears to have important long-term learning implications is the learning of background contexts and levels for stimulation. These contexts and levels could reflect a variety of diverse stimulation patterns, including deficiency-maintenance conditions of stimulation. By "level" is meant an abstraction for the numbers, types, ranges, and similar features of stimuli experienced. These levels may function as background or setting conditions to qualify the effectiveness for behavior of stimuli presented on any particular occasion. The residues of these experience patterns with stimuli may play a systematic role in the control exercised over behaviors by environmental events. This acquired control must be included tentatively under the rather flexible learning heading we have been using. One of our tasks, therefore, is to study systematically the roles of a number of salient classes of such levels of stimulation.

A level or rate of stimulation may itself acquire stimulus value for the organism, even to the point where it can exert close control over behaviors related to basic organismic requirements. This point can be stated in a manner not unlike one which Helson (1964) has termed "adaptation level": the level or rate of stimulation the organism has experienced through time and hence comes to "expect" might itself, through some as yet inadequately identified learning process, acquire the capacity to function as a stimulus context (background or schema) that qualifies the functioning of a relevant stimulus, provided at a given point in time, in determining behavior. That is, the organism will respond in a manner that will maintain or restore the level of occurrence of stimulation when it deviates from the adaptation or maintenance level. This level might best be estimated as a central tendency of the range and frequency of the stimuli experienced by the organism up to that point in time, and would provide the context for the organism's subsequent responses to the stimuli in that class.

Thus, through some process of learning, the organism becomes conditioned to the maintenance pattern of the classes, rates, frequencies, ranges, and types of stimuli received, and these learned maintenance levels can themselves function to control behavior. This learning should occur readily when the rate of stimulation is regular rather than intermittent. On the basis of this maintenance-level conception, one could predict an organism's approach to food, for instance, in the sense that its "hunger" at any given time would depend on temporal conditioning factors, based perhaps on some average time span between earlier feedings and the average number or amount of food stimuli received per feeding. The learning assumed to be involved in such cases can be illustrated with a simple hypothetical, but possible, example of deprivation and satiation conditions controlling the efficacy of organismic stimuli for behavior.*

Suppose that we have two groups of animals. From birth onward, the first group has been on a maintenance schedule for food stimuli involving regular twelve-hour feedings, and the second group has received regular feedings every twenty-four hours. Assume also that the groups are equivalent in all other ways; for example, in the type and amount of food they are given and the regularity of feeding. Now let us deprive both groups of food for eighteen hours. The question that now arises is for which group would we expect food to function as a more effective stimulus in terms of the control it exhibits in evoking or reinforcing behaviors; or, to put it differently, which group can we expect to show more hunger-relevant behaviors at eighteen hours? Most of us will probably agree with the assumption that, other things being equal, food will function as a more effective stimulus in controlling the behaviors of the organisms in the group on the twelve-hour maintenance schedule for food than it will for those in the twenty-four-hour group. If we overlook what may be an irrelevant fact, that food or its equivalent is required for organismic survival, the case may be made that, in many of the important ways in which stimuli can acquire control over behaviors, food may be no different from any other functional stimulus. The notion being advanced here is that some form of learning must be involved in such cases. In the present example, this learning is based simply on the regularity of exposure to the food stimulus. Moreover, the example includes the suggestion that this learning can qualify the

---

* The author does not believe the required experiment has been done, although he has attempted with limited success to conduct experiments on the role of maintenance conditions in determining the efficacy of nonappetitive social stimuli for behavior (Gewirtz, 1967a).

deprivation-satiation laws that govern the effect of long-term maintenance conditions for behaviors in connection with food and diverse
other stimuli. That is, eighteen hours of food deprivation may be
said to operate as a relative *deprivation* condition for organisms regularly fed more frequently (e.g., every twelve hours) and as a relative
satiation condition for organisms regularly fed less frequently (e.g.,
every twenty-four hours), depending upon their maintenance schedule for the stimulus commodity. This outcome may constitute a
paradox under the more conventional conceptions for the functioning
of stimuli, for drive and setting conditions, and the like.

To extend these notions even further, it is quite possible that
operations for stimulus classes other than food may be qualified by
the distributional characteristics of the subject's experience with a
particular stimulus commodity or with the range and other distributional characteristics of classes of stimuli. For example, Gewirtz,
Jones, and Waerneryd (1956) found that subjects' generalization-
discrimination response gradients for visual-angle stimuli within a
particular range were displaced in the direction of the range of stimuli
they had earlier experienced. These findings are consistent with what
would be expected on the central-tendency basis of the concept of
adaptation level. The learnings of background contexts and levels of
stimulation are thus important factors which must be reconciled by
any learning approach to the outcomes of early life experience.

The conceptual milieu for the functional relationships at issue
has been reviewed by the writer (Gewirtz, 1961b, 1967a). At any
given moment one or more of a great variety of context or background
conditions can determine the effectiveness or salience of stimuli in
any one of their several roles in the control of behavior—in producing
or eliciting it, in signaling (cueing) occasions for its occurrence, and
in strengthening or weakening it when made contingent upon it.
Such diverse "setting" or "drive" contexts can qualify the effectiveness of stimuli on response performance and on the learning inferred
from systematic changes in such performance. We have seen that
a generally recognized set of such conditions involves the availability
(relative to some modal level) of classes of functional stimuli to the
organism in the interval preceding a test for stimulus efficacy, particularly in the context of deprivation and satiation operations for
food and water stimuli. Another often neglected issue involves the
circumstances ("ground") present when stimuli ("figures") are provided. Thus, in perceptual research, background contexts have often
been varied systematically to lower or heighten the discriminability

or salience of a stimulus-figure. Another context determinant of stimulus efficacy for behavior will be illustrated in Chapter 8. This context determinant is based on the "Premack principle"; namely, that the occurrence of a more probable response could reinforce a less probable one when the occurrence of the former is made contingent upon the latter (Premack, 1959, 1962).

Summary

The purpose of the functional analysis in this chapter was to consider how to conceptualize the role of environmental stimulation and its effects on behavior in child development. On the assumption that "environment" has no meaning other than in terms of stimulus effects on behavior, and that "behavior" has no meaning except in terms of its functional relationships to the controlling stimuli of the environment, some concepts heretofore used in child development, such as those of environmental "wealth" and "deficiency," were examined and found inadequate or misleading. In the conceptual analysis presented, it was seen that many important behavior outcomes depend not only on whether stimuli are available, their number, identities, or rate, but in addition on whether the stimuli provided are *functional* for behavior, i.e., discriminable (as under appropriate context conditions and/or in the absence of competing or masking stimulation) and occurring in effective temporal relationships with behavior. Thus, emphasis is placed on the sequential flow or interchange between available functional stimuli and child behaviors.

Given the properties and implications of the short-term hunger model, it was concluded that that conception was not an appropriate analogue for the long-term deficiency-hunger model for ordering the cumulative effects of stimulation (deficiencies). The shifts in a child's response patterns occurring under the changed conditions of stimulus provision when he is moved to a new setting have often been used under the deficiency model either as an index of the complete or partial "satiation" of earlier stimulus deficiency (and hence, "hunger") when the new response pattern increasingly included socially valued behaviors, or as an index validating an earlier inadequate supply of these stimuli when the new response pattern included an increase in rate of responses for those stimuli (e.g., for attention or affection). It was proposed in our stimulus-control learning analysis that these deficiency indices may reflect the adjustment of the rate of the child's behaviors to a new and higher rate of stimulus provision available in the new setting, and that many socially valued behavior outcomes in the changed setting can be explained parsimoniously as new learning by the child due to new response-reinforcement contingencies.

The *asymptotic* learning approach was proposed as potentially more fruitful for understanding and enhancing child behavioral development. Examples of enhanced development were given, and emphasis was placed on the necessity for a detailed specification of the behaviors to be fostered, as well as, in parallel detail, of the environmental conditions that could effect changes. Explanations of privation and deprivation in terms of the deficiency and the learning models were compared. It was seen how *privation* phenomena are typically explained under the deficiency model as involving an inadequate supply of "essential" stimuli to the child for long periods in early life. Under a learning conception, however, it was proposed that privation may not represent a lack in the amount of the stimuli provided, but rather the failure of the stimuli presented to be discriminable and functional, in effective contingencies with behavior. *Deprivation* phenomena, occurring when there are abrupt changes in the availability of important cue or reinforcing stimuli (as in separation from a person to whom the child is attached), were also considered. Under the learning conception, the behavior outcomes of deprivation are thought to result largely from irrelevant emotional responses, such as those typically found when behavior sequences are blocked. It was also suggested that many "retarded" or "backward" behavior patterns may result from the unintentional reinforcement of extreme instrumental dependency and other maladaptive behaviors, accompanied by a severe limitation of the functional stimuli made available to the child. A subsequent increase in the rate of such behaviors then may "confirm" the often casual diagnosis that the child is "backward" or "retarded."

Finally, some limitations were examined in the application of basic conditioning relationships and models to the conditions of child development (including deficiency conditions of stimulation), and some directions were indicated for required extensions of conditioning conceptions. These directions involved particularly the role of stimulus registration in dimensional learning and of the acquisition of background contexts for stimulation (e.g., adaptation levels) which qualify the efficacies of the stimuli provided to the developing child.

In the context of the assumptions advanced in this chapter, the chapter that follows presents an approach to devising a technology for enhancing the behavioral development of young children via differential stimulation by bringing particular desired behaviors to maximal levels. These may be above the levels attained even in the most privileged settings.

REFERENCES

Bakwin, H. Loneliness in Infants. *American Journal of Diseases of Children*, 63: 30–40, 1942.
———. Emotional Deprivation in Infants. *Journal of Pediatrics*, 35: 512–521, 1949.
Bijou, S. W. Theory and Research in Mental (Developmental) Retardation. *Psychological Record*, 13: 95–110, 1963.
Bowlby, J. The Influence of Early Environment in the Development of Neurosis and Neurotic Character. *International Journal of Psychoanalysis*, 21(2): 154–178, 1940.
———. *Maternal Care and Mental Health*. World Health Organization, Monograph Number 2. Geneva: World Health Organization, 1952.
Gesell, A., and C. S. Amatruda. *Developmental Diagnosis*. 2d ed. New York: Hoeber, 1947.
Gewirtz, J. L. A Learning Analysis of the Effects of Affective Privation in Childhood. *Acta Psychologica*, 19: 404–405, 1961(a).
———. A Learning Analysis of the Effects of Normal Stimulation, Privation and Deprivation on the Acquisition of Social Motivation and Attachment. In B. M. Foss (Ed.), *Determinants of Infant Behaviour*. New York: Wiley, 1961(b), pp. 213–299.
———. The Course of Infant Smiling in Four Child-rearing Environments in Israel. In B. M. Foss (Ed.), *Determinants of Infant Behaviour III*. New York: Wiley, 1965, pp. 205–260.
———. Deprivation and Satiation of Social Stimuli as Determinants of Their Reinforcing Efficacy. In J. P. Hill (Ed.), *Minnesota Symposia on Child Psychology*, vol. 1. Minneapolis: University of Minnesota Press, 1967(a), pp. 3–56.
———. Detrimental Usage of Drive in Social-learning Theory. Paper presented at the annual meeting of the American Psychological Association, Washington, D.C., September 1967(b).
———, and B. C. Etzel. Contingent Caretaking as a Solution for Some Child-rearing Paradoxes. Paper presented at the biennial meeting of the Society for Research in Child Development, New York City, March 1967.
———, L. V. Jones, and K. E. Waerneryd. Stimulus Units and Range of Experienced Stimuli as Determinants of Generalization-Discrimination Gradients. *Journal of Experimental Psychology*, 51: 51–57, 1956.
Goldfarb, W. Psychological Privation in Infancy and Subsequent Adjustment. *American Journal of Orthopsychiatry*, 15: 247–255, 1945(a).
———. Effects of Psychological Deprivation in Infancy and Subsequent Stimulation. *American Journal of Psychiatry*, 102: 18–33, 1945(b).
———. Emotional and Intellectual Consequences of Psychologic Deprivation in Infancy: A Re-evaluation. In P. H. Hoch and J. Zubin (Eds.), *Psycho-*

pathology of Childhood. New York: Grune & Stratton, 1955, pp. 105–119.

Helson, H. *Adaptation-level Theory.* New York: Harper & Row, 1964.

Keys, A., J. Brozek, A. Henschel, O. Michelson, and H. L. Taylor. *The Biology of Human Starvation,* 2 vols. Minneapolis: University of Minnesota Press, 1950.

Levy, D. M. Primary Affect Hunger. *American Journal of Psychiatry,* 94: 643–652, 1937.

Premack, D. Toward Empirical Behavior Laws: I. Positive Reinforcement. *Psychological Review,* 66: 219–233, 1959.

———. Reversibility of the Reinforcement Relation. *Science,* 136: 255–257, 1962.

Ribble, M. A. *The Rights of Infants.* New York: Columbia University Press, 1943.

———. Infantile Experience in Relation to Personality Development. In J. McV. Hunt (Ed.), *Personality and the Behavior Disorders.* New York: Ronald, 1944, pp. 621–651.

Spitz, R. A. Hospitalism: An Inquiry into the Genesis of Psychiatric Conditions in Early Childhood. *The Psychoanalytic Study of the Child,* vol. 1. New York: International Universities Press, 1945, pp. 53–74.

———. Hospitalism: A Follow-up Report. *The Psychoanalytic Study of the Child,* vol. 2. New York: International Universities Press, 1946(a), pp. 113–117.

———. Anaclitic Depression. *The Psychoanalytic Study of the Child,* vol. 2. New York: International Universities Press, 1946(b), pp. 313–342.

———. The Role of Ecological Factors in Emotional Development in Infancy. *Child Development,* 20: 145–156, 1949.

———. Unhappy and Fatal Outcomes of Emotional Deprivation and Stress in Infancy. In I. Galdston (Ed.), *Beyond the Germ Theory.* New York: Health Education Council, 1954, pp. 120–131.

Yarrow, L. J. Maternal Deprivation: Toward an Empirical and Conceptual Re-evaluation. *Psychological Bulletin,* 58: 459–490, 1961.

8

On Designing the Functional Environment of the Child to Facilitate Behavioral Development

JACOB L. GEWIRTZ

This chapter attempts to bring concepts and data from diverse areas of molar psychology to bear on an analysis of the environment as the determinant of behavior and as the context for it. Such an analysis is essential in light of the recent emphasis on the design of caretaking settings and "stimulating" environments for young children, and because of the steady accumulation of empirical research on the effects of differential "experience" on behavior, particularly early experience. The focus of this literature has been the proposition that varieties of environmental input can determine the subsequent behavior of the organism. This is by no means a novel proposition in psychology and in one form or another (e.g., "nature-nurture," "maturation-learning," "the child is father to the man") has commanded attention through the years in the fields of comparative, developmental, personality, physiological, psychoanalytic, and social psychology.

169

Renewed interest in the effects of environmental contact derives in part from recent neurophysiological speculation (e.g., Hebb, 1949, 1955), which has pointed up the necessity for considering revisions in traditional views of the nature of stimulation and its consequences for behavior. In recent years, there has been much research with lower organisms on early experience (summarized in Haywood and Tapp, 1966), by those in Hebb's tradition and by others (e.g., Denenberg, 1964; Levine, 1962). While attempts to explicate theoretical parallels between the functions of environmental stimulation at the behavioral level and those of its neurophysiological and biochemical counterparts are interesting and potentially useful, the problem for the molar behaviorist remains the articulation of the precise manner in which differential stimulation facilitates and controls the ongoing behaviors of the organism. Thus, while physiological discoveries of neural correlates of stimuli and behavior, or organic changes corresponding to operations and responses grouped under concepts like "arousal" and "emotionality," might be relevant for the molar behaviorist, it would still remain necessary for him to specify in appropriate detail the conditions under which stimuli are differentially effective in controlling behavior at a given moment and through time.

The Scope of the Analysis to Follow

The functional environment is comprised of stimulus events which can control behavior by *evoking* it, *signaling* occasions for its occurrence, and *strengthening* or *weakening* it. We will emphasize a few simple learning and performance concepts in order to illustrate their utility and power (1) in approaches to deficiency conditions of stimulation and their outcomes (consideration of which was begun in the preceding chapter); (2) in general approaches to adaptive and social learning in early childhood; and (3) in the engineering of practical programs to enhance the behavioral development of the child. The generic concepts of this analysis will be potentially compatible with those of diverse approaches, such as Montessori's (1912) and Piaget's (1952; see also Hunt, 1963). If the definitions or implications of principles under other approaches involve learning concepts and hence are similar to those we will be emphasizing in our analysis, they would constitute alternatives for facilitating behavioral development; if they do not, the behavior concepts emphasized here would have to be modified to take account of these implications. The important point is that the basic conceptual tools of the present analysis are open to modification or qualification. The attempt will be made to determine the extent to which such simple concepts can account for rather complex outcomes in some important areas of a child's development.

In order to highlight the main conceptual theme of this analysis, issues in the definition of stimulus and response, principles of acquired stimulus control, and changes in the maintaining environment are given greater emphasis than are the precise identities of such events, the contexts in which they occur, or the results of particular studies. Even so, a list of stimulus conditions which can have short- and long-term impact on some socially desirable behavior patterns at different points in development is included, as are the operations by which these effects can be achieved. Earlier attempts have been made by the author to take account of the *content* of stimuli and responses in a fine-grain analysis of the many ways in which differential stimulation and gross environmental changes can effect important behavior outcomes (Gewirtz, 1956, 1961b). Some of these outcomes involved maladaptive behaviors which created problems for the maintaining environments, while other outcomes involved socially desirable behavior patterns. Although those analyses detailed ways in which particular stimulus and response classes would be affected, they were directed to an end different from the one of this chapter.

A *functional analysis* attends to the direct impact of both short- and long-term stimulus conditions on behaviors. Many such conditions may be operating at any given moment. When the deficient or disturbed behaviors of children are considered in the context of a functional analysis, the engineering of better child-rearing environments to produce more socially desirable behaviors can be facilitated. Throughout our functional analysis, the focus for positive growth is neither passive nor remedial. We attend more to designing improved environments that facilitate the development of socially desirable behaviors in the child during the period of his earliest learning and the "realization of his potential," and less to remedying the child's behavioral deficiencies once they are identified as serious behavior problems. To be sure, these foci are two aspects of the same process, the basis of which might be thought to be adverse reinforcement histories and sometimes simply the failure for stimulus and response functions to have been coordinated in a child's history (e.g., Bijou, 1963; Ferster, 1961, in press; Gewirtz, 1961b). Another possible basis for deficient outcomes might be the absence of stimuli that for short periods increase nonspecifically the incidence of a variety of behaviors (e.g., via "arousal").

The Conceptual Milieu for Designing Improved Child-Development Settings

Today's conception of the individual in his environment is different from that prevalent in the period immediately following World War II, when the approaches of Freud and Hull set much of the tone in analyses of psychological functioning. In Freudian and Hullian theory, the organism is a passive, unresponsive being; satisfaction of biologically derived needs or drives (for example, for food, water, or removal of noxious stimuli) are the prime forces behind behavior. The radical change to the view of an *active* organism in commerce with his environment has been supported from many sources by research on behaviors characterized by the "search for stimulation" and those that are maintained by such stimulus consequences as "novelty," "complexity," and "variety." Other behavior patterns reflecting the organism's active interaction with his environment have been labeled "curiosity" (Berlyne, 1950), "exploration" (Montgomery, 1951), "intrinsic motivation in objects" (Harlow, 1950, 1953), and "manipulation" (Harlow, Harlow, and Meyer, 1950).

The above approaches generally propose "drive" as the basis for behaviors which seek out stimulation, and they differ in many ways from those approaches which regard the *reduction of stimulation* as the primary motivational force. However, they also differ from the theoretical viewpoint which assumes that, as a highly alert and responsive being, the child is in continual *active* interaction with the myriad stimuli occurring in his environment, even when his basic organismic requirements are satisfied. This view that the human organism is responsive to and his behavior is maintained by a great variety of unconditioned and conditioned stimuli that have no apparent survival value (at least in terms of the traditional conception of organic "drives") is not a new one. It has been advanced in various ways by theorists who have held very different approaches to the origins of adaptive and intelligent behavior in humans, as well as to the methodological issues of psychology (e.g., Baldwin, 1906; Piaget, 1952; Skinner, 1938; White, 1959; Woodworth, 1958); it has also been advanced by investigators of animal and child play (e.g., Beach, 1945; Welker, 1961). Supported by relatively recent empirical evidence on exploratory and curiosity behaviors, the emphasis in these approaches is based on a certain view of the fundamental nature of the human organism: responses can be evoked and maintained by a great variety of environmental stimuli, and the infant may be responsive to his environment even when his bodily wants are satisfied (Gewirtz, 1967b).

A variety of approaches and prescriptions have been offered for engineering improved environmental conditions to foster better, even optimal, development of specific behavior systems in young children. Traditional educational procedures, which have had as their point of departure fairly rigid notions of fixed intelligence, predetermined development, a rather limited notion of brain function, and a lack of emphasis on the importance of early experience,* have served as the basis for fostering the development of more capable individuals. However, there are limitations to such procedures, among them that formal education usually begins in the fifth or sixth year of life and employs some methods which are now regarded as inefficient and which often seem to violate many of the principles on which programmed instruction is currently based (e.g., Skinner, 1954).

Outside the conventional educational establishment is the work of Montessori (1912), who stressed fostering sensory and information processes and perseverance. Also, demonstrations by Wellman, Stoddard, Skeels, and Skodak at the Iowa Child Welfare Research Station were pioneer successes in demonstrating that various child-behavior systems could be fostered. These demonstrations, accomplished against a theoretical milieu in which hereditary and genetic determinants were thought most important (with children assumed to have a fixed IQ), proved that "enriched" nursery school and care-taking environments could raise intellectual performance and enhance the acquisition of social skills (see especially Skeels, 1965, 1966; Skeels and Dye, 1939; Skeels et al., 1938).

Finally, in recent years, we have seen the rapid growth of a technology for the application of behavior laws to practical affairs, involving in particular the management of stimulus-response contingencies via reinforcers (e.g., Skinner, 1953; Ullman and Krasner, 1965; Verhave, 1966). Under the experimental procedures of this

* See Hunt (1964) for a useful summary of background details.

approach, the demonstration of the conditions of stimulus control of behavior and the diagnosis of bases of problem behavior are one and the same process. The potential power of the approach has been increasingly appreciated over the years.

Summaries of ways of enriching preschool environments to facilitate the development of specific behavior systems for disadvantaged children can be found in a variety of sources. Hunt (1964) stresses the necessity for exposing the preschool child to a variety of objects and circumstances in order to establish the representative images which are the referents for verbal symbols through experiential learning. He conceives that a problem to be encountered involves *matching* new material and experience to the familiar environment already experienced by the child. Emphasis on a preschool acquisition of various aspects of language skills and their development is also common to the concerns of John and Goldstein (1964) and others; these researchers underline the importance of the early acquisition of "labels" as a foundation for more complex language and verbal mediational processes for the child. Consonant with Fowler (1962), Deutsch (1964) suggests that early cognitive enrichment is critical to the culturally deprived child, but that this child must first acquire the language tools for this enrichment through stabilized expectancies of his environment, which can be reinforced via verbalized routines and regulations.

In the conceptual milieu described, it seems constructive to concentrate on cataloguing the behaviors of children in terms of the great number and variety of stimuli which potentially may evoke and subsequently reinforce those behaviors. Yet this seems to be only part of the task necessary for achieving desired behaviors in children. Assuming environmental conditions of the child to be his primary mediator for learning socially desirable or otherwise valued behaviors, one of the prime concerns in implementing these behaviors is to provide an environmental context for him which will supply the stimulation and stimulus-response contingencies required for these learnings. At the same time, it is recognized that there have been faults apparent in the outcomes of child rearing in institutions, foster families, day-care centers, and many types of family settings. It follows that our attention might profitably be given to improving environmental conditions for children in order to increase the learning opportunities afforded by these conditions and to "upgrading" children in *any* child-rearing setting, whether "deficient" or "privileged."

What is "Environment"?

An assumption underlying our approach is that to specify behaviors without close attention to the controlling stimuli of the environment does not have validity at any level of analysis. Further, it is meaning-less at any conceptual level—at the level of "health" or "discomfort," at the level of behavior systems, or even at the level of an elementary response—to speak of these concepts for behavior without simul-taneously specifying the relevant stimuli at a *parallel* level of analytic detail.

DEFINING STIMULUS AND RESPONSE

Many of the major advances in psychology have involved attempts to improve the description of the stimulus. Thus Dewey, in his now classical analysis of the reflex arc (1896), contended that the central problem of reflexology was that of discovering the stimulus. More generally, in the functional analysis of the control of behavior by the environment or of the impact of the environment on the behavior of the organism, emphasis must be on the stimulus-response (S-R) *unit*, for there can be no meaningful definition of "stimulus" inde-pendent of its response or potential response; similarly, there can be no meaningful definition of "response" independent of its stimulus coordinate. Hence, the correlated concepts "environment" and "con-tact with the environment" become meaningless abstractions without specification of the organism's behaviors that are actually or poten-tially affected by the stimuli which comprise such an environment.

Demographic classifications, such as "culture group" or "age," are sometimes used as crude indices of those processes. In principle, these gross terms are reducible to patterns of stimulation and their interchange with behaviors (J. L. Gewirtz and H. B. Gewirtz, 1965; H. B. Gewirtz and J. L. Gewirtz, in press). More frequently, perhaps, global variables have been emphasized and used in research on the outcomes in child-behavior patterns of child-rearing conditions. These variables have been devised to summarize, over lengthy time spans, either the stimuli provided by the environment (e.g., "nurturance," "warmth") or the behaviors of the child (e.g., "dependence," "re-sponsiveness"), but not both interaction facets simultaneously. Gen-erally, such global variables are not sufficiently differentiated to be optimally useful under the more powerful models available (in particular, learning models) or even under the theoretical approaches that have spawned them, since they do not account in the required detail for systematic behavior changes effected by the functional environment, particularly because they do not deal directly with the sequential details of the interchange between the environment and the individual's behavior (Gewirtz, 1964). In a parallel fashion, instead of defining child-rearing environments in terms of caretaker roles or at the level of informal description (methods typically used to date), they might more fruitfully be described in terms of the functional stimuli comprising the environments.

Under our functional approach, the behavior outcomes desired must be specified *before* a meaningful attempt can be made to identify the aspects of the environment that must be manipulated or controlled in order to effect those particular behavior outcomes. A specification of the stimulus conditions maintaining those desired behaviors is likely to have greatest utility when made at the same level of analysis as is involved in the description of the behaviors. The sequential details of the interchange between behaviors and stimuli must be specified as well.

Behavior concepts for performance and learning phenomena provide keys to an understanding of the impact of recurring contingencies in the environment on systematic changes in response strength in early human life. At the same time, they offer the means for identifying an organism's functional environment. That is, an analysis in conditioning terms can facilitate the identification or isolation of those relatively few events in the environment that actually can and do function as stimuli for an organism's behavior, and, hence, that can have a systematic impact on behavioral development. On this basis, a corollary of the conditioning concept is that simply cataloguing the types and frequencies of environmental events offered to infants has limited predictive value. Rather, it seems more fruitful to consider the circumstances under which given stimuli are provided to the infant, particularly whether the stimuli enter contingencies with the infant's behavior in such a way that behavior strength can be acquired and maintained.

The information required for a functional analysis could be gathered efficiently either through systematic observation of occurrences and contingencies in selected life contexts and field experiments or through observation in experimental settings established to represent in abstract form the essentials of a set of naturally occurring conditions. All assumptions about the effects of environment on behavior must then be demonstrated experimentally in order to show their basis in behavioral technology. There is a continuity of purpose in such analyses, from theorizing to theory testing to application, and in appropriate instances, from application to prevention.

IMPLICATIONS OF OUR APPROACH FOR SUCH CONCEPTS AS "ENVIRONMENTAL WEALTH"

One consequence of this functional approach is the abandonment of nonbehavioral criteria for the "good" environment for children, in favor of environments characterized by their functional aspects for behavior control. Thus, "environmental wealth" in the sense of a dimension extending from deficient ("poor") to abundant ("rich") is a meaningless term, because there is no universal a priori concept of wealth in behavioral analysis or technology. A concept of "environment" can proceed only if it has a basis in the stimulus control of behavior; it cannot antedate the development of such a behavior technology.

Let me illustrate this limitation on the concept of environmental wealth. It is a truism that stimuli must be available before they can affect the behavior of the organism. And in a gross way, therefore, this fact of stimulus availability, or "richness," might be expected to relate to or predict behavior outcomes. However, limits on this conception must arise immediately when concepts like "environmental wealth" are subjected to scrutiny. First, the precise identities of the eliciting, cueing, or reinforcing stimuli provided are critical. Second, the roles of those stimuli in relation to responses can vary and have to be specified before immediate and long-term behavior outcomes can be predicted. Third, we know from motivation-set and similar researches that the unencumbered organism may sometimes be unresponsive to stimuli (including those to which he often responds) that have recently been made available in abundance, or the organism may be responsive only under particular "setting" conditions. It is also known that stimuli may function to reinforce behaviors only if they are discriminable and are provided in effective temporal relation (contingencies) with the behaviors. Hence, any analysis of the relative availability of stimuli (in the sense of a "rich" or a "poor" environment) must, from the outset, focus on details of the interplay between environmental stimuli and the relevant behaviors of the organism, as well as on contextual factors which could influence the efficacy of the stimuli provided.

Behavior patterns that enable the child to manipulate aspects of his environment as he copes with new or potentially stressful situations are often termed "intelligence" or "flexibility." The probability of the child's acquiring these diverse behaviors depends only partially on environmental "richness" in the sense of an abundance of potential stimulus events. Rather, these acquisitions depend more on the *nature* of the particular stimuli provided, as well as on the extent to which the available stimuli evoke various novel behaviors and enter into effective contingencies with the child's behaviors.

RELEVANCE OF "FEELINGS" AND "AFFECTS" IN THIS ANALYSIS

An assumption concerning the feelings and affective responses of caretakers and their charges for each other is sufficiently important to be emphasized early in our analysis. We will focus on stimuli, responses, and their interchange from the vantage of both the infant and the caretaker. Abstract terms such as "feelings" and "affects" imply responses by one of the interactors which provide stimuli that are discriminated by the other interactor and that control his behaviors. The phenomenal events implied by those abstract terms are taken into account insofar as they are reduced to the functional terms of our analysis. Thus, the infant does not discriminate *feelings*. He may discriminate animated faces from expressionless ones, soothing sounds from harsh ones, gentle squeezes from hard ones, gradual movements from sudden ones, or one complex of these events from another. If the events implied by "feelings" are not discriminated by the infant or his caretaker and do not affect in any way the behaviors that are of concern in an analysis, then by that token they are irrelevant and hence are ignored.

THE "OBJECTIVE" VS. THE "PHENOMENOLOGICAL" APPROACH TO ENVIRONMENT

While some approaches are deemed useful in organizing particular areas, they may not engender a fruitful orientation to delineating relevant aspects of the environment and thus may be of limited value for increasing the knowledge of how stimuli control or come to control behavior. In this sense, a phenomenological approach, although pragmatic, is limited in the leverage it can provide on the specification of the controlling environment for behavior systems. This approach emphasizes *how* the individual sees stimuli, defining the problem so that certain of the individual's evaluative responses are used as the subjective equivalents of physical stimuli. The application of phenomenological principles comes down to a search for response-response (R-R) laws. In the case of early human development, the R-R approach is particularly limited in its attempt to define the relevant aspects of the controlling environment. Because this approach precludes a primary focus on the physical stimulus, it is not possible to predict the response *in advance* of the individual's showing some behavior to the physical stimulus. This is particularly so in settings where an individual exhibits only one salient response to the physical stimulus and does not provide a response index of the subjective stimulus.

Concepts Reflecting Behavior
Development and Control

We have been attempting to outline the conditions that determine which of the myriad events comprising the environment are, or can become, functional for child behavior. This outline is a precondition for engineering child-care procedures and should aid in the design of environments (such as in residential wards in institutions, in day-care centers, and even in routine family settings) to "upgrade" the behavior systems of children, or to realize their "latent capabilities." Under the asymptotic model, which was described in Chapter 7, the goal of such technological designs may be stated as that of preparing patterns of experiences for each child that will efficiently bring to maximal level the adaptive behavior systems which are valued by society.

A large variety of phenomena involving diverse paradigms and behavior systems are currently grouped under the headings of *conditioning* and *learning*. As typically used, concepts ordering environmental operations that effect almost any systematic and reversible change in an identified or defined behavior are grouped as learning concepts (mechanisms). The number of such concepts and the labels assigned to them are arbitrary. Thus, under this inevitably loose working definition there is always a place for concepts which order previously unidentified phenomena. As the study of environmental impact on behavior develops, it is probable that most of the existing concepts grouped at present under the open-ended heading of "learning" will become increasingly differentiated and refined. This continuous process will lead to new concept labels and groupings.

In a sense, then, concepts of learning belong to every theorist who studies systematic effects of recurring environmental conditions on behavior. This is true whatever the theoretical approach, its degree of development, the particular phenomena ordered by the theory, its language, the level of analysis and detail employed, and the particular heuristic tone given to the concepts (e.g., behavioristic, cognitive, or even animistic). Learning concepts are at issue whether a theory refers to "ego enhancement, growth, or changes," to the "growth of self-awareness," or to the "development of a substitute interpersonal attachment." In the same sense, concepts ordinarily grouped under such headings as "ethology," "perception," or "intelligence," which have evolved to order environmental phenomena effecting changes in behaviors, *overlap* learning concepts at various levels as well as each other.

In order to delineate the operations and concepts involved in behavior development and control from those in other areas, a list is given here of some of the mechanisms stemming from and successfully utilized in analyses of fundamental behavioral development and control, both short- and long-term. This list is not intended as exhaustive.* Rather, it is put forth to highlight the fact that there are a substantial number of standard procedures to facilitate and effect systematic changes in adaptive behavior patterns and to provide a basis for understanding the performance dynamics of those behaviors. Many of these procedures may be implemented simultaneously.

Stimulation Effects
These are conceived to operate through short time spans. Examples include:

1. *Adaptation, habituation:* systematic decreases in the probability of responding to a stimulus (the conditioning history of which is usually not known) and decreases in other response attributes after successive presentations of the stimulus; often short-term and subject to recovery with time.

2. *Sensitization, arousal, facilitation:* raising the probabilities of various behaviors or lowering response thresholds; included are spe-

* Additional concepts, as well as procedures for implementing the concepts presented here, can be found in standard textbooks of psychology, particularly in books which emphasize learning conceptions (e.g., Keller and Schoenfeld, 1950; Kendler, 1963; Kimble, 1961; Kimble and Garmezy, 1963; Skinner, 1953).

cific effects on a particular response and general effects on groups of responses.

Conditioning Effects

These are conceived to operate usually through longer time spans. Examples include:

1. *Reinforcement:* in the instrumental or operant case, when a stimulus is made contingent upon a response and the response attributes (e.g., probability, amplitude, latency, resistance to extinction) are affected systematically, the stimulus is termed "reinforcing"; when the response rate is increased, the stimulus is termed a "positive" reinforcer ("reward"); when the response rate is decreased, the stimulus is termed a "negative" reinforcer ("punishment"); the systematic removal of the contingency is termed *extinction*, which can be thought of as "learning not to respond." (In the Pavlovian or classical conditioning case, which is of secondary concern to us in this paper, the unconditioned eliciting stimulus is said to function as a reinforcer when the probability of the conditioned response changes systematically.)

2. *Contingency:* a stimulus which is an immediate consequence of a response is contingent upon it and may imply reinforcement in the operant case; a response contingent upon a stimulus may imply that the latter functions as an eliciting, evoking, or discriminative stimulus.

3. *Scheduling:* the provision of contingent stimuli can constitute reinforcement that is continuous (following each response occurrence) or intermittent (following the response on a specific irregular basis); an intermittent reinforcement schedule may be conceived as "fortifying" against a change in response rate when contingent stimulation is changed.

4. *Response differentiation:* shaping of the response through reinforcement of successive approximations to the desired response; emergence of a new response.

5. *Discrimination, cueing:* learning the occasion for responses. (The reciprocal process is termed *generalization*.)

6. *S-R chaining:* sequential contingencies between an individual's responses and stimuli, including those provided by preceding responses of another person in an interaction context, as opposed to "one-sided" variables for stimuli alone or for responses alone.

7. *Conditioned reinforcement:* a conditioned discriminative stimulus comes to maintain responses when made contingent upon them, particularly if the responses are those which had preceded it in an S-R chain.

8. *Habituation:* may involve "learning" not to emit a possible unconditioned response to a particular stimulus; although sometimes subject to recovery, habituation is often long-term (complete).

9. *Assimilation-accommodation:* following Piaget's usage, these concepts refer to systematic changes in behavior effected by the or-

ganism's experience with the environment. In *assimilation* a ready-made "schema" comes to be evoked; for example, looking, which is evoked at first only by changes in visual stimuli, is later evoked by changes in sounds that have occurred in connection with the original light-change stimuli. In *accommodation*, the structure of the action is modified to fit the situation. (An analysis of the learning implications in these conceptions of Piaget is found in Hunt [1963].)

Performance Factor Effects
These effects are thought to operate directly on responding.

1. *Reactive (work) inhibition:* response fatigue, associated with decreases in responding in short-term operations, and subsequent response recovery with the dissipation of the fatigue factor.

2. *Conditioned inhibition:* long-term fatigue component conditioned to response cues (may also be classified as a conditioning effect).

Setting-Drive Effects
These result from setting conditions that determine stimulus efficacy for behavior on a particular occasion. These conditions may operate:

1. At *one* time point concurrent with the functioning focal stimulus (e.g., "ground" for "stimulus-figure").

2. *Immediately prior* to the point of stimulus functioning (e.g., a cue as to the region in which the focal stimulus will appear).

3. *Across* time points prior to the functioning of the focal stimulus to heighten or lower its efficacy for behaviors (e.g., providing deprivation or satiation contexts for a stimulus) (Gewirtz, 1967a).

QUALIFICATIONS OF THESE CONCEPTS

While the implications of the concept classes listed above for the analysis of the functional environment are presented in detail later, several qualifications and preliminary implications can be listed here:

1. The stimulus-response relations ordered under each of the above headings represent the *properties of the organism;* by extension they index the different ways in which environmental conditions can have a durable impact on the developing child.

2. The possibilities under each of them are qualified by such factors as behavior *thresholds* for particular stimuli, and the *capacities* of the child at each point in his behavioral development (maturation).

3. The relationships indexed by these concepts may vary from one developmental period to the next.

4. Insofar as evoking or reinforcing stimuli have acquired their roles through learning, the way in which they control behavior can differ from child to child. Hence, the provision of these stimuli must

be adapted to the individual child in order to provide stimuli that are relevant for him.

5. To the extent that stimuli (without unconditioned value) provided on any occasion are not meaningful in terms of a child's history (they have no conditioned value), they will be minimally effective on the occasion (trial) of presentation. Across trials, if the stimuli are presented in a recurring way in contingent relation to behaviors, they can effect or be involved in new learnings.

All of the preceding operations will affect behavior on any single occasion of application. The history of repeated applications will reflect a cumulative effect different from, or more extensive than, the effect of any single application.

Analysis of environments conducive to development along socially desirable lines therefore requires programming principles for providing stimuli in specific relations to behaviors in the child's repertoire. Some examples of such principles will be sketched after organismic factors are briefly considered.

THE ROLE OF ORGANISMIC FACTORS

Thus far we have given little attention to differences in innate characteristics, to apparently unlearned stimulus-response associations, to changes in children's capacity with developmental level, and to species-specific and individual differences. Such factors must always be accounted for in analyses of experiences designed to enhance the growth and development of children in the early years. In recent years behavior scientists have not found fruitful the attempt to separate behavior functioning from environmental context, as was the emphasis in the "heredity vs. environment" ("nature vs. nurture") controversies of several decades ago. Such concepts as "capacity," "ability," "level of functioning," and the like cannot be used independent of behavior as it occurs *within* an environmental context.

When considering the role of behavior capacities, it is axiomatic that an infant cannot perform tasks requiring responses which he is physically unable to make. Hence, no amount of stimulation, exposure, or training will facilitate those responses. (However, it may sometimes be possible for the child to use alternative responses to achieve the same ends.) If a child's receptors or motor and locomotor skills are insufficiently developed, the number and types of stimuli from all sources to which he can respond and which can reinforce his responses are limited. Moreover, the child who is *classified* as not

184 Translating Child Care Goals

up to the norms of his peer group (perhaps as a result of these organismic limits for receiving and operating on stimuli) may be provided with a more restricted range of stimuli and behavior opportunities than his peers. (See the section on "backward" behavior patterns, Chapter 7, p. 158.)

The Facilitation of Valued Behavior Outcomes

Socially-desirable behaviors can be made more likely to occur in unified groups as a result of the application of equivalent environmental processes to all of them. This holds particularly for attempts to raise the incidence of socially-desirable behavior classes from zero to low initial rates. To *facilitate* the emergence and strengthening of valued adaptive and coping behavior outcomes as well as behaviors that are under the control of a variety of social events and combinations (e.g., attachments), and to effect early dimensional and contextual learnings, operations of the following classes can be applied:

1. *Reinforcement.* Reinforcing stimuli can be provided to strengthen or weaken the ongoing behaviors on which they are contingent. Their effects as reinforcers are qualified by such factors as temporal gradients of delay between response and stimulus application, schedules of reinforcement, and the program or temporal sequence of application.

2. *Shaping.* Socially desirable response outcomes in the child's behavior can be fostered by reinforcing successive approximations to the desired response. The occurrence of primitive behavior elements that permit shaping to be implemented can be promoted by providing appropriate evoking stimuli. Various behaviors can be shaped to progressively higher levels as the changing capacities of the child permit.

3. *Extinction.* In order to extinguish a child's behavior like fussing that has been identified as asocial or undesirable, it is first necessary to identify the reinforcing stimuli that maintain or support that behavior. One method of modifying the child's behavior involves the removal of the reinforcing stimuli which previously followed the nonvalued behavior; another method involves reinforcing preferred responses that are incompatible with the nonvalued behavior. These processes are complementary and if used jointly will enhance differentiation. Thus, infantile modes of response to the environment

can be supplanted by responses more appropriate to the child's age group.

In contrast to extinction, *punishment*, which entails making a noxious stimulus systematically contingent upon a response, is not an efficient means for eliminating undesirable behavior. Punishment merely inhibits the behavior to stimuli in the given situation (that in which it was punished), and if the situation changes, the undesirable behavior can recur. Further, punishment often leads to emotional behaviors that may be disorganizing (even if not directed toward the punishing agent). Since these emotional behaviors are usually negative and consensually regarded as undesirable, the result of punishment may be merely the exchange of one undesirable behavior for another.

4. *Context-setting conditions.* The effectiveness of stimuli in evoking or in reinforcing behavior on a particular occasion may be enhanced by manipulating the context-setting conditions of stimulus provision. Behavior occurrence may thus be promoted by providing stimuli (unconditioned or conditioned) in terms of operations which enhance evocation effects by maximizing stimulus salience, for example, deprivation operations. Some conditions can also facilitate the dropping-out of undesirable responses (e.g., startle-avoidance behaviors).

5. *Stimulus exposure.* Early dimensional, categorical, and contextual learnings can be facilitated by exposing the child to stimuli from a large variety of classes, levels within classes, and combinations, so that they may be registered by him and so that emotional responses to some of them may be habituated. It is assumed that if, in addition to reinforced responses, motor or other discriminated responses are made to these stimuli and these responses are not followed by reinforcement, even more effective dimensional learning trials will result. (See the section on stimulus registration, Chapter 7, p. 160.)

6. *General responsiveness.* Implementation of conditions for curiosity and exploratory behaviors may facilitate general responsiveness to the environment. Two conceptually overlapping types of behavior should be supported: (1) *coping behavior*, occasioned when the behavior pattern established by a S-R chain is interrupted by a break ("frustration"); and (2) *problem-solving behavior*, involving the identification of alternative solutions to a problem and the choice of the most efficient one. The support of these behaviors makes possible a great variety of responses (realistic or fantasy) for the child.

7. *The Premack principle.* The relationship isolated by Premack' (1959, 1962) provides a basis for evoking and reinforcing a large variety of child behaviors. Stated briefly, this principle maintains that in a situation where a *more* probable (i.e., frequent) response A and a *less* probable but independent response B are identified, response A can function as a positive reinforcer for response B, when the occurrence of A is made contingent upon the occurrence of B. Conversely, making response B contingent upon response A can decrease the rate of response A and is equivalent to negative reinforcement or punishment of response A (Weisman and Premack, 1966).

This relationship, originally isolated in research with lower animals, can be readily extended for use with infants or with children of school age and can preclude the need for shaping or special training to bring infrequent behaviors into a child's repertoire. For children who understand verbal instruction, it is necessary merely to indicate to a child that he will be permitted to engage in what is, for him, a frequent behavior *only after* he exhibits a specified novel response (one which he might not exhibit in the ordinary course of events). Moreover, in school and day-care settings this method could be a useful alternative to the inefficient method of punishment that is often used in the attempt to suppress many undesired behaviors of high probability at the time when the teacher is encouraging behaviors of lower probability. The approach outlined here, which avoids the use of penalties and their ensuing negative emotional effects on the child, could ease the caretaking efforts of teachers and simultaneously permit the evocation and reinforcement of diverse socially-desired behaviors. In a nursery-school setting, Homme et al. (1963) increased the rate of originally low-probability behaviors, such as sitting quietly in a chair and looking at the blackboard, by making contingent upon them such high-probability responses as running around the room, screaming, pushing chairs, or working jigsaw puzzles. While this application was a preliminary one, it demonstrated the potential utility of the principle for the constructive control of the behaviors of young children.

8. *Generalized imitation.* A child can acquire behavior patterns through imitation by exposing him to models who perform the behaviors that one wishes the child to acquire. An imitative response is not classifiable by content; it is similar to a behavior of another person (the "model") and is matched to the cues provided by the model's response (but is not emitted because of common stimulus antecedents or environmental constraints). A generalized tendency to

imitate involves the child's copying many responses of models in diverse situations, often in the absence of those responses being directly reinforced. This *generalized-imitation* tendency can be established by teaching the child a discrimination through the use of many of the techniques listed earlier, particularly through the frequent reinforcement of a variety of specific imitative behaviors, and it can then be maintained by occasional direct reinforcement of those behaviors.* Once established in the child, this generalized-imitation tendency is pervasive, it can be focused on one model, it can occur in situations where there is no extrinsic reinforcement for imitation, and it can ease the acquisition of novel behavior sequences and eliminate lengthy trial-and-error learning in many realms. Further, generalized imitation can account as well for the imitation of more general attitudes and values, which may result in behaviors that are in form (topographically) quite different from the model's. Indeed, the generalized-imitation paradigm can provide a parsimonious basis for the phenomena usually grouped under the concept of *identification,* by which the child is said to acquire the motives, values, and ideals of significant individuals in his life. An analysis of the acquisition and maintenance of the generalized-imitation pattern in life settings, and its relation to vicarious reinforcement, observational learning, and identification is to be found in a recent paper by Gewirtz and Stingle (in press).

Observational learning has been defined as the immediate or delayed matching of a subject's response to that of a model, without the response having been exhibited before being correctly made; while *vicarious reinforcement* has been defined as the increase in likelihood that an observer (i.e., imitator) will copy a model's behavior that he has seen being reinforced. In life settings, a child's

---

* In work with most children, the conditions for the acquisition of this generalized-imitation response class often go unnoticed. However, a dramatic example of an extreme case will illuminate the process involved. A generalized-imitation response was shaped in retarded, initially nonimitative child subjects by making the word *good,* followed by food, contingent upon their imitating each of a series of specific behaviors exhibited by an adult model (Baer, Peterson, and Sherman, 1965). Initially, direct tuition in the form of physical assistance to the child by the model was necessary to provide response occasions for reinforcement. After several imitative responses had been reinforced in this manner, the children began making some imitative responses that were not reinforced, maintaining this nonreinforced imitation until extinction of all imitation was effected by presenting reinforcement noncontingently or not at all. Although in life settings, due to the intermittency of most reinforcement, this extinction may require a longer period of nonreinforcement than was found necessary in the study described, these results suggest that for imitative responses to persist, pairing with reinforcement must somehow be maintained.

matching responses to models' responses are very often directly reinforced. Indeed, opportunities for new learnings that are clearly free
of the child's having been extrinsically reinforced for imitating are
rare. Hence, for the range of life settings to which we have been attending, this conception of generalized imitation may be functionally
equivalent to that of observational learning and to encompass vicarious-reinforcement phenomena.

ECOLOGICAL FACTORS

It is possible to engineer ecological conditions in a setting to facilitate and subsequently reinforce certain desirable behavior outcomes
in an individual child or in a sub-group of children. At times it may
be best to insulate children against interference from adults, other
children, or activities, in order to facilitate their successful completion of tasks in which they are engaged. If individual children interfere with group activities or the activities of particular other children,
it may be useful to insulate potential victims from these children. It
may sometimes be reasonable to consider increasing the number of
children in a limited area or otherwise manipulating them ecologi-
cally in space in order to increase the probability of various positive
interactions between the children and the probability of particular
activities: role play or thematic play. It is also possible to manipulate
the ratio and kind of props to space in order to foster constructive
use of them or particular patterns of interaction. Thus, the occurrence of various desirable behavior systems may be facilitated and
subsequently reinforced by conditions brought about by systematic
manipulations of the available space, the type and number of materials positioned in that space, and the number of peers and adults
in that space. Although the principles underlying such ecological
manipulations are not as yet well understood, an illustration of their
utility can be found in Shure (1963).

For our purposes, other situations may be considered as ecological
conditions. For instance, the greater availability of active adults in
a child's environment provides a wider range of behaviors for the
child to use as models for his own behavior (in generalized imitation
and identification). A similar situation prevails if children's groups
include heterogeneous age groups of children. For example, when
there are young children in a group, caretaker models are more apt
to exhibit nurturant responses which the older children may copy.
Moreover, socialization by imitation is more possible for the young

child when there are a large number of older individuals in his environment who exhibit a variety of behaviors that he can copy. Whether a child is part of a family unit or in a group-care setting, the socializing agents must decide, on the basis of those behaviors assumed appropriate for the child's present age level or for the next higher age level, which of his behaviors to reinforce differentially. This means that the caretaker must continuously monitor the child's behaviors and be prepared to respond to them. If the socialization process occurs in the absence of older models who could directly reinforce a child's behaviors, it is more difficult for the child to acquire more mature behaviors.

Some Consensually Valued Behavior Systems

Before the principles of behavior facilitation and change can be implemented, it is instructive to consider a list of outcomes that should be fostered early in life. As such lists vary with the aims of different analyses, we will not attempt a complete listing here but instead will provide categories of socially desirable behaviors stated in general terms, specifying only some preliminary operations for facilitating such behaviors. The various operations just enumerated provide the basis for the facilitation of specific behaviors under the general behavior categories listed in this section.

Various *bodily skills* are certain to be consensually valued. The control of *gross movements* of the arms, hands, legs, and trunk (as are involved in reaching and locomotion) can be facilitated by large environmental props (for example, furniture and large push toys) which can both support the child and also provide opportunities and challenges for increasing his mobility. *Articulate movements,* such as grasping, can be facilitated through play with manipulable, movable toys, such as pegboards, screw-in toys, blocks, puzzles, and other props that require coordination of small muscle movements.

Social responsiveness, another valued behavior outcome, can be facilitated most easily by providing stimuli from social sources contingent upon such responses as the infant's smiles, laughter, and vocalizations. These stimuli will then come to control his behaviors by acting in either a discriminative or reinforcing role. (These behaviors thus become appropriately social.)

As the child matures, *speech* and *language* skills become increasingly relevant. The child can build up repertoires of speech sounds through stimulation provided by an adult and also possibly by the child's attempts to imitate these stimuli. This process may also be facilitated by reinforcement of the child's spontaneous verbalizations with verbal replies, as well as by provision of verbal labels for objects and action processes. Over repeated occasions, these sounds may acquire meaning for the child.

Self-reliance is shown in the child's fending for himself over periods of time. It may be facilitated by establishing occasions (and general environmental conditions) for the child to perform acts to care for himself, as in eating, toileting, dressing, and attaining objects. Apart from his being reinforced by the successful completion of the activity (for example, receipt of food when he feeds himself), his responses may be strengthened further by social reinforcement mediated by the caretaker.

A degree of *emotional independence*, which is manifested in the child's not requiring a high maintenance rate of receipt of social stimuli (as is provided through intensive interaction with others), may be facilitated by reinforcing autonomous behaviors of the child and by providing him with a lower maintenance rate of social stimuli.

The child can *gain information* about his environment through his experiences with the animate or inanimate materials provided by the environment. Experiencing instances of stimuli from a variety of classes and in many modalities can facilitate factual and dimensional learnings. This information also can facilitate fantasy and play behaviors.

In early life, emotional, startle, defensive, and aversive response complexes may occur to a variety of apparently unconditioned stimuli, such as sudden, intense sounds, and these may interfere with desired behavior outcomes. Some of these responses may undergo complete habituation if their evoking stimuli are provided in abundance. Thus, interference responses are unlikely to become associated with the range of material and social stimuli in the infant's environment. Infants unresponsive to such potentially disorganizing stimuli can operate more freely, and as their early experiences are far less encumbered, their developmental learnings should be more rapid and occur in a wider sample of settings.

Behaviors which are identified as *asocial* (e.g., crying for attention) are generally considered undesirable and may be extinguished by removing the reinforcing stimuli which the child has learned are contingent upon these acts.

The learning of *tolerance for delay of reinforcement* can enable the child to adapt more easily to the range of situations present in most environmental settings, where latency, duration, and type of reinforcement are extremely varied. Tolerance for delay of reinforcement will be dealt with in detail here, for besides its clear advantages in family settings, its fostering is particularly important in group-care settings, where the caretakers are generally overburdened and unable to attend immediately to the responses ("needs") of each child. In such settings, often the noisiest child is fed first, for caretakers often indicate that they equate the amount of the child's crying with the degree of his hunger and thus may inadvertently reinforce disruptive behaviors.

Tolerance for delay may be conditioned in younger children by the periodic provision of a delay cue by the caretaker to bridge the time gap between the child's acceptable request (e.g., one which does not involve crying) and its reinforcement. For older infants the cue may be a verbal statement by the caretaker, for instance, "I am busy now," followed by an appropriate response after the caretaker's task is completed. This training can be facilitated by providing reinforcement after varying lengths of time and after low response amplitudes, thus preventing the establishment, for instance, of temper tantrums through the reinforcement of high response amplitudes, or of nagging through reinforcement of long response durations.

Mealtime interactions between caretaker and infant constitute the bulk of such interaction opportunities in many group care and family settings. In addition to the specific delay behaviors being taught, these interactions which take place when the infant is not near his limit for hunger and frustration can make the meal more pleasant for both caretaker and child. Moreover, learning of socially desired behaviors (including attachment behavior) by the infant during meals can be effected more efficiently.

Implications of the Analysis

In relation to the concepts for environmental control over behavior, the present analysis has emphasized the learning *contingencies* provided to the infant by his parent-caretaker and the valued behavior outcomes achieved through the control of these contingencies. These contingencies are the basis for the infant's acquisition of patterns of social behavior which are under the control of social discriminative and social reinforcing stimuli. Instead of stressing which or how many of a given class of stimuli are provided to the infant, this analysis has emphasized whether or not stimuli available to the infant are functional for him and whether or not these stimuli, paired with his responses, comprise effective contingencies for learning.

STIMULI AVAILABLE TO THE INFANT

The following questions must be asked about the available stimuli and their control functions:

1. Are potential evoking or reinforcing stimuli actually provided? If they are, are they discriminable for the infant?

2. If stimuli are provided that elicit emotional-startle behaviors (presumed here to be unlearned), does the pattern of their occurrence allow the relatively complete habituation of these behaviors?

3. Are potential evoking (including arousing) stimuli provided in a pattern and at a rate conducive to the occurrence of the behaviors these stimuli could affect?

4. Are potential reinforcing stimuli dispensed immediately contingent upon the infant's behaviors (especially those consensually defined as "social") so the behaviors can be conditioned?

5. Are originally neutral cue stimuli (e.g., provided by the caretakers' attention or appearance) followed closely by potential reinforcing stimuli in order for the cues to acquire reinforcer value that will remain effective as long as the pairings take place?

6. Are there current or immediately preceding background-context conditions which qualify the effectiveness of the evoking, reinforcing, or cue stimulus? (Examples are satiation for a repeatedly presented stimulus or fatigue of a frequently repeated response.)

SPECIFIC IMPLICATIONS OF THE PROVISION OF COMPLEX STIMULI

The stimuli which can lead to the acquisition of valued behaviors by the developing child can be referred to as "abstract stimulus complexes" (e.g., stimulation, love, mothering). The following are some specific implications of the assumptions of stimulus provision and control outlined here:

1. The components of these stimulus complexes can be dispensed only as physical stimuli. That is, they must be visual, auditory, tactile, or olfactory, or combinations of these types of stimuli. From the earliest phases of an infant's development, the component elements of these stimuli may operate as *unconditioned* evoking or reinforcing

stimuli for the infant. These same stimuli cease to be functional for the infant as his responses to them habituate.

2. An abstract stimulus complex has functional significance for the infant only to the extent that it has involved effective learning contingencies for him. (Component elements of the stimulus complex may also provide unconditioned stimuli for the infant's responses.)

3. The infant's responsiveness to stimuli (in this case, social stimuli) appears to be established and maintained by unconditioned and conditioned reinforcing stimuli dispensed by people in his environment. In terms of this working assumption underlying the present approach, the proposition that the human infant has certain *innate* needs for social stimuli (such as mothering and love) appears only remotely useful heuristically. Under the learning model, the infant cannot thrive in an environment devoid of stimuli to establish and support his behavior and learning. Also, in the context of this model, if an originally neutral stimulus is provided by the infant's caretakers as discriminative for reinforcement, it will acquire reinforcing value for him.

4. It is apparent that there will be differences among children in the composition and importance of a stimulus complex as a result of the differing conditions existing in the early establishment and maintenance of such stimulus complexes. Stimulus complexes presented by the child's parent or main caretaker can be most effective as reinforcers. These complexes are usually composed of the particular stimuli which were salient in the acquisition of reinforcing value by the stimulus complexes. However, if an identical stimulus complex is offered to the child by others, its reinforcing value for the child may differ, until he learns the functional equivalence of the diverse stimulus sources.

Various stimulus complexes intended by the dispenser to represent stimulation or love to the child will not be efficient as reinforcing stimuli because they have not been conditioned as such in behavior settings different from the ones in which the child's basic learnings occurred. Children will also differ in regard to the relative importance these conditioned reinforcing stimuli have for them. They will differ, too, in regard to the amount of the stimulus considered sufficient and the rate at which they have learned to receive it.

Some of the possibilities stemming from the provision of a stimulus complex (for example, love) by different people in different settings include the following:

a. In the instance where different attributes of a learned behavior are required before reinforcement is provided, variations of that behavior may occur.

b. The reinforcement source may be able to predict the stimuli which will function as reinforcers for the child by observing the stimulus-response contingencies that operate for him. This source can then provide the stimuli in the appropriate timing relationships with the responses.

c. If the child adjusts to the new situation, new stimuli can acquire conditioned reinforcing value and can maintain his behavior in the new environment.

d. In the instance where a child's responses are not reinforced in their usual way, he may emit emotional behavior of various sorts and intensities, similar to behavior occurring when extinction procedures are begun after continuous reinforcement or when a behavior chain is blocked.

e. If effective reinforcing stimuli are provided in a new setting on a schedule different from the former one, the child may emit responses at a rate corresponding to the altered schedule. (Thus, if stimuli are provided more frequently in a new setting, the child may respond at a higher rate.)

5. As was seen in Chapter 7, there is a fallacy in the proposition that simply giving a child "enough" stimulation, attention, or love can compensate for an earlier "inadequate" supply of these stimuli. A sudden change to a higher rate of stimulus provision, whether or not the stimuli are provided contingent upon behavior, can bring about abrupt disruptive changes in many interrelated behaviors, including social behaviors, and can lead to new behavior patterns which may differ greatly from those that might have been adopted otherwise. This disorganization, actually created by the child's transition to the new caretaking setting, may be used under a long-term deficiency-hunger model as an index of the inadequacy of the supply of these stimuli received by the child in the earlier setting. Changes in existing habit systems toward valued patterns of more social and mature behaviors may occur when the stimuli in the new setting are repeatedly presented to the child in effective contingencies with valued behaviors, when this was not the case in the prior setting. These newly established behavior patterns may, in turn, serve under the deficiency model to indicate that the child has become more "secure," since he no longer *appears* to need so much attention and

love; and it is thus often concluded that the "hunger" for these stimuli has been reversed. Also, if it is assumed that the conditioned-reinforcer class dispensed is the most effective one for the child, different discriminative stimuli can control the occurrence of behaviors for that reinforcing stimulus in a new setting (e.g., a move to a new home or into a therapeutic setting).

6. Environmental events which have no unconditioned stimulus value and have not been previously paired with any positive or negative reinforcement will not, even when associated with intense affect responses, have any effect on the child's behaviors.

The final assumption brings all the earlier ones into focus:

7. A child's social learning is characterized by his acquisition of social-behavior patterns which are under the control of social discriminative and reinforcing stimuli. This process is dependent upon the contingencies with his behaviors that are constituted by the stimuli provided to the child in his behavior setting. In this context, caretakers can be pivotal in providing efficient conditions (contingencies) for optimal social learning. Unfortunately, this is rarely the case. The approach often taken by parents, as well as by many theorists in this area, is to stress only the provision of a commodity (as, food or love) and not the circumstances under which these commodities are given. More specifically, the question is how do these potential discriminative and reinforcing stimuli influence the child's behavior? It is important to consider this latter point, for it is the key factor in the child's social learning.

BEHAVIOR CHANGES DUE TO SHIFTS IN THE MAINTAINING ENVIRONMENT

It is axiomatic that a child will bring to a new environmental setting behavior systems that have been maintained by (and possibly acquired on the basis of) the stimuli in the setting from which he has come. It follows that the child's initial behavior to stimuli in a new setting will be a function of the similarity of the new stimuli available to those which controlled his behavior in the earlier context. These initial behaviors in the new setting are also determined by the rate at which his behaviors to novel stimulus conditions will habituate (sometimes a slow process with disruptive effects when abundant startle and noxious stimuli are found there).

One factor on which the child's adjustment in the new environment depends is likely to be whether the new caretakers learn from his behaviors the relevant discriminative and reinforcing stimuli and then provide those stimuli.* Other factors can include whether the child, through new learning facilitated in the new caretaking setting, acquires responses and reinforcing stimuli appropriate to the new setting. Further, a sudden and extreme shift from a setting in which the child's behavior systems have been under close stimulus control to a setting in which they are not may lead to a considerable weakening, deterioration, or even cessation of those behaviors. That is, because the controlling stimuli are no longer available, if the child exhibits any behaviors in the new setting, many of these behaviors may be less complex, even primitive, relative to the responses of his repertoire which are specific to the previous setting. In the extreme case, if the caretaking agency in the new setting is inflexible and fails to reinforce successively more appropriate instances of originally simple behaviors, the child may not acquire a substitute behavior repertoire there. These conditions may thus eventuate in a pathological outcome in the child. This outcome is especially likely if, at the same time, his behaviors are not advancing in complexity appropriate to his age group, and this pattern is contrary to the expectations of his reinforcing agents.

Shifts in the maintaining environment are reflected mainly in responses to different or novel stimuli in the new settings (Gewirtz, 1961). The effects of such shifts can be examined in three contexts:

1. *The single-occasion shift.* There may be differences between a child's responses in a context providing already conditioned discriminative stimuli and one providing stimuli which are not discriminative for the infant's behaviors (e.g., the presence of a substitute caretaker who is different from the mother or regular caretaker). If the stimuli provided in a new setting are markedly dissimilar from the discriminative stimuli in the former setting, the child may not respond to them. Otherwise, he may respond to the stimuli in the new setting in proportion to their similarity to those with discriminative control over his behaviors in the previous setting.

2. *Shifts across occasions.* With repeated presentations, new stimuli can acquire discriminative value for the infant. Alternatively, when the responses from the former setting are now inappropriately emitted in the present setting and are unreinforced, emotional or other maladaptive behaviors may result. These maladaptive behaviors may be incompatible with the emission of new adaptive responses in the

---

* The writer has considered the bases for the acquisition of initial and substitute attachments in an earlier analysis (Gewirtz, 1961).

setting, as has been illustrated in the section on deprivation phenomena in the preceding chapter.

3. *Simultaneous control by multiple environments.* A special case of shift in controlling stimuli involves differences in discriminative control of a child's behavior in independent but sometimes overlapping environmental settings (as in "multiple mothering"). Each caretaker can maintain different caretaking settings for a child by providing discriminative stimuli for responses that are appropriate in each setting. A problem of discrimination between caretakers or caretaker roles in the child's different environments may occur. Another problem may arise when there are multiple caretakers in a setting, each of whom provides different discriminative stimuli for him. The child's response to the discriminative stimuli of one caretaker may be incompatible with the response to the discriminative stimuli provided by another. These issues may become important for the institutional child, for the child in a day-care center or nursery school during the day, for the child left for a time with a babysitter or relative, or for one cared for simultaneously by a relative or maid and a parent.

Control of the Environment by the Infant

The caretaker-child interaction setting provides ample opportunity for mutual stimulation and reinforcement. It follows that this is an occasion for learning by the caretaker or parent—the environment—as well as by the child. This conception of the environment's behaviors adapting to the child's has to date received little emphasis in analyses of caretaker-child interaction.* Just as the caretaker promotes the child's growth by mediating stimuli that are valued by the child (and hence reinforcing) in learning contingencies, the child can also mediate reinforcing stimuli (in the form of his smiling, eating "well," ceasing to cry) that can affect learning by the caretaker in important areas.

THE INFANT AS CONDITIONER

By providing *positive* reinforcing stimuli, an infant can shape (via differential reinforcement) and eventually control a variety of his

---

* For exceptions see papers by Bell (1967) and Gewirtz (1961).

environment's behaviors, as behaviors directed toward his emission of vocal responses, such as *ma ma* or *da da*. Smiling and differential responsiveness by the infant toward the adult appear to constitute potent reinforcing stimuli for the behavior of most adults in many societies. Through these operations, the child can effect changes in his caretaker's behavior which will produce subsequent changes in his own behavior, and which will become, in turn, reinforcing for his caretaker's behavior. On this basis, "baby talk" and outlandish grimaces will enter the caretaker's behavioral repertoire as a function of the differential reinforcement provided by her charge. In this sense too a caretaker may become "attached" to her charge on the same conditioned-reinforcement basis that underlies the child's attachment to the caretaker. That is, stimuli provided by the young child acquire conditioned reinforcement value for the caretaker's behavior because they are associated with a variety of potent reinforcing stimuli for her behavior.

The control of the caretaking environment by behavior that provides *aversive* stimuli can be illustrated by the infant's instrumental crying and the environment's responses to such crying. High rates of crying appear to have strong aversive qualities for most adults, possibly unconditioned as well as conditioned. Hence, caretakers often respond by attempting to eliminate the infant's crying. Indeed, to do so they often stop some activity with another infant. This cessation of aversive stimuli can constitute potent reinforcement for the caretaker's behavior and hence increase the likelihood of her picking up the child when he cries again. However, picking up the infant when he cries can also constitute potent reinforcement for the infant's crying. Consequently, even though there is momentary relief for the caretaker each time the infant ceases to cry when he is picked up, the long-range effect is to increase the very behaviors of the infant that are aversive to the caretaker.*

TRAINING THE CHILD TO CONTROL HIS ENVIRONMENT

The child's potential for controlling his environment is especially important when he is in a group care setting. Much of his experiential learning is then taking place in a situation where the ratio of caretakers to infants is low, where the rate of caretaker turnover is high, when the time the caretakers have for each of their charges is severely

* See Etzel and Gewirtz (1967) for a detailed analysis of instrumental crying in infants and of its impact on caretakers.

restricted and mostly spent with caretaking routines, and where un-encumbered and "motivated" caretakers are not always available. Hence, where possible, it seems constructive to teach the child posi-tive social responses instead of negative or emotional "desperation" responses (e.g., crying or fussing), so that he will be able to control his caretaker most efficiently through the use of stimuli provided by his responses.

The child's caretaking setting can be tailored to enhance the opportunities for him to learn responses that "charm" (and particu-larly those which are potent reinforcing stimuli for caretaking be-haviors) in situations where sequential caretaking is provided by different caretakers or with diverse caretakers providing concurrent care. The more effectively the child is trained, the more able he will be to secure reinforcing opportunities for himself. Thus, there is an advantage in providing opportunities for the child to learn selected social skills that will give him some resilience in his environment and enable him to maximize his use of inconsistent settings toward whole-some development. For instance, at an early point the child can be reinforced heavily for smiles and for a variety of interesting vocal responses. These responses are highly effective in controlling be-haviors of caretakers.

It is also important to design methods to strengthen habits for the control of caretaker behaviors under the present design in order to achieve the child's unencumbered development, given that each experience (trial) can modify the effects of his past learning. Hence, special effort must be made to maintain the responses valued for caretaker-behavior control. This operation not only holds for institu-tional and day-care situations, but also may be applied as a form of preventive therapy for babies and children who have incompetent or unmotivated parents or caretakers.

On Love and Contingencies

Many consider it a truism that children thrive under or require tender loving care—popularly referred to as "TLC"—affection, and similar stimulus commodities. However, in the context of this chapter, where myriad environmental conditions that impinge on children and differentially affect their behavior have been identified, we must ask, "What is TLC?" It appears that the use of this term reflects concern for and sensitivity to children in an indifferent and sometimes hostile world. Hence, the term "TLC" apparently serves as a label for wholesome or ideal conditions in an environment concerned with socially desirable child development, but it is unspecific as a prescription for the behaviors required of the environment. In these chapters, we have been attempting to demonstrate the logic and utility of considering that environmental conditions for wholesome child development include those which provide the child with *contingencies* between his socially valued behaviors and behaviors of the environment, in a manner such that conditions for learning are optimal; but we are unspecific about the *motivation* of the caretaking environment. The combination of these two sets of factors can provide an interesting illustration of the main thesis of our analysis.

Recently, attention has been focused on the need for stimulation of children in institutions and substandard environments. This emphasis on stimulation per se is of little use without also attending to the response the child makes and the way in which it is reinforced. However, in group care settings, when much caretaker time is spent with one child (like one who "cries for attention"), less attention can be given to stimulation, responses, and reinforcement for the remaining infants. In principle, these infants can thrive with special care and certainly can do better if exposed to a well-defined program for providing caretaking attention. Otherwise, in essence, the "wrong" behavior (crying) will be reinforced for the "wrong" child (his instrumental crying, for instance, brings him the desired attention anyway) at the "wrong" time (the caretaker may be occupied with another child).

It should be apparent in this general context that conditions for wholesome child development are not restricted only to environments including "natural" parents. *Any* environment which effectively implements conditions consonant with the support and maintenance of consensually valued behavior systems for the child is one which can foster the development of that child. In addition, "natural," intact families are often worse than some institutions in terms of the unwholesome behavior outcomes that can be acquired by the child. Institutions can be engineered to provide relatively good environments for children, while a family may provide a relatively poor caretaking environment. That is, there is no necessary correlation between institution or foster home residence and unwholesome outcomes or between natural family membership and wholesome outcomes.

A SOLUTION: TLC THROUGH CONTINGENT CARETAKING

Thus far, this analysis has emphasized the issue of defining "environment" and "stimulation" and has provided some examples of concept classes which reflect environmental control of behavior on both short- and long-term bases. The analysis has detailed some consensually desirable behavior systems and has suggested ways in which they may be facilitated. In addition to the suggestions offered, a quite different and important tack can also be followed to improve conditions of experiential learning for infants and young children in group-care settings (Gewirtz and Etzel, 1967). This procedure does not require the use of environmental props nor does it necessitate programming the child's environment in a way similar to that for enhancing his social responsiveness or his learning of language skills. It calls for a modification of the caretaker's pattern of responsiveness to children, conforming to an explicit conditioning model similar to the one outlined in this paper. If discriminative and reinforcing stimuli (the caretaker's "love" and "attention") are provided to children under optimal learning conditions, two desirable results can be achieved simultaneously.

The first desirable result is the child's acquisition of a variety of socially valued behavior patterns, including those which insure that he will benefit maximally from his experiences. Indeed, this can be so effective as to allow the child to learn how to manipulate his environment to bring on such experience, independent of his caretaking or teaching setting. The desirable behaviors include those evoked and maintained by social stimuli, as well as speech, adaptive and coping behaviors, smiling, and the like.

Of equal importance, the subsequently learned habits of approach and response to conditions in his environment can fortify the child against the inconsistencies and vicissitudes of group care. Future adjustments can be made more easily once fortification has taken place. For example, when instrumental crying is subject increasingly to extinction procedures as the child grows older, the more mature behaviors that are increasingly required of him can be reinforced. Vocal behavior, for example, plays a key role in the socialization of children and in the establishment of social relationships. Deficits in such behavior patterns are often exhibited by infants in residential institutions. Hence, it is advisable to start early vocal training of infants in institutions by effectively reinforcing this response class. This prescription is especially called for if the infant is to remain in an institutional environment.

The second desirable result of a provision of optimal learning conditions is the satisfaction experienced by parents and caretakers, stemming from their active role in evoking and reinforcing socially desirable infant behavior with their "attention" and "love," for in this way they are contributing directly to the child's development. Caretakers are often ambivalent to a child when they must respond to him on his terms, particularly given the vehemence of the injunctions and prescriptions in our society regarding the proper adult orientation toward their charges. Taking a focused, disciplined role by reinforcing particular socially desirable behavior patterns and not reinforcing antisocial or immature responses may require a greater sensitivity than does undisciplined responding to the child, but should also prove more satisfying and to involve less ambivalence for mature caretakers than should attempts to follow such vague maxims as "be good to the child" or "give infants as much tender loving care as they need."

In other words, caretakers and parents can improve the level of functioning of each child in their charge, bring out the child's capabilities, and fortify him for gaining the most from his environment in a sometimes deficient group setting. At the same time, the caretaker may experience considerable satisfaction from knowing *how* and *when* it is constructive to provide attentive concern, care, and love for the child. An example of what may occur if this reasoning is not employed is the disruptive instrumental crying by infants which occurs both in homes and in group-care settings. In this example, the caretaker may find herself in the paradoxical position of reinforcing the immature or antisocial behavior of a child by continuing to respond to his insistent crying (for attention), while at the same time she may be ignoring other infants who also require her attention and care.

It is our experience that most caretakers are warm and loving persons. What is needed are roles to facilitate the translation of their love into effective reinforcement for the infant, that will be provided contingent upon those behaviors that society deems important for him to have in his repertoire. This may be done to compensate for developmental deficiencies in the infant due to busy, overworked caretaking environments, or simply to attempt to bring out the most advanced levels of adaptive behavior of which the infant is capable by tailoring environments to provide appropriate experiential learning.

Some Issues in the Learning Approach

In Chapter 7, there were listed several directions in which learning concepts might be extended to encompass more adequately some cumulative effects of experience. It may be useful at this point to consider several conceptual issues that can provide a better basis for understanding the learning approach we have employed in these chapters, including the conditions that can qualify learning, the generalizations that can be drawn from this approach, as well as its open-ended nature.

THE ROLE OF REINFORCEMENT IN THE LEARNING MODEL

Many of the ways in which a response may be strengthened are generally termed "reinforcing conditions." In this sense, when the critical stimulus apparently responsible for the strengthening or maintenance of a response is identified, it is usually termed the "reinforcing stimulus." There are at least two paradigms for the operation of such reinforcing stimuli. In the most frequently used paradigm, that of operant conditioning (which has come to give the term "reinforcement" much of its contemporary tone), reinforcing stimuli are those which systematically make more or less probable (i.e., strengthen or weaken) an identified response when made repeatedly contingent upon it. Under the respondent-conditioning (Pavlovian) paradigm, the repeated pairing of a preceding neutral stimulus with an unconditioned stimulus that elicits an unconditioned response is termed reinforcement when the result is a systematic increase in the probability that the previously neutral stimulus will elicit a response similar to or a derivative of the unconditioned response. Experimental characteristics have been identified which are typical of each paradigm, and others which overlap. It is evident, however, that the second reinforcing operation described is of a different order than the first even though both operations have been termed "response strengtheners." In the same sense, there are many possible sequence and timing patterns between response and stimulus which, when repeated often enough in an experimental context, will affect the strength of the response. Also, there exist a large number of conditions (stimulus deprivations, response sets, and the like) which can qualify the effective operation underlying reinforcing events.

We tend to label any recurring event as "reinforcing" if it makes more probable a response which it follows. The class of reinforcing operations is therefore open and the difference between the labels "reinforcement" and "learning" is thus often one of semantics. In principle, any of a large number of stimulus-response contingency operations may be classified as "reinforcing" when response strength is systematically affected by the provision of a stimulus. However, there are sometimes situations in which a systematic change in behavior is identified but the discriminative and reinforcing stimuli are not. In such a case it is sometimes assumed that the maintaining stimuli will later be identified, and the process is tentatively termed "learning."

An arbitrary use of the term "reinforcement" is seen in the following example. There sometimes appears to be a systematic change in attributes of a response (its strength) in a context where the contingency between that response and a stimulus is not identified. The behaviors involved are often labeled "self-reinforcing" (e.g., Harlow, 1950; Harlow, Harlow, and Meyer, 1950) or "intrinsically motivated." Where a reinforcing stimulus for behavior has not been identified, an efficient and parsimonious approach would be to identify the conditions under which the response occurs or appears to be strengthened. In this example, the response may have been strengthened only because of the opportunity for it to occur. A sufficient provisional "explanation" would be to present the network of functional relationships governing the occurrence of the response. These would include its relationships with various stimuli and time factors, showing changes in the response indices as a function of the pattern of preceding response occurrence (habituation). This procedure would preclude some possible costs of the gratuitous introduction of the term "reinforcement," which carries with it also some of the excess meaning of the "drive" concept. By labeling such responses "self-reinforcing" and hence implicitly contending that a vague reinforcing event controls them, researchers may effectively ignore some relevant determinants of response strength which may be of a different order from the ones usually involved in conventional reinforcement analyses of such determinants. Assuredly, the term "self-reinforcing" may be but a euphemistic label meaning, first, that the response determinants are not conventional and, second, that the exact nature of these determinants has not yet been established. In some instances, this usage may be due to the requirement that the researchers who use this label, while remaining open-minded, must be consistent within the over-all theoretical framework in which they are working.

In this context, Bandura (1965) has proposed that no response trial vicarious-reinforcement and observational learnings can take place. These would follow the standard laws of learning, were it not for the fact that they seem to occur in the absence of overt responding trials. Thus, these learnings appear not to involve the reinforcement contingencies characteristic of most learning situations, in particular those discussed in this and the preceding chapter. Nevertheless, they can illustrate additional ways in which the reinforcement concept has been used and can identify some interesting substantive issues that these uses index. This is the concern of the present section. Equally important under the purpose of this chapter, however, these apparently nonstandard learnings and the attempt I have made in the earlier section on the facilitation of valued behavior outcomes to explain vicarious-reinforcement and observational-learning effects in life settings in terms of a standard operant-conditioning conception can provide a potentially useful model in terms of which environments for enhancing child development could be designed.

The theme of this paper is that it is very convenient to use the open-ended reinforcer model for understanding the determinants of behavior and the conditions under which behavior can be evoked or changed. It has been demonstrated that this model provides a most convenient operational method for closely describing the dependence of behavior on environmental stimuli and the dependence of stimuli on behavior. This approach is useful in diverse settings that have been analyzed systematically. An attempt has been made to show how useful it can be in the approach to the phenomena of systematic upgrading of changes in children's behavior, as well as in handling the general issue of moment-to-moment changes in the maintaining environment (including such dramatic changes as involved in the separation of the child from a person with whom he has his primary relationship).

It follows in principle that an open-ended operational approach such as is outlined here can accommodate changes in environmental behavior patterns that are effected by unindexed conditions. This possibility derives from the fact that the definitions of the units of stimulus and response (i.e., size, complexity, and subtlety) are arbitrary and hence completely flexible for the purpose of any given analysis. In addition, an operational approach does not require any particular language system. However, because it derives historically from certain behavioristic analyses of associations and learnings, its concepts will be continuous with those of its antecedents, and the researchers who have typically worked within its framework will very likely favor certain directions in their approach. Because the approach outlined here is open-ended and operational, and hence permits analysis in terms of any size unit that appears relevant, it should protect the researchers who use it from their biases—that is, it is self-corrective.

THE NEED TO EXPLICATE "SETTING" CONDITIONS IN CHILD RESEARCH

In recent years there have appeared an increasing number of conditioning studies with infants and young children. The range of discriminative and reinforcing stimuli that has been shown to function in controlling a variety of child behaviors, for the most part through instrumental learning, has grown considerably (e.g., Stevenson, 1965). These studies have increased our understanding of adaptive learning in early life by providing tools to aid in designing environments that lead to desirable behavior outcomes, and they have increased our understanding of environmental stimulus classes that exercise moment-to-moment control over behavior.

Nevertheless, the experimental operations in a significant proportion of conditioning studies with children tend to be reported incompletely. Although discriminative and reinforcing stimuli are often described in appropriate detail, the *setting* and *maintenance* conditions that qualify the efficacy of those stimuli are often inexplicit. If potential reinforcers are not made relevant to the child via the implementation of appropriate setting conditions, they are not likely to function effectively and uniformly. For example, because achievement is emphasized in the school setting, the reinforcing effectiveness of remarks implying evaluation, such as the word *good* dispensed by an adult, would be high initially and would remain high for extensive periods after the child has left the classroom. A physically identical stimulus provided by a younger child or by an adult who is scorned by the neighborhood children would be less effective in the same setting. Further, an objectively identical stimulus provided by a machine with which a child might be interacting in a peer's home or even in a school which the child has entered secretly after closing hours, would probably show less reinforcing effectiveness than the "good" dispensed by the adult in the classroom. All too frequently these setting conditions are only implied in descriptions of experimental procedures with children, whereas they are rarely omitted from the description of experimental procedures in animal learning and drive literatures (e.g., the length of time during which the organism has been deprived of food prior to a conditioning task which tests the discriminative or reinforcing efficacy of food). Since there are a large variety of situations in which the functional effectiveness of the reinforcing or discriminative event is qualified or determined by setting conditions implemented concurrently with, immediately preceding, or through long time spans preceding the learning tasks, it is equally important to specify the setting conditions as the learning conditions in experiments with children.

LIMITS IN THE APPLICATION OF BASIC LEARNING
CONCEPTS TO CONDITIONS OF CHILD DEVELOPMENT

The learning relationships and the models, which are the basis of the conditioning approach to the impact of environment on early human adaptive and social behavior, are derived both from work with lower organisms and from simplified situations with humans in which several apparently salient aspects of naturally occurring phenomena are manipulated systematically. Attempts are made simply to identify both the stimulus events in the environment and the key behaviors which they appear to control. There is, however, a fundamental limitation in this approach which has often gone unrecognized when basic learning paradigms are applied uncritically to early human development and learning.

Typically, in investigations modeled on basic stimulus-response acquisition and performance paradigms with either lower organisms or humans in highly abstracted settings, some salient conditions are systematically manipulated in an *extreme* way, keeping minimal the number of cues or competing responses in a task setting, and employing operations to make the stimuli involved maximally salient for the organism (e.g., by manipulating background contrast factors). Thus, if food is to be employed as a discriminative or reinforcing stimulus in a discrimination task with pigeons, the subjects are frequently reduced to about 80 per cent of their normal body weight and are, in addition, deprived of food for an additional twenty-four or thirty-six hours. Further, the food stimulus is then dispensed in relatively small amounts so as to preclude the subject's satiating markedly for it during the experimental session and to insure its homogeneous effectiveness throughout the session. In this way, the salience of the food stimulus for the organism is maximized by the implementation of conditions which fall toward the extreme of a postulated dimension of operations for food salience.

In experiments with young humans, however, it is rarely possible to implement such extreme conditions, and more than minimal operations along this dimension are seldom attempted. The impact of discriminative and reinforcing stimuli on behaviors can be studied only within the intensity ranges permitted by everyday conditions in those environments. Thus, experiments and systematic observational studies cannot be carried out as efficiently as is possible with lower organisms in highly contrived situations.

This last point, however, indicates only a surface aspect of the limitation inherent in the approach questioned here. The basic reason for the limited scope of most of the work accomplished with lower organisms is, paradoxically, the success with which these contrived and extreme experimental conditions have been implemented. Consequently, in the conditioning literature and, oddly enough, in the deprivation-satiation motivation literature as well, remarkably little attention has been devoted to the functioning for behavior of stimuli through the lower and intermediate segments of their intensity ranges. Hence, the generalizations that can be drawn from experimental work apply minimally to the rapidly developing young human who is normally subjected only to stimuli of low and intermediate intensity values in life settings (for example, he is not deprived of food for more than a very few hours), and is in situations which contain various competing stimuli and have only minimal contrast (setting) conditions that can operate to heighten stimulus discriminability. Hence, an understanding of the operation of stimuli in the *lower* portion of the stimulus-attribute ranges is precisely what is required in order to understand the impact of the environment on the behaviors of the young organism, and paradoxically it is about this lower portion that we know very little. Moreover, in the attempt to understand the impact on behavior of these less extreme conditions, the tendency has been to use concepts like "attention" and "vigilance." These concepts, however, contain considerable excess meaning and have proved gross and unwieldy. Consequently, they can aid little in providing an understanding of adult human behavior for which they were devised, and much less in the understanding of the stimulus-response relationships that are focal in early life.

It is for these reasons that we have emphasized the variety of setting conditions that could qualify the impact of stimuli on behaviors (even in the lower portion of the intensity range of their functioning), as well as the apparently learned long-term background contexts for some classes of setting conditions. If we are to understand the functioning of stimuli in the lower segments of their intensity ranges and hence through the gamut of conditions in life settings, a deliberate attempt must be made in the study of early human-developmental learning to identify setting operations which qualify the functioning of stimuli for behaviors of the young organism.

Summary

In the context of the conceptions advanced in this and the preceding chapter, an approach was outlined in this chapter for enhancing the behavioral development of children in the early years via differential stimulation to bring their socially desirable behaviors to maximal levels. These levels may be above those such behaviors could attain even in the most privileged child-rearing settings.

Some of the requirements of a functional approach to the effects of stimulation on child behavior were discussed. It was seen how, to be meaningful, behavior outcomes had to be defined in relation to their controlling stimuli and, at the same level of analysis, the concept "environment" had meaning only when specified in terms of the effects of its component stimuli on behavior. An additional requirement was for the socially valued behavior outcomes of the child to be explicated before a meaningful attempt could be made to specify the stimulus conditions that would facilitate these desired behavioral outcomes. Implications of a functional approach included first, the abandonment of *non*behavioral criteria for the "good" environment of the child, and, second, the need for experimental validation of all assumptions about the effects of environment on behavior.

The current conceptual milieu for designing improved child-development settings was surveyed to set the scene for a discussion of concepts that reflect behavioral development and control. Selected concepts from conditioning theory were summarized, as were concepts for stimulation effects, performance-factor effects, and setting-drive effects. Behavior changes due to shifts in the maintaining environment were also considered. Finally, procedures were sketched for implementing these concepts to foster some representative socially-valued behavior systems.

It was seen, too, how the child comes to control his environment by the effective dispensation of reinforcers valued by parents and caretakers, such as smiles and vocalizations. Means were emphasized for fostering behaviors in the infant that would enable him to control his environment effectively.

We have attempted to demonstrate the logic and utility of considering that environmental conditions for wholesome child development include those which provide the child with contingencies between his socially valued behaviors and behaviors of the environment, such that conditions for learning are optimized. When this approach was tied in with the affection of caretakers for their charges, it was possible to illustrate the mutual benefits that could accrue for both children and their caretakers.

Finally, some conceptual issues were considered to provide a more adequate basis for understanding the learning approach we have outlined in these chapters.

REFERENCES

Baer, D. M., R. F. Peterson, and J. A. Sherman. Building an Imitative Repertoire by Programming Similarity between Child and Model as Discriminative for Reinforcement. Paper read at the biennial meeting of the Society for Research in Child Development, Minneapolis, Minn., March 1965.

Baldwin, J. M. *Mental Development in the Child and the Race: Methods and Processes.* New York: Macmillan, 1906.

Bandura, A. Vicarious Processes: A Case of No-trial Learning. In L. Berkowitz (Ed.), *Advances in Experimental Social Psychology,* vol. 2. New York: Academic Press, 1965, pp. 3–55.

Beach, F. A. Current Concepts of Play in Animals. *American Naturalist,* 79: 523–541, 1945.

Bell, R. Q. A Reinterpretation of the Direction of Effects in Studies of Socialization. *Psychological Review,* 75: 81–95, 1968.

Berlyne, D. E. Novelty and Curiosity as Determinants of Exploratory Behavior. *British Journal of Psychology,* 41: 68–80, 1950.

Bijou, S. W. Theory and Research in Mental (Developmental) Retardation. *Psychological Record,* 13: 95–110, 1963.

Denenberg, V. H. Critical Periods, Stimulus Inputs, and Emotional Reactivity: A Theory of Infantile Stimulation. *Psychological Review,* 71: 335–351, 1964.

Deutsch, M. Facilitating Development in the Pre-school Child: Social and Psychological Perspectives. *Merrill-Palmer Quarterly,* 10: 249–263, 1964.

Dewey, J. The Reflex Arc Concept in Psychology. *Psychological Review,* 3: 357–370, 1896.

Etzel, B. C., and J. L. Gewirtz. Experimental Modification of Caretaker-maintained High-rate Operant Crying in a 6- and a 20-week-old Infant (*Infans Tyrannotearus*): Extinction of Crying with Reinforcement of Eye Contact and Smiling. *Journal of Experimental Child Psychology*, 5: 303–317, 1967.

Ferster, C. B. Positive Reinforcement and Behavioral Deficits of Autistic Children. *Child Development*, 32: 437–456, 1961.

————. An Operant Reinforcement Analysis of Infantile Autism. In S. Lesse (Ed.), *An Evaluation of the Results of the Psychotherapies*. Springfield, Ill.: Charles C Thomas (in press).

Fowler, W. Cognitive Learning in Infancy and Early Childhood. *Psychological Bulletin*, 59: 116–152, 1962.

Gewirtz, H. B., and J. L. Gewirtz. Caretaking Settings, Background Events, and Behavior Differences in Four Israeli Child-rearing Environments: Some Preliminary Trends. In B. M. Foss (Ed.), *Determinants of Infant Behavior IV*. London: Methuen (in press).

Gewirtz, J. L. A Program of Research on the Dimensions and Antecedents of Emotional Dependence. *Child Development*, 27: 205–221, 1956.

————. A Learning Analysis of the Effects of Normal Stimulation, Privation and Deprivation on the Acquisition of Social Motivation and Attachment. In B. M. Foss (Ed.), *Determinants of Infant Behaviour*. New York: Wiley, 1961, pp. 213–299.

————. On the Choice of Relevant Variables and Levels of Conceptual Analysis in Parent-child Interaction Research. Paper presented to the Conference on Methodology in Parent-child Interaction Research, Department of Pediatrics, Upstate Medical Center, State University of New York, Syracuse, October 1964.

————. Deprivation and Satiation of Social Stimuli as Determinants of Their Reinforcing Efficacy. In J. P. Hill (Ed.), *Minnesota Symposia on Child Psychology*, vol. 1. Minneapolis: University of Minnesota Press, 1967(a), pp. 3–56.

————. Detrimental Usage of Drive in Social-learning Theory. Paper presented at the annual meeting of the American Psychological Association, Washington, D.C., September 1967(b).

————, and B. C. Etzel. Contingent Caretaking as a Solution for Some Child-rearing Paradoxes. Paper read at the biennial meeting of the Society for Research in Child Development, New York City, March 1967.

————, and H. B. Gewirtz. Stimulus Conditions, Infant Behaviors, and Social Learning in Four Israeli Child-rearing Environments: A Preliminary Report Illustrating Differences in Environment and Behavior between the "Only" and the "Youngest" Child. In B. M. Foss (Ed.), *Determinants of Infant Behaviour III*. New York: Wiley, 1965, pp. 161–184.

————, and K. G. Stingle. The Learning of Generalized Imitation as the Basis for Identification. *Psychological Review* (in press).

Harlow, H. F. Learning and Satiation of Response in Intrinsically Motivated Complex Puzzle Performance by Monkeys. *Journal of Comparative and Physiological Psychology*, 43: 289–294, 1950.

————. Motivation as a Factor in the Acquisition of New Responses. In *Current Theory and Research in Motivation*. Lincoln, Nebr.: University of Nebraska Press, 1953, pp. 24–49.

————, M. K. Harlow, and D. R. Meyer. Learning Motivated by the Manipulation Drive. *Journal of Experimental Psychology*, 40: 228–234, 1950.

Haywood, H. C., and J. T. Tapp. Experience and the Development of Adaptive Behavior. In N. R. Ellis (Ed.), *International Review of Research in Mental Retardation*, vol. 1. New York: Academic Press, 1966, pp. 109–151.

Hebb, D. O. *The Organization of Behavior*. New York: Wiley, 1949.

————. Drives and the CNS (Conceptual Nervous System). *Psychological Review*, 62: 243–254, 1955.

Homme, L. E., P. C. de Boca, J. V. Devine, R. Steinhorst, and E. J. Richert. Use of the Premack Principle in Controlling the Behavior of Nursery School Children. *Journal of the Experimental Analysis of Behavior*, 6: 544, 1963.

Hunt, J. McV. Piaget's Observations as a Source of Hypotheses Concerning Motivation. *Merrill-Palmer Quarterly*, 9: 263–275, 1963.

———. The Psychological Basis for Using Pre-school Enrichment as an Antidote for Cultural Deprivation. *Merrill-Palmer Quarterly*, 10: 209–248, 1964.

John, V. P., and L. S. Goldstein. The Social Context of Language Acquisition. *Merrill-Palmer Quarterly*, 10: 265–275, 1964.

Keller, F. S., and W. N. Schoenfeld. *Principles of Psychology*. New York: Appleton-Century-Crofts, 1950.

Kendler, H. H. *Basic Psychology*. New York: Appleton-Century-Crofts, 1963.

Kimble, G. A. *Hilgard and Marquis' Conditioning and Learning*. 2d ed. New York: Appleton-Century-Crofts, 1961.

———, and N. Garmezy. *Principles of General Psychology*. 2d ed. New York: Ronald, 1963.

Levine, S. The Effects of Infantile Experience on Adult Behavior. In A. J. Bachrach (Ed.), *Experimental Foundations of Clinical Psychology*. New York: Basic Books, 1962, pp. 139–169.

Montessori, M. *The Montessori Method*. New York: Stokes, 1912.

Montgomery, K. C. The Relation between Exploratory Behavior and Spontaneous Alternation in the White Rat. *Journal of Comparative and Physiological Psychology*, 44: 582–589, 1951.

Piaget, J. *The Origins of Intelligence in Children*. New York: International Universities Press, 1952.

Premack, D. Toward Empirical Behavior Laws: I. Positive Reinforcement. *Psychological Review*, 66: 219–233, 1959.

———. Reversibility of the Reinforcement Relation. *Science*, 136: 255–257, 1962.

Sears, R. R. Identification as a Form of Behavioral Development. In D. B. Harris (Ed.), *The Concept of Development*. Minneapolis: University of Minnesota Press, 1957, pp. 149–161.

———, L. Rau, and R. Alpert. *Identification and Child Rearing*. Stanford, Calif.: Stanford University Press, 1965.

Shure, M. B. Psychological Ecology of a Nursery School. *Child Development*, 34: 979–993, 1963.

Skeels, H. M. Effects of Adoption on Children from Institutions. *Children*, 12: 33–34, 1965.

———. Adult Status of Children with Contrasting Early Life Experiences. *Monographs of the Society for Research in Child Development*, vol. 31, no. 3 (serial no. 105), 1966.

———, and H. B. Dye. A Study of the Effects of Differential Stimulation on Mentally Retarded Children. *Proceedings of the American Association of Mental Deficiency*, 44: 114–136, 1939.

———, R. Updegraff, B. Wellman, and H. Williams. A Study of Environmental Stimulation: An Orphanage Pre-school Project. *University of Iowa Studies in Child Welfare*, 15: 1–191, 1938.

Skinner, B. F. *The Behavior of Organisms*. New York: Appleton-Century-Crofts, 1938.

———. *Science and Human Behavior*. New York: Macmillan, 1953.

———. The Science of Learning and the Art of Teaching. *Harvard Educational Review*, 24: 86–97, 1954.

Stevenson, H. W. Social Reinforcement of Children's Behavior. In L. P. Lipsitt and C. C. Spiker (Eds.), *Advances in Child Development and Behavior*, vol. 2. New York: Academic Press, 1965, pp. 97–126.

Ullmann, L. P., and L. Krasner (Eds.). *Case Studies in Behavior Modification*. New York: Holt, 1965.

Verhave, T. (Ed.). *The Experimental Analysis of Behavior: Selected Readings.* New York: Appleton-Century-Crofts, 1966.

Weisman, R., and D. Premack. Punishment and Reinforcement Produced by Reversal of the Probability Relation between Two Responses. *Program of the Seventh Annual Scientific Meeting of the Psychonomic Society* (Abstract) 1966, pp. 20–21.

Welker, W. I. An Analysis of Exploratory and Play Behavior in Animals. In D. W. Fiske and S. R. Maddi (Eds.), *Functions of Varied Experience.* Homewood, Ill.: Dorsey, 1961, pp. 175–226.

White, R. W. Motivation Reconsidered: The Concept of Competence. *Psychological Review,* 66: 297–333, 1959.

Woodworth, R. S. *Dynamics of Behavior.* New York: Holt, 1958.

PART III

Contemporary Programs and Strategies

Reports on selected programs—proposed and in progress, in the United States and abroad—are brought together in this section. Although the authors focus on parents and children who are apparently in need, the reader possibly may feel that the benefits should be available to all. Whatever the income level, parents are people in their own right. Family relationships are as complex and vital for adequate child rearing in suburbs as in slums. There is an almost universal tendency for child-care professionals to overlook fathers. It is likely that the majority of middle- and upper-income parents fall considerably short of practicing "ideal" child-rearing and family relationship patterns. And most parents, not just poor ones, probably have more growth potential than society recognizes or implements.

In like fashion, the services and opportunities available to children—while undoubtedly more complete and well implemented in "good" neighborhoods—are only moderately available in most urban settings today. The approaches suggested here for low-income families, for the working mother, or for those somehow "needy," "impoverished," or "deprived" might well apply, with appropriate adaptations, to families and children of all income levels.

ཨ§ 9 ཀ֍

Poor Families and Their Patterns of Child Care: Some Implications For Service Programs

CATHERINE S. CHILMAN

Concern for healthy physical, psychological, and social development of infants and young children often leads to a tendency to overlook the physical, psychological, and social needs and characteristics of the parents of these children. Parents—especially the father—are seldom seen as individuals in their own right.

Very poor parents are particularly apt to be neglected. The term "very poor" is used here to describe the chronically unemployed or underemployed portion of our population, who also tend to be undereducated and to come from backgrounds of long-term poverty. We are distinguishing between the so-called "working class"—often termed "lower class," or "class IV"—and the very poor—often termed "lower-lower class," or "class V." A number of sources indicate that there are probably greater differences in cultural patterns between class IV and class V than between class IV and class III, the middle class (Herzog, 1963; Komarovsky, 1964).

217

According to studies and clinical observations, the very poor have a greater tendency than other socioeconomic groups to consider themselves alienated from the rest of society (Myers, 1959; Rainwater, 1960; Riessman, 1964). Their alienation and distrust of authority figures—doctors, teachers, social workers, and nurses—tend to make it especially difficult for professionals in the child-care field to reach these parents in any meaningful way. Alienation frequently blocks in both directions: Child-care professionals also tend to distrust and dislike the parents of poverty.

This mutual alienation plays into the already existing tendency for pediatricians, child psychiatrists, child psychologists, and child-welfare workers to focus their energies and empathies on babies and children. Reinforced mutual alienation is likely to have a variety of outcomes, including the tendency to design health, education, and welfare programs primarily for the very young. While lip service is given to parents in many of these programs, parents are often seen as minor auxiliaries to the major effort. For instance, in the anti-poverty efforts, great emphasis is placed on such programs as Head Start, maternal and child health clinics, experiments in new ways of infant care, and—at a slightly older age level—educational enrichment in the elementary and high school years and job training for youth. Although parents, especially mothers, are involved to some extent in some of these programs, they are brought into the act in a supporting role rather than as star performers.

While there are public and voluntary local, state, and Federal programs which emphasize services and programs for adults—and, to some extent, total families (most notably in family social service agencies)—the major push is in child- or youth-centered services. While there are excellent research-based reasons for placing major program emphases on the very young (Bloom, 1964; Caldwell and Richmond, 1964a; Hess, 1964; Hunt, 1964), and while saving babies and children has greater popular and professional appeal than salvaging parents, there are also excellent research-based, theoretical, and cultural reasons for a family-centered approach in health, education, and welfare programs (Ackerman, 1958; Nimkoff, 1965). These reasons will be considered now in detail.

The Family as a Dynamic Interaction System

Theory, clinical experience, and a limited amount of research supports the principle that the social and psychological well-being of children is strongly related to the social and psychological well-being of the entire family to which they belong (Ackerman, 1958). The marital relationship of parents, for instance, apparently has a strong effect on the capacity of both father and mother to be adequate parents. Direct research evidence on this point is mostly lacking, although it is supported by theory, clinical experience, and indirect research findings (Block et al., 1958; Burgess and Cottrell, 1939; Chilman and Kraft, 1963; Levine, 1964; Levy, 1943; McCord, McCord, and Thurber, 1962; Strodtbeck, 1965b; Terman, 1938).

Healthy development of children appears to be closely associated with their relationships to both their fathers and mothers, as well as to their siblings (Ackerman, 1958; Burgess and Cottrell, 1939; Lynn and Saurey, 1959; McKinley, 1964; Mussen and Distler, 1959; Stolz et al., 1954; Strodtbeck, 1965b; Terman, 1938). Later patterns of adolescent and adult adjustment, including dating, courtship, mate selection, marital, and parental patterns are associated with life experiences of children in their family of origin (Burgess and Cottrell, 1939; Cavan, 1964; Chilman and Meyer, 1963; McKinley, 1964; Terman, 1938). These observations do not necessarily mean that, at all costs, the family must be saved as a child-care unit. Apparently, some families are unable to assume this function even with considerable professional help (Young, 1964). Differential diagnosis is called for, with a judicious approach that avoids a too ardent endorsement of the concept that "all infants and young children must remain with their mothers," or its antithesis, "infants and young children need to be saved from the damages imposed by their inadequate parents."

Differential, experimental approaches are needed, ranging from programs that attempt to substitute for parents on a more or less permanent, round-the-clock basis, to temporary, or part-time child-care arrangements that complement parental care. In all intervention strategies, attention must be paid to their impact on the total family interaction and behavior patterns, as well as on the child for whom treatment plans are made. Much attention has been paid to the "separation anxiety" that babies and children may experience when they are removed from their parents. Little heed is generally given to the separation anxiety that the parents and siblings may experience when a child is removed from the family, even on a part-time basis.

Studies of typical child-rearing and family life patterns of lower-lower-class parents indicate that these life-styles tend to be in direct contradiction to the patterns that a large number of studies show to be associated with positive child development.* When parental patterns positively associated with mental health, educational achievement, social acceptability, adequate conscience formation, and family stability are compared with parental patterns reported to be more prevalent in poverty groups, it appears that, comparatively speaking, lower-lower-class parents tend, in effect, to rear their children for failure in the five areas examined. However, this conclusion must be regarded as tentative for several reasons: Deficiencies and gaps in available research exist, and there may be a middle-class bias in the criteria used in existing studies to define the five areas being scrutinized. Furthermore, child development and behavior is based on a number of variables, only one of which is the child-rearing approach of the parents. There are adverse effects of the poverty situation itself and its multiple deprivations.

There are troubles with the samples, too. Increasing evidence shows that boys and girls respond differently to parental practices. Much research has failed to define adequately this issue (Bayley and Schaefer, 1964; Crandall, 1963). Most studies concerned with parental practices and their relation to the five criteria cited have used older children in their research samples. There are few studies of parental practices and their outcomes that focus on infants and preschool children, especially studies of parents and children together (Caldwell and Richmond, 1964b).

In spite of these deficiencies, there are clues that economically impoverished parents tend to employ inadequate child-rearing patterns with their infants and preschool youngsters (Hess, 1965; Sewell and Haller, 1956). Parental patterns which studies indicate are conducive to positive child development are compared to research findings concerning the behavior of very poor parents (Table 1).

A natural reaction to these findings might be a strengthened conviction that children of poverty must be "saved" from their parents. A more reflective reaction might be a consideration of the way in which parents might be helped to modify their patterns. Undoubtedly these fathers and mothers, as other fathers and mothers, want "the best" for their offspring. Their goals are similar to the goals of our larger society: more education, more opportunities, better health, better homes, greater happiness for their sons and daughters. Yet they lack knowledge of how to go about achieving these goals. They may rely on a quirk of fate, rather than believing that strategies can

---

* See Chilman (1965, 1966) for a detailed analysis of research in this area.

Table 1.* Child-Rearing and Family Life Patterns More
Characteristic of the Very Poor Compared with Patterns
Associated with Successful Adaptation to Middle-Class Society

Patterns Reported to be Characteristic of the Very Poor	Patterns Conducive to Adaptation to Middle-Class Society
1. Inconsistent, harsh, physical punishment.	1. Mild, firm, consistent discipline.
2. Fatalistic, personalistic attitudes, magical thinking.	2. Rational, evidence-oriented, objective attitudes.
3. Orientation in the present.	3. Future orientation, goal commitment.
4. Authoritarian, rigid family structure; strict definition of male and female roles.	4. Democratic, equalitarian, flexible family structure.
5. "Keep out of trouble," alienated, distrustful approach to society outside family; constricted experiences.	5. Self-confident, positive trustful approach to new experiences; wealth of experiences.
6. Limited verbal communication; relative absence of subtlety and abstract concepts; a physical-action style.	6. Extensive verbal communication; values placed on complexity, abstractions.
7. Human behavior seen as unpredictable and judged in terms of its immediate impact.	7. Human behavior seen as having many causes and being developmental in nature.
8. Low self-esteem, little belief in one's own coping capacity; passive attitude.	8. High self-esteem, belief in one's own coping capacity; an active attitude.
9. Distrust of opposite sex, exploitive attitude; ignorance of physiology of reproductive system and of contraceptives.	9. Acceptance of sex, positive sex expression within marriage by both husband and wife valued as part of total marital relationship; understanding of physiology of reproductive system, effective use of contraceptives.
10. Tendency not to differentiate clearly one child from another.	10. Each child seen as a separate individual and valued for his uniqueness.
11. Lack of consistent nurturance with abrupt and early granting of independence.	11. Consistent nurturant support with gradual training for independence.
12. Rates of marital conflict high; high rates of family breakdown.	12. Harmonious marriage; both husband and wife present.
13. Parents have low levels of educational achievement.	13. Parents have achieved educational and occupational success.

* This table, because it is so condensed, may be misleading since several topical fields have been merged (i.e., mental health, educational achievement, social acceptability, conscience formation, and family stability). For data differentiating these fields, see Chilman (1965, 1966).

help their children overcome the conditions that condemn the poor to failure and rejection. They lack economic, social, and psychological resources to implement their aspirations.

In many instances, professionals, working in a cooperative partnership with parents, may be able to give these parents the know-how, the resources, and the belief that their children can shift from the cycle of poverty to the cycle of prosperity. Of course, such a shift cannot come about simply through different parental methods and attitudes. Opportunity for education, better housing, employment, health, and other services must also be open to them. But opportunity alone isn't the whole story. As opportunities develop, individuals must have the attitudes, motivations, and personality characteristics to make effective use of them. Thus, family change-agents and community change-agents both have important roles to play.

Changing Parental Patterns

To what extent the parental patterns of the very poor can be changed is open to question. That some of them do change is obvious in terms of the history of our country. Perhaps those parents who are the most resistant to change are the ones who remain at the lower-lower-class level. This may be more true for white families than nonwhite, because the upward movement of nonwhite persons has been more drastically blocked by prejudice and a host of disadvantages. Experimental and evaluative projects are called for in upgrading families. Perhaps a few tentative principles can be stated as guides.

Very poor parents may have more intellectual potential than they appear to have. Constricted life experiences, lack of education and illiteracy, low self-esteem, and poor health may be holding very poor parents back. Adults may be more capable of mental growth than we know. Little experimental study, especially of lower-class subjects, has been done (Chilman, 1966). The classic adult intelligence curve of declining abilities may be inaccurate.

Parents are seldom given enriching experiences along the lines of their needs and motivations as persons in their own right. Many parents need emotional, physical, social, and intellectual nourishment for themselves. Before they can give these life ingredients to their children, they themselves must first receive them. One cannot give what one does not have. Studies of AFDC * families, for instance, paint a picture of parents who have had little security of any sort in their own growing-up years. Thus, the professional who seeks

* Recipients of the Aid to Families of Dependent Children Program.

to serve the children of these families may need to provide experiences which have direct relevance to the ego needs of the parent. These parents need some chance to taste specific quick mastery and to offset the frustrations and failures which have been their main diet.

Studies have shown that providing discipline is essential for positive human development. Research related to child-rearing patterns associated with adequate conscience formation (Kohlberg, 1964; White and Lippitt, 1960), later marital stability (Burgess and Cottrell, 1939; Peck and Havighurst, 1960; Terman, 1938), and positive ratings of good emotional health in children (Baldwin, Kalhorn, and Breese, 1945; Peterson et al., 1959) indicates that "firm, mild, consistent discipline" is a crucial, associated variable. Except for marital stability, these findings apply to child-rearing outcomes in terms of children's behavior. It is reasonable to assume, however, that adult behavioral patterns are deeply intertwined with the childhood experiences. Research evidence plus clinical observation (Young, 1964) indicates that many low-income parents lacked "firm, mild, consistent discipline" in their own growing-up experiences. The tendency for a larger proportion of poor parents to behave impulsively and with higher levels of overt aggression is probably related to the harsh, punitive, inconsistent child-rearing patterns to which many of them were exposed in their own youth.

Many of the very poor suffer from a chronic, deep depression, linked to a hopeless anxiety springing out of a lifetime of frustration, failure, and rejection (Chilman, 1966). Often this depression is dealt with in an impulsive, dramatic, expressive style, rather than in the more compulsive, intellectualized, instrumentalist style generally employed by the middle class in dealing with their hopeful, goal-oriented anxiety. The seemingly "don't care," irresponsible, "live it up" attitude sometimes observed among the very poor may be seen as a defensive, but ineffectual, maneuver to make life bearable. The professional who understands these defensive maneuvers can empathize, perhaps partly because of his own sense of frustration in attempting to help the very poor parents themselves. Any means by which poor parents can become less anxious, less depressed, and less constricted may be reflected in their child-rearing patterns.

Opportunities for social experience are needed for many parents of poverty. The loneliness, fear, and alienation of families in large cities have been noted in a number of studies (Duhl, 1963; Strodtbeck, 1965a). Estrangement is noted especially for the recent arrival in the city and in neighborhoods drastically changed by urban renewal.

The first need of families may be for help with housing, income, food, medical care, family planning, legal assistance, clothing, employment training, and placement. Parents pressed with specific concrete problems of survival are hardly in a position to consider the subtleties of a "rich, total developmental attitude" toward their children. Involvement of poor parents in social action projects at advisory and participative levels, employment of these parents in service programs, and the development of one-stop, multi-service centers may all be indicated as a way of working *with* disadvantaged adults.

Implementation of the Principles

Techniques by which desired changes could be achieved might be borrowed from other areas of practice and tailored to the population under concern.

GROUP PROGRAMS FOR PARENTS

Social workers, home economists, parent educators, and mental health workers report that education and treatment programs designed somewhat along the lines of a social club are effective. In a publication focused on helping low-income families through parent education groups, Chilman and Kraft (1963) summarize these reports. They suggest that the leader should be warm, enthusiastic, mature, flexible, and empathic. In addition, he needs some basic program skills. If he lacks professional training, he needs initial orientation, continuing in-service training, and good supervision.

The program should be built on the perceived needs of the parents. Especially in the early stages of the group, an emphasis may be placed on doing rather than talking. Sewing, cooking, and home-making groups adapted to the life realities and values of the participants may be effective.

As parents work on activity projects, they talk intensively and extensively about their concerns for their children and their families. At such times, a sensitive leader can pick up the cues that are offered and use the strength of group members. Such a technique seems to be far more effective than a planned discussion or lecture on child rearing and the family. The activity program can lead to field trips and expeditions designed to expand the experience, information, and self-confidence of the parents. A trip to the supermarket or the department store, for instance, is more likely to be greeted with enthusiasm than a trip to the library or the art museum. In time, a club may expand its interests toward more patently cultural aims. The development of friendship groups within the club is an allied aim of the program. By decreasing their social isolation, parents can be assisted by others in problem-coping situations and in more extended life experiences outside club meetings without the help of the leader.

New social skills—appearance, language, interpersonal relations, etc.—may be acquired and re-enforced by the group. These social skills can be useful to parents in their communities and in jobs; they may also transfer to family relationships and child-rearing practices.

If parents are to attend a group, some provision for babies and young children is usually necessary. The majority of low-income parents do not feel comfortable about employing baby-sitters to stay with their children even if money is provided or if free baby-sitters are made available. The cultural tradition of these families may dictate that parents take their children with them.

Although it may be difficult to locate suitable rooms for the meetings, a search may turn up a number of places. Space is sometimes available in public housing projects, pediatric clinics, day-care centers, and nursery schools, including those established under the Head Start program. Funds for the construction of appropriate centers may be obtained from a variety of sources, including those under the Mental Health Facilities Act and recent urban renewal legislation. Although schools and churches might seem suitable, experience shows that low-income parents may be loath to attend activities in settings that they associate with "the middle-class authority system." Not all schools and churches are so regarded and, of course, one of the aims of the group programs would be to help parents make effective use eventually of community resources that are in the mainstream of our culture.

In order to attract members to the programs and clubs, assertive reaching-out methods may be necessary at the outset. Leaders and club members may need to visit potential participants in their homes to encourage them to come and make them feel wanted for themselves.

It is especially necessary to find new ways to reach fathers. It has been extremely difficult to attract fathers to the programs. Their diffidence may be partially related to a tendency toward matriarchal structures in the lower socioeconomic class. A male leader would seem to be one of the requirements, yet even when this has been attempted, the results are meager. Observers have suggested that those working with "hard-to-reach" fathers should meet them in the places where they spontaneously gather and which seem natural and comfortable to them.

Group activities for poor adults can take forms other than the social club. The recently developed community action program, literacy classes, and vocational training programs are examples. These programs, however, are not directly concerned with child-rearing and family relationship patterns.

INDIVIDUAL COUNSELING

It is well known that the usual therapeutic approach of a one-to-one relationship fails to attract and hold most low-income parents. Reasons for this failure have been well documented (Riessman, 1964; Strodtbeck, 1965a). A number of caseworkers have evolved adaptations of the individual counseling approach in the past ten years (Fantl, 1964; Weinandy, 1964; Young, 1964). They suggest going to parents in their own homes rather than waiting for them to come into agency offices. They recommend firmness, setting of specific limits, and a reality orientation to immediate pressing problems. Their approach seems to rest on evolving a climate of assertiveness without aggression, nurturance and protection without domination and overprotection, responsible use of authority without authoritarianism, dependability without exploitation of dependency, recognition of family crisis and a clear meeting of these crises without the development of a crisis orientation, and empathy without overidentification.

In recent experimentation with the use of untrained family counseling aides, some good results are reported. Group supervision of the aides might be tried, rather than relying entirely on individual supervision. A similar technique might be used in supervising subprofessional leaders of the parent clubs discussed earlier. Group supervision may require less effort. Participation with others may develop staff morale, generate enriched insights and knowledge, and reinforce attitude changes.

Family counseling is a variation on individual counseling. Some social workers are adapting the concepts of recent work in family therapy to their work with entire families of the very poor (Levine, 1964). Recognizing that verbal insights have less meaning and less immediate appeal to people of low educational and economic levels, some workers have experimented with role playing and games in which all members of the family participate. New ways of behaving and insights about behavior in the family are worked out in the context of action.

TWENTY-FOUR-HOUR FAMILY EMERGENCY SERVICE

For those who have limited coping ability, the numerous difficulties in coping with family life in an urban setting presumably have accumulative negative effects that add to the sense of hopelessness and apathy of low-income parents. To assist with such problems, neighborhood counseling centers have recently been set up in some communities, sometimes with grants from the Office of Economic Opportunity. A variety of models are being used and it is probably too early to evaluate their effect (Parad, 1965). However, further experimentation with neighborhood counseling centers seems to be indicated. One feature of many of these centers is an emergency service. By this plan, professional and semiprofessional staff members are on call around the clock for help with family emergencies. Emergencies might be less severe than a real family crisis, although help in meeting crises would certainly be part of the service. A "family emergency" might be acute illness in a child, especially when the parents are also ill, a marital quarrel, an intoxicated family member, a neighborhood altercation, and so on. If small emergencies are met, more full-blown crises might be prevented or reduced in number. An emergency service should maintain links with other community agencies, including social agencies, health, police, housing, schools, legal services, and the city sanitation department. It might be operated by the public welfare department.

DAY-CARE SERVICES AND PRESCHOOL PROGRAMS

Although day-care centers and preschool programs, such as Headstart projects, recognize the importance of reaching and working with parents, this has proven to be extremely difficult. Parents who are working or who have other children at home have limited time. The subcultures of poverty and the tendency of staff members to identify with children rather than with the total family also create communication difficulties. There are a number of compelling reasons why staff members of child-care centers should reach the entire family. If young children are exposed to one set of values and attitudes at home and another in a child-care center, a discontinuity in life is created. It is important that a child-care program recognize the vital link that the parents provide and view itself as a complementary, but not substitute, child-rearing service. Parents can give the staff members special understanding of their children, as well as the other way around. The suggestions made earlier regarding the use of social clubs and counseling services for low-income parents might well be applied to work with fathers and mothers of children in day-care and other pre-school services.

It would seem important to have men, as well as women, serving in these programs. Many of the children of the very poor come from broken homes and have very little contact with adult males. Yet it is well recognized that both boys and girls need positive relationships with men as well as with women for their total development. Adolescent boys and girls who are either high school dropouts or who are given released time from school could work with preschool centers provided they are carefully chosen and are given skilled supervision. The staff placement of young people can become a laboratory experience tied to high school courses on child development or incorporated in such programs as Vista or the Job Corps. From work of this sort, psychosocial and educational gains could be made by the adolescents as well as by the young children whom they serve.

EXPANSION OF DAY-CARE HOMES

Homes that furnish day care for a few children are frequently recommended for infants and youngsters under the age of three when their natural parents are unable, for whatever reason, to care for their children full time themselves. Studies of day-care arrangements of working mothers have indicated that a considerable number of children are informally placed in such settings (*Child Care Arrangements,* 1965).

The Children's Bureau of the Department of Health, Education, and Welfare strongly recommends that states institute licensing for day-care homes. Thorough coverage of day-care homes through licensing procedures appears to be a desirable but difficult and minimal goal. Many parents may need help in locating suitable homes for day care. Often the daytime mother herself needs guidance in methods of good child care. A clear understanding between the parents and the day-care substitutes is needed as to the roles of each, methods of child care to be used, and the needs and characteristics of the individual child.

Development of competent, dependable day-care homes could probably be greatly facilitated through a social service agency, which has funds available for supplementary payments to daytime parents, since many low-income families cannot afford adequate payment for child care. It should be possible to find and further develop day-care homes within low-income neighborhoods, thereby providing at-home employment for some mothers who would otherwise need to work outside their homes or be dependent on public assistance. The day-care home represents a possible advantage to group care in that it may be nearer to the child's own home and represent less cultural distance between the home environment and the day-care setting. Furthermore, the daytime caretaker might teach the child's parents improved patterns of child care.

Although concepts such as those sketched above are well known to child-welfare professionals and although the Children's Bureau has worked to expand such programs under authorization of 1962 legislation, the number of professionally supervised day-care homes is still low in many communities. An adequate program is expensive and public funds for day care (at federal, state, and local levels), have tended to be sparse. Recent amendments to the Social Security Act (1967) promise a greater emphasis on day care for children of AFDC mothers combined with work-training and placement of such mothers.

HOMEMAKER SERVICES

The concept of using homemakers as helpers in a family crisis is well understood. Yet the concept of this service has more understanding and acceptance than actual implementation; the majority of the communities in this country do not have a homemaker service. Not only is this basic service needed, but also it might be expanded to use homemakers as family life teachers (Hill, 1963). Such teachers would not necessarily work full time for one family; they might work with different families for several hours a day, one or more times a week. The homemaker might aid low-income families when the mother returns from the hospital with a newborn. She would not only help with care of the baby and with housework, but also could serve as a "child development and family relations teacher" at a crucial and teachable moment in the life of a family. Such a service might be especially relevant for very young families with their first child. Homemakers who are carefully selected, trained, and supervised could be drawn from the ranks of the unemployed poor and experimentation along these lines is currently going on in some communities.

IMPROVED HEALTH SERVICES FOR PARENTS

Health services for low-income parents need to be greatly improved. The significance of poor health as a deterrent to adequate parenting among low-income families is made explicit by a variety of studies, such as an investigation of AFDC cases (Burgess and Price, 1963), which showed that three-fourths of the mothers had serious health problems. A study of child placement reveals that poor health of the mother was a leading factor in the removal of children from their own homes for institutional or foster-home placement (Jenkins and Sauber, 1966).

There is already considerable emphasis on providing excellent, routine health care for infants and for expectant mothers in high-risk maternal and infant mortality groups; this is accomplished through such services as the Child Health Conference and maternal and child health clinics. Recent Federal legislation (Title XIX of the Social Security Act) provides grants to states for improved health services for parents as well as for children in some low-income families, chiefly those receiving AFDC. Implementing these services is a gigantic task, partly because of the shortage of medical personnel. Among the suggestions for the alleviation of this shortage is to expand the use of indigenous nonprofessionals who perform clerical and paramedical services under supervision and with in-service training. Recent evidence from community action projects and from studies of very poor families points to the importance of providing health services in uncrowded settings that avoid long waiting periods, that assure regard for each individual, and that coordinate medical care with recommendations to the family and to social services.

CLUBS FOR TEEN-AGE MARRIED COUPLES

A concentration of health, education, and welfare services for very young married couples, especially those of low-income levels, would appear to be pertinent. Among the services might be a "social club" somewhat like that sketched earlier. Such a club could help young, disadvantaged husbands and wives learn, early in their marriage, more effective interpersonal relations. Various studies (e.g., Komarovsky, 1964) strongly indicate that one of the central problems of very poor husbands and wives is their lack of ability to communicate with each other in terms of their social lives and to plan cooperatively for such aspects of family life as housing, homemaking, family expenditures, control of family size, and employment plans. A club for couples of this kind might give them opportunities for social learning through group interaction and might also provide an opportunity for subject-matter learning in areas such as those indicated.

Group and individual programs for both unmarried mothers and unmarried fathers are also indicated. Efforts along these lines are going on in a few clinic and group-work settings.

FAMILY PLANNING SERVICES AND SEX EDUCATION

It is well recognized that the very poor, more than other socioeconomic groups, tend to have families larger than they say they want (Freedman, Whelpton, and Campbell, 1959). It is also reported that their known illegitimacy rates are higher (Lunde, 1965), as well as their rates of family breakdown (Lieberman, 1964). A number of research studies (e.g., Chilman, 1965) also indicate that the very poor tend to know less about the physical and psychological aspects of reproduction and marital relationships than do other socioeconomic groups. There is a tendency to distrust sex education for children and adolescents, and a fearful, fatalistic attitude toward sex is more likely to prevail. Marital happiness and sex satisfaction in marriage generally receive lower ratings by groups of very low-income men and women (Blood and Wolfe, 1960; Komarovsky, 1964).

Since studies also indicate that children in large families are less likely to achieve their full potential of development, it would seem to be highly strategic to conduct family planning programs especially designed for the very poor. Probably these programs should include family life and sex education, group and individual counseling, as well as medical services for contraception (Corkey, 1964; Herzog, 1960; Chilman, 1967).

That these services need to be skillfully adapted to the values, attitudes, situations, and informational levels of low-income families does not imply that they are not needed for other families, nor does it necessarily imply that they should be reserved for disadvantaged parents. If neighborhood clinics are developed—as they undoubtedly should be—the approach to family life and sex education (including contraceptive advice) will probably need to be handled sensitively in terms of the specific populations of the areas that the clinics are meant to serve.

EMPLOYMENT COUNSELING, TRAINING, PLACEMENT, AND CHILD-CARE PLANNING

Vocational services are obviously basic to the economic framework underlying the welfare of children and their parents. Low-income parents have a greater need for these services because of their tendency toward multiple handicaps in the employment field today. This subject is too large for full presentation here, but it is directly related to the fact that adequate child-care programs are essential if mothers are to enter the employment market. At present, child-care services are in dangerously short supply (*Child Care Arrangements,* 1965).

BETTER COORDINATION OF COMMUNITY RESOURCES

The need for coordination of community resources and more teamwork among the various professions has received a large amount of publicity but relatively little action over the years. The problem of fragmented services becomes increasingly acute as specialties grow, agencies proliferate, and public and private research and demonstration projects evolve under a wide array of sponsorships. While this explosion in services, specialties, and knowledge is mostly to the good, the coordination and application of these facilities to the lives of families frequently fall short.

At various points in this chapter, reference has been made to the concept of a neighborhood center. Neighborhood centers might be extended to meet a number of family needs; these centers would include emergency services, parent clubs, young married couple's clubs, family-planning services, educational and employment counseling, preschool programs, and so forth. Such centers might incorporate staff members from a number of community agencies, such as public welfare, public health nursing, public schools, juvenile courts and family relations workers from the courts, and others. In the past few years, neighborhood centers of many kinds have developed rapidly. Research is needed in the relative effectiveness of their programs.

In the neighborhood center, an interprofessional staff could be organized to diagnose and treat specific cases as a team. Not only would the cases benefit from such a team approach, but the team members themselves might benefit in increased knowledge, respect, and understanding of each other so that further interdisciplinary coordination would be implemented.

Data-processing techniques might be applied to the various possible and existing programs on local, state, and Federal levels so that, in effect, there would be a "service and program information retrieval service" similar to research information retrieval services that are now available. Information retrieval could be highly useful at all levels of public and voluntary organizational systems.

Summary

The focus in this chapter has been on the child-rearing and family life patterns of the very poor. Since these patterns arise out of poverty conditions, the conditions themselves require deep and extensive alleviation in such areas as increased employment opportunities, more adequate public assistance, extension of civil rights, and so on. Although changes such as these are recognized as being basic, a full discussion of them is beyond the scope of this chapter.

A wide range of services for poor parents has been suggested. It has not been possible to detail how these services may be operating currently in various parts of the country or how they might be set up in areas where they do not now exist. The services discussed have been chosen primarily because they seem particularly suitable for low-income families with young children. How effective they may be is still largely unknown. An experimental attitude and, whenever possible, provision for objective evaluation should accompany development of these services.

REFERENCES

Ackerman, N. The Psychodynamics of Family Life. New York: Basic Books, 1958.
Baldwin, A. L., J. Kalhorn, and F. H. Breese. Patterns of Parent Behavior. Psychological Monographs, 48: 3, 1945.
Bayley, N., and E. Schaefer. Correlations of Maternal and Child Behavior with the Development of Mental Abilities. Monographs of the Society for Research in Child Development, vol. 29 (serial no. 97). No. 6. Chicago: University of Chicago Press, 1964.
Block, J., V. Patterson, J. Block, and D. Jackson. A Study of the Parents of Schizophrenic and Neurotic Children. Psychiatry, 21: 387–397, 1958.

Blood, R. O., and D. M. Wolfe. Husbands and Wives: The Dynamics of Married Living. New York: Free Press, 1960.

Bloom, B. S. Stability and Change in Human Characteristics. New York: Wiley, 1964.

Burchinal, L. Research on Young Marriages. In M. B. Sussman (Ed.), Sourcebook on Marriage and the Family. Boston: Houghton Mifflin, 1963.

Burgess, E., and D. Price. An American Dependency Challenge. Chicago: American Public Welfare Association, 1963.

Burgess, E., and L. Cottrell. Predicting Success or Failure in Marriage. Englewood Cliffs, N.J.: Prentice-Hall, 1939.

Caldwell, B., and J. Richmond. Programmed Day Care for the Very Young Child. A Preliminary Report. Journal of Marriage and the Family, 26: 481–488, November, 1964(a).

———, and ———. Social Class Level and the Stimulation Potential of the Home. Paper presented at the 1964 meetings of the American Psychological Association, Los Angeles. Available from Upstate Medical Center Department of Pediatrics, State University of New York, Syracuse, New York. (Mimeographed), 1964(b).

Cavan, R. Subcultural Variations and Upward Mobility. In H. Christiansen (Ed.), Handbook of Marriage and the Family. Chicago: Rand McNally, 1964.

Child Care Arrangements of the Nation's Working Mothers. A Preliminary Report. Washington, D.C.: U.S. Department of Health, Education, and Welfare, Children's Bureau, and U.S. Department of Labor, Women's Bureau, 1965.

Chilman, C. S. Child Rearing and Family Life Patterns of the Very Poor. Welfare in Review, 3: 9–11, January, 1965.

———, Growing Up Poor. Washington, D.C.: U.S. Department of Health, Education, and Welfare, Welfare Administration, 1966.

———, Poverty and Family Planning in the United States: Some Social and Psychological Aspects and Implications for Programs and Policy. Welfare in Review, 5: 3–15, April, 1967.

———, and I. Kraft. Helping Low Income Families through Parent Education Groups. Children, 10: 127–136, July–August, 1963.

———, and D. Meyer. Aspirations, Attitudes, and Related Characteristics of Married and Single Undergraduates. Syracuse University (Mimeographed), 1963.

Corkey, E. C. A Family Planning for the Low-income Family. Journal of Marriage and the Family, 26 (4): 478–484, 1964.

Crandall, V. J. Achievement. In H. A. Stevenson (Ed.), Child Psychology. Sixty-second Yearbook for the National Society for the Study of Education. Chicago: University of Chicago Press, 1963, pp. 416–459.

Duhl, L. (Ed.). The Urban Condition. New York: Basic Books, 1963.

Fantl, B. Integrating Social and Psychological Theories in Social Work Practice, J. Cohen (Ed.). Smith College Studies in Social Work, vol. 34, no. 35, June, 1964.

Freedman, R., P. Whelpton, and A. Campbell. Family Planning in the U.S. Scientific American, 200 (4): 50–55, April, 1959.

Herzog, E. Children of Working Mothers. Washington, D.C.: U.S. Department of Health, Education, and Welfare, Children's Bureau, 1960.

———. Some Assumptions about the Poor. Social Service Review, 37 (4): 389–402, December, 1963.

Hess, R. Educability and Rehabilitation: The Future of the Working Class. Journal of Marriage and the Family, 26: 421–429, November, 1964.

———. Social Class Differences in Maternal Teaching Methods. Unpublished paper delivered at the American Psychological Association Annual Conference, Chicago, Illinois, 1965.

Hill, E. Helping Low-Income Families Through Homemaking Consultants. Children, 10: 132–136, July–August, 1963.

Hollingshead, A. B. Cultural Factors in the Selection of Marriage Mates. *American Sociological Review*, 15: 619–627, 1950.

Hunt, J. McV. The Psychological Basis for Using Pre-school Enrichment as an Antidote for Cultural Deprivation. *Merrill-Palmer Quarterly*, 10: 209–248, 1964.

Jenkins, S., and M. Sauber. *Paths to Child Placement.* New York: Community Council of Greater New York, 1966.

Jones, H. E., and H. S. Conrad. The Growth and Decline of Intelligence. *General Psychology Monographs*, 13: 223–298, 1933.

Kohlberg, L. Development of Moral Character and Moral Ideology. In M. L. Hoffman and L. W. Hoffman (Eds.), *Review of Child Development Research*, vol. 1. New York: Russell Sage Foundation, 1964, pp. 383–432.

Komarovsky, M. *Blue Collar Marriage.* New York: Random House, 1964.

Levine, R. A. Treatment in the Home: An Experiment with Mental Health of the Poor. In F. Riessman, J. Cohen, and A. Pearl (Eds.), *Mental Health of the Poor.* New York: Free Press, 1964, pp. 329–335.

Levy, D. *Maternal Overprotection.* New York: Columbia University Press, 1943.

Lieberman, E. J. Preventive Psychiatry and Family Planning. *Journal of Marriage and the Family*, 26(4): 471–477, November, 1964.

Lunde, A. S. White-Nonwhite Fertility Differentials in the United States. *Health, Education, and Welfare Indicators.* September, 1965, pp. 28–38.

Lynn, D. B., and W. L. Saurey. The Effects of Father Absence on Norwegian Boys and Girls. *Journal of Abnormal and Social Psychology*, 59: 258–262, September, 1959.

McCord, J., W. McCord, and E. Thurber. Some Effects of Paternal Absence on Male Children. *Journal of Abnormal and Social Psychology*, 64: 361–369, May, 1962.

McKinley, D. *Social Class and Family Life.* New York: Free Press, 1964.

Mussen, P. H., and L. Distler. Masculinity, Identity, and Father-Son Relationships. *Journal of Abnormal and Social Psychology*, 59: 350–356, November, 1959.

————. Some Antecedents and Consequents of Masculine Sex Typing in Adolescent Boys. *Psychological Monographs*, 75:2: 1–24, 1961.

Myers, J. K., and B. H. Roberts. *Family and Class Dynamics in Mental Illness.* New York: Wiley, 1959.

Nimkoff, M. F. *Comparative Family Systems.* Boston: Houghton Mifflin, 1965.

Pacaud, S. Psychological and Psychomotor Functions in Aging. In R. H. Williams et al. (Eds.), *Processes of Aging.* New York: Atherton Press, 1963.

Parad, H. J. (Ed.). *Crisis Intervention: Selected Readings.* New York: Family Service Association of America, 1965.

Peck, R. F., and R. J. Havighurst. *The Psychology of Character Development.* New York: Wiley, 1960.

Peterson, D. R., W. C. Becker, L. A. Hellmer, J. J. Shoemaker, and H. C. Quay. Parental Attitudes and Child Adjustment. *Child Development*, 30: 119–130, 1959.

Rainwater, L., and K. K. Weinstein. *And the Poor Get Children.* Chicago: Quadrangle Books, 1960.

Riessman, F. *New Approaches to Mental Health Treatment for Labor and Low Income Groups.* Mental Health Report No. 2. National Institute for Labor Education, New York, 1964.

Sewell, W. H., and A. O. Haller. Social Status and the Personality of the Child. *Sociometry*, 19: 114–125, June, 1956.

Stolz, L. M., et al. *Father Relations of War-born Children.* Stanford, Calif.: Stanford University Press, 1954.

Strodtbeck, F. The Hidden Curriculum in the Middle-class Home. In J. D. Krumboltz (Ed.), *Learning and the Educational Process.* Chicago: Rand McNally, 1965(a), pp. 91–112.

————. Family Communication and Child Development. *Research Project Summaries*, no. 2, NIMH, July, 1965(b).

Terman, L. M. *Psychological Factors in Marital Happiness*. New York: McGraw-Hill, 1938.

Tyler, L. E. *The Psychology of Human Differences*. 3d ed. New York: Appleton-Century-Crofts, 1965.

Weinandy, J. Case Work with Tenants in a Public Housing Project. *Journal of Marriage and the Family*, 26: 4, 1964.

White, R. K., and R. O. Lippitt. *Autocracy and Democracy*. New York: Harper & Row, 1960.

Young, L. *Wednesday's Children*. New York: McGraw-Hill, 1964.

✑ 10 ✑

Group Care of Infants
in Other Countries

DALE R. MEERS
and ALLEN E. MARANS

In the United States, widespread acceptance of the importance of early experience for the child's later development has led to a search for more adequate methods of care for babies, especially those whose natural parents and home environments do not provide for healthy growth. One consequence of the search has been the formulation of the foster-home concept; another has been the cautious reintroduction of part-time group care for very young children.

Recently, the department of psychiatry of the Children's Hospital, Washington, D.C., planned a research project in rearing groups of babies from birth to three years of age in both day and residential care. (See full description in Chapter 11.) Appropriate models on which to base the program were not available within the United States. But programs which have flourished in other countries for many years seemed worthy of investigation. While the trend in the

United States has been toward improving and increasing the availability of nursery schools for children aged three to five, other countries have focused on intervention at even earlier ages. Knowledge of these programs was often second hand and incomplete, however. Published accounts often were not readily comprehensible or replicable, because scientific validation of reputed results was rare and the goals of the programs were frequently incompatible with the "American way of life." That is, group child-rearing programs in some countries have aimed at developing nationally esteemed characteristics in the children which emphasize collective, rather than personal, responsibility.

The information reported in this chapter was obtained by personal visits to selected centers, discussions with leading authorities and policy makers in these countries, and reviews of their literature, training curricula, and textbooks. The programs were selected to explore a variety of solutions for differing national, social, and cultural problems and to make clear the wide range of "techniques" of early child care. Some programs illustrate pitfalls to be avoided while others demonstrate successful innovations worthy of emulation. The findings reported here have been compared with those of other professionals visiting from the United States.

In this review, we will attempt to highlight philosophic or ideological views of several other countries, relevant to and reflected in the methods of selection, training, and practices of the child caretakers in group day-care and residential centers. The caretakers themselves are given special attention because of their obviously crucial responsibility for the outcome of their programs. It is through the caretakers that whatever is considered to be the "essentials of mothering" is made available to the child.

Great differences exist between supposedly similar institutions in the same country and even between different units within the same institution. We have generalized sometimes in an effort to highlight directions and degrees of success most representative of the programs under consideration. Philosophical and ideological orientations have been forced on us in comparing the differing prescribed methods of care. Here, as elsewhere, a great disparity between ideals and practices often exists; but we have considered it important to be aware of the idealized and intended techniques and goals. We have been interested in learning of the best technical management possible, and have concluded that facilities in the United States can match the *worst* institutional care elsewhere.

Centers in the U.S.S.R., East Germany, Czechoslovakia, Hungary, Israel, Greece, and France will be presented. Emphasis has been given to the programs of the Communist countries for several reasons. For one, the enormity of the undertaking in these countries merits attention in and of itself. The need for large numbers of facilities and personnel, all under government supervision, has required the formulation of programs which could be enacted on a large scale while maintaining specific goal directions. For another, descriptive literature concerning these programs has not been readily available in the West. The consequences of caring for millions of babies under such a radical change in child-rearing methods are of greatest importance for science and society.

U.S.S.R.—The Children's Collectives

In 1956, Khrushchev introduced a nationwide program aimed at "the creation of the new Soviet man" (Bronfenbrenner, 1963). To accomplish this objective, a major portion of the responsibility for child rearing was deliberately shifted from the family to the children's collectives, the U.S.S.R. day nursery. The collectives are designed to free mothers for more active social and economic roles and to provide, in a semi-institutional setting, a superior environment for better emotional, intellectual, physical, and social development of the children. Underlying this approach was the judgment that the present generation of parents, having been "deprived of a proper upbringing," could not be expected to rear the "New Soviet Man" without help from state-supervised facilities. The state thus recognized the role of the "upbringer" as the purveyor of the new culture for young children, and in the children's collectives provides mother-substitutes who have been selected and trained to achieve the several aims of the state for its future citizens.

Children from three months to seven years of age are considered preschoolers. Nurseries, formerly for children up to three years of age, have been combined with kindergartens (formerly for three- to seven-year-olds) for the purpose of providing greater continuity of care for the individual child. There are three types of preschool care: *Day care*, the most common, comprises 85 per cent of extra familial preschool care. Five to ten hours of care are given daily during the work week and the child remains in his family home at night and on weekends. *Boarding care*, used much less, is next in frequency.

The child is cared for five days a week, returning home on weekends and holidays. *Residential care*, in which the child remains full time, is used only in the absence of other alternatives.

In 1964, it was reported that over seven million children, representing almost 10 per cent of the Soviet population of preschool and school-age children, were being raised in such facilities (Zaporozhets, 1964). Of these, about five million were enrolled in the nonresidential nurseries and kindergartens. The entire program is expected to involve one-third of all Soviet children by 1970 and 100 per cent by the 1980's.*

A sustained effort is made to involve the family in the social education of the child. Creches (day-care centers) are seen not as substitutes for the family but rather as partners in the rearing of children. Parents participate in a PTA-like organization out of the sense of duty to their child and to their country. They attend frequent conferences and lectures in addition to having personal daily contact with the director and teachers of the day-care center when they bring or pick up their children. Through these contacts, they too become better citizens. "There is no attempt in the creche to copy the ideal mother-child relationship; in fact, it is the other way around. The nurse is urged for the good of the baby to teach mothers to carry out at home routines established in the center" (Robinson, 1965).

By Soviet law, every working mother is entitled to 126 days of full pay after her baby is born. For up to one year, she may remain home with her child but retain the right to return to her former job thereafter. Most mothers reportedly take advantage of this option so that relatively few babies under one year of age are in the day creches. If the baby is placed early (during the first year), the mother is given time off from work to visit the creche in order to breast-feed.

There has been some recent controversy as to whether day care should be made available at all for babies under one year of age (Zaporozhets, 1964). Some authorities in the U.S.S.R. are in favor of giving each mother a full year's leave with pay after her baby is born. Others are concerned with the emotional reactions of babies who first enter nurseries in their second year of life. They feel that if the baby is to go into the nursery for at least a part of its care, it is better for him to enter at an earlier age.

---

* More recently, informants in other Communist countries have indicated that this Soviet plan is being reappraised as a result of less than complete satisfaction with the outcome of the programs to date.

In the "better" Soviet institutions for child care, each group of seven or eight babies is attended by a nurse and her assistant, a *nyanya*. As the children become older, a group twice this size would have the same number of "upbringers." In less well-staffed nurseries, the younger groups might contain as many as twelve to fifteen babies and the older group, eighteen to twenty.

The directors of these institutions are trained by a special faculty in pedagogical colleges, a level of education between high school and other colleges. The nurse "upbringers" also receive their three years of training in these pedagogical colleges. The nyanya, less well-trained, is often educated by on-the-job training via the nurse "upbringer." All too often, a shortage of trained personnel necessitates the utilization of older women (*babushkas*) who formerly cared for their grandchildren in their own homes. Despite the training and supervision, it is reputed that the babushkas frequently care for the babies in traditional ways, rather than the "right"—state-approved— methods.

PRESCRIPTIONS FOR CARE

The prescribed methods for the rearing of children in both full- and part-time institutional settings are determined by researchers and the administration in power. Their recommendations frequently become required practices throughout the Soviet Union. One Soviet scientist of high position wryly noted, in this regard, "When we make a mistake, it is a big one." Unfortunately, research data are not available which might afford a basis for an objective comparative evaluation of the effects of the various programs on the physical, emotional, social, and cognitive development of the children.

The Ministry of Education formerly administered only the kindergarten programs (for children aged three to seven) and the Ministry of Health carried primary responsibility for the nurseries (for children aged six weeks to three years.) With the merger of nursery and kindergarten into one unit, the Ministry of Education has been given increasing responsibility for the program. This change has been stated to be the result of dissatisfaction with the achievements of the Ministry of Health in "education" of the younger babies (the President's Panel on Mental Retardation, 1962).

Among the researchers most influential in establishing programs for infants is Professor Tur of the Institute of Pediatrics in Leningrad

(1954). In his department of healthy children, an institution for children aged two weeks to three years, work is directed toward devising and improving the way of life in the institution (day care and full-time residential care) that will avoid the development of "hospitalization psychic disorders," and maximize children's developmental progress. In the laboratory of growth and development, the regimen of life for children is formulated according to age. Exercises and programmed play periods are begun at two and one-half months of age.

At the Institute of Pediatrics at the Academy of Medical Science in Moscow, Shchelovanova (1964) has conducted studies of the development of the physiology of the central nervous system in children from birth to three years of life (Report of Medical Exchange Mission, 1960). Through the study of conditioned reflexes, particular methods of exercises and massage have been devised which are reputed to facilitate good muscular coordination. Experimental studies have also led to the construction of a "system" to promote speech development. Underlying such work is the hypothesis that proper management of the first year of life through conditioned reflexes is fundamental to "good brain development." These findings have supplied components for the nationally authorized programs for all infant-care facilities in the Soviet Union and have become the basis for the training programs for the nurse "upbringers" who staff them.

The textbook by Shchelovanova and Aksarina (1960) * is the major textbook for schools which train nurses for child-care facilities for the first three years of life. In addition to providing specific methods of child upbringing, a clear and fervent picture is presented of the Soviet view of the importance of the day-care centers and the roles of nurse and nyanya in preserving and strengthening the health of children. The discussion which follows has been largely derived from the precepts of this book.

Preserving the physical health of the babies by proper nutrition, hygiene, and adequate clothing is seen as a major concern of group care. Fresh air and sunshine is emphasized. Babies are bundled up warmly to nap outdoors even in the coldest weather. Pediatricians frequently attend all creches. There is the reminder that:

* Translation of this important reference was sponsored by the Center for Studies on Children and Youth of the Community Research and Services Division of the National Institute of Mental Health.

Prerevolutionary Russia was ill-famed for its high rate of infant death, this sad companion of exploitation, unemployment and poverty—social conditions prevalent among the working masses in capitalist countries. . . . After the great socialist October revolution, the rates of infants' diseases and death have been cut drastically (p. 8).

The other serious complication of group education is seen as "hospitalism"—"the absence of conditions necessary for the normal life and development of children, which leads to an underdevelopment of the organism and of the neuropsychological activity of children as well as to generally bad health and condition." "Hospitalism" is said to develop in poorly organized nurseries (especially where infants live permanently) "where the development of the higher nervous system of children is neglected."

The fallacy of the concept that the development of the neuropsychological activity and behavior of a child (e.g., his physical movements) is the result *merely* of the organic maturation of the nervous system has been discussed by Shchelovanova and Aksarina:

. . . According to this theory, a child at a certain age starts to crawl, sit, and walk exclusively because his nervous system, as well as his bone structure and muscular system, has sufficiently matured. To achieve this, a child must be fed properly, so as to establish a metabolism providing sufficient matter to build all organs and tissues. From this assumption, the erroneous conclusion was drawn that the upbringing of infants consists merely of properly feeding him and keeping him clean. This conclusion was supported by the reasoning that within a family no special training (or educational) techniques are applied but the child still develops well (normally) as far as neuropsychological aspects are concerned. Such reasoning overlooked the fact that within a family an intensive kind of natural education is exerted frequently even though there might be a complete lack of educational goals or intentions. For a child grows literally on the hands (or in the arms) of adults, who exert an influence on him evoking and maintaining positive emotional states of mind, developing by introducing games, a variety of complex movements as well as the sense organs. All this creates the necessary conditions for a normal neuropsychological development of the child.

Thus, real life refutes the above mentioned erroneous concept of education and proves convincingly the necessity of starting a child's education from the very first month of his life (p. 22).

The manner in which nurse and nyanya are to function is explicitly stated. Children are to be separated into four age groups: infants up to nine or ten months of age; toddlers up to twelve or fifteen months;

an intermediate group of children up to twenty or twenty-two months; and children twenty months to three years of age. If only three groups can be formed, infants and toddlers are combined. Specific schedules and sequences of activities (sleeping, feeding, and playing, in that order) are recommended for each age group.

There is much emphasis on regulating routines, with the awareness that "where groups of children are being raised, only a regular routine will allow the staff to serve the individual needs of the children in an effective, efficient way." For example, it is recognized that infants of the same age vary in their need for sleep. Since the procedure of getting all the babies up or down may take twenty to thirty minutes, a baby requiring more sleep could be put down first and picked up last. By this means he may be able to sleep an hour longer than the others. The procedure can be reversed for one who requires less sleep.

The steps by which nurses and nyanyas should provide stimulation (or education) of the baby appropriate to his stage of development are clearly spelled out for each stage and process for the first three years. For example, a summary of beginning toilet training:

> A child can be trained not to wet or dirty his diaper at the age of 3–4 months. A baby of this age must be held atop a potty at the appropriate times. A child can be seated on a pot after he has learned to sit well by himself. To train a child to be neat, he must be made to associate a certain position of his body and sounds, produced by the adult and stimulating his physiological functions with the act of urinating and defecation. To train a child to use the pot for urinating or defecating, he must, at first, be seated on the pot only at such times when positive results are certain. While the baby sits on the pot, the adult must be with him all the time, repeating such sounds as "a-a" (such as in moder*a*te, he*a*rt, gu*a*rd) or "pe-pe." Just as soon as a baby relieves himself, he must be taken off the pot. He must also be taken off the pot after having sat there for 3–4 minutes without producing any results (p. 82).

Although this method is described in detail it is also made clear that the nurse is "catching the child," that she must be alert to signs produced by the child. The point when the child can control this function himself and can indicate to the nurse when he is ready is said to come much later in his life. But it is also claimed that almost all their babies are toilet-trained by eighteen months of age.

Another example of specific instructions follows:

A strong leg support is one of the bases for the development of the child's ability to stand up and walk. Raising children of this age group, special attention must be given to gradually strengthening their leg support. Therefore, at the age up to 4–4½ months, children must be exercised as described before, i.e., they should be made to "dance," letting them stand on their feet for very brief periods of time, holding them under their arms at all times. The child learns to stand up ever more steadily, and at five months of age, being held under his arms, he can stand up quite steadily, fully straightening his legs at his knee and hip joints (p. 118).

Shchelovanova and Aksarina make frequent statements about the most desirable *sequence* of developmental steps. A child should be able to turn onto his stomach before learning to grasp objects, so that he will not become passive, (i.e., lying on his stomach and not playing with toys). It is never explicitly stated that "undesirable" patterns of development should be discouraged, but the student nurse could easily gain such an impression.

ENCOURAGEMENT OF POSITIVE EMOTIONS

Accompanying the description of every task of the nurse or nyanya is the instruction to be happy, tender, gentle, and encouraging. Nowhere is there mention of stern measures to be taken, no negative responses, no punishment. The role of the worker in the child-care facility is to set an example for the behavior of her charges, to take a positive approach to the learning of appropriate skills at each stage of development. A positive emotional state is seen as important for the physical well-being of the child, as well as providing a better atmosphere for learning. "One of the most important tasks of bringing up children in creches and nurseries is the creation of conditions which contribute to making children happy, cheerful and active according to their age." When a child cries or is unhappy, it is seen as a failure of the upbringer.

The methods employed in these institutions also emphasize training in "collective living" and productive group activity. Upon entry, at three months of age, infants are placed in group playpens with five to seven other children of the same age. Particular stress is placed on teaching children to share and engage in cooperative activity. Frequent reference is made to common ownership, "Mine is ours; ours is mine." As soon as the children are able to talk, they are given training in evaluating and criticizing each other's behavior from the point of view of the group. It becomes the upbringer's task to develop each collective into a self-reliant unit in which members both help and discipline each other. For example, the upbringer helps the other children in the unit to change from ridiculing a fearful member to praising him for every sign of progress in overcoming his fears (Bronfenbrenner, 1963).

The Russians clearly recognize that there are differences in potential despite their "apparent" uniform treatment of all the children. However, they believe that it is possible to enhance the progress of any normally endowed child by exposing him to programs of appropriate stimulation. Defective babies are recognized early because of close medical supervision and they are either referred to special settings or are placed with children of a developmental level that will serve as a stimulus to the handicapped child.

The major problem for the foreign observer is the absence of research which could validate the good results which the Russians claim for their methods. Shchelovanova and Aksarina's textbook offers fascinating but limited evidence that methods have been worked out to mold the kind of child desired for the Soviet way of life. The nurse and nyanya are given credit for the importance of their roles in the healthy development of each individual child and the future of their country. Whether child-care practices actually carried out approximate the stated Soviet methods has not been well documented. For example, it is unknown how often the babushkas actually subvert the programs despite supervision by nurses schooled in the more modern methods of child rearing. It is extremely unfortunate that objective studies of this vast undertaking to "create the new Soviet man" are lacking.

Child-care Programs of East Germany, Czechoslovakia, and Hungary *

The programs in Eastern Europe present certain over-all differences which reflect both the varied economic and cultural conditions in the several countries, as well as their varied ideological commitments. The Hungarian programs had their inception in the indigenous need

* We are indebted to the many East Europeans who provided exceptional opportunities for visiting various child-care facilities. Particular thanks are due to Dr. Eva Schmidt-Kolmer, Humbold University, East Berlin; Dr. Z. Matcheck, Children's Psychiatric Clinic, Prague; Dr. E. Peter-Pikler, National Methodological Institute for Child Education and Research, Budapest; and Mrs. Magdo Lazlow, Ministry of Child Care, Budapest.

of communities to provide shelter, care, and food for the parentless children who were incidental victims of the war. Equally pressing, however, was the need for able-bodied adults, mothers as well as fathers, to find employment, to sustain the family under the frugal conditions of a postwar economy. The tremendous need of an entire community for day-care programs was matched by the political, administrative readiness to implement them. From meager beginnings in Budapest with day-care centers established in any acceptable building, such as an unused factory, the Hungarian programs have proliferated during the last two decades with an intent to provide equal care throughout the country.

While there have been continued changes and improvements in physical design, physical equipment, staff ratios, quality of food, etc., the day-care of infants under the age of three has been consistently viewed an "economic necessity." The program has been considered one that should be progressively *limited* and eventually terminated as soon as economic conditions permit. The Hungarian conviction is not based solely on the question of potential damage or retardation to the babies concerned. Rather, there are humanitarian concerns for the apparent discomfort and unhappiness that substitute care creates for the small child who is separated from both mother and home.

In East Germany, one suspects that a confluence of factors, besides the press of economics, have affected the emergence of their child-care programs. Under the Communist government, a "feminist" reaction of considerable magnitude proves quite germane to the day-care programming. The East Germans seem ideologically intense yet not as dedicated as the Soviet Union. Instead, the emphasis of day care is to give women equal opportunities.

The East Germans were plagued by the decimation of their professional population, a loss of personnel who might have facilitated an easier transition in their child-care programming. In one generation, a new industrial state was constructed and a man-power shortage has persisted with a combined effect both vast and continuous. Industrialization brought subsequent demands for extensive child-care programs, necessitating the use of relatively untrained staff and inexperienced administrators. Younger women have been needed in technological employment with the result that child day-care staffs in East Germany appear to be considerably older than elsewhere in Eastern Europe. War deaths and the subsequent emigration of the middle-age professionals have left behind a disproportionate, aging population of East German women who are perhaps less adequately equipped by either background or temperament for giving care in the present nurseries.

Prague, Czechoslovakia, was spared much of the worst devastation in World War II; its industrial base and professional population were left relatively intact. The social revolutionary zeal of the Czechoslovakian Communists, when they came to power, recalls some of the earlier organizational errors of the U.S.S.R. in the 1920s. Without research, apparently on the basis of ideological assumptions, the Czechs terminated foster-home programs and adoptions in 1952, placing parentless children in state residential institutions, while simultaneously introducing massive day-care programs along the lines of the other East European countries.*

While the emphasis of these programs seems more "ideologically" oriented in Prague than in Berlin or Budapest, it remains less so than the U.S.S.R. A distinction perhaps is needed with respect to economics and social attitudes in the different countries. While there is pressure for East German mothers to work because there is insufficient labor, Czechoslovakia gives the impression that the high cost of consumer (luxury) goods has induced many mothers into an employment market that is already glutted.

Because of the sheer massiveness of the programs, which encompass approximately one-third of the preschool children of Hungary, Czechoslovakia, and East Germany, there have been extensive problems in the staffing and programming of the child-care centers. Organizational problems and the lack of training facilities contribute to significant differences in appearance and programming between individual day-care centers even in the same community. Yet, whatever the differences that persist, there are also many common emphases and points of view throughout the Eastern European countries.

Although certain differences in the programs have been noted, in one way or another all the countries in Eastern Europe have established an extremely comprehensive and complex set of programs as a result of their philosophic and ideologic point of view covering the child from conception through his years of education. The programs are aimed at remedying irregularities of opportunity for both the child and his parents. The Socialist countries share the egalitarian principle that the female citizen and mother should have equal op-

* The Czechoslovakian government, it should be added, also abolished the professional standing and training of their psychologists, who might have been used in the assessment of these new programs.

portunities with men for work and participation in the community. Given the female's biological productivity and consequent vulnerability, she has need to be protected from excesses of work, to be given options for paid vacations and leaves of absence with full pay for pregnancy, etc. Prenatal care is a recommendation, if not a legal requirement. Postnatal care is the right of both the mother and the child.

Economic necessity, however, remains a prime motive for the average parents in Eastern Europe to use day-care and institutional facilities for their younger children. The work week is long (forty-eight hours) and incomes are relatively low with respect to the cost of consumer goods. While dire poverty seems to have been abolished, the national emphases and needs for productive labor and for the recruitment of mothers to work provide both incentive and justification for the placement of children in day care. These do not appear to be child-oriented cultures, in the sense of the Israeli kibbutzim or in the U.S.S.R. The role of the female, as mother and child caretaker, does not seem highly valued and the status of the substitute caretaker seems even less favorable or rewarded. Indeed, some East European research and administrative staffs appeared surprised with the idea that a mother might actually enjoy or prefer remaining home with children who may vex yet also delight her. The inception of research into the vast child-care programs seems minimal at best. While the East European physical sciences have advanced at a relatively high rate, there has been no comparable progression in the study of infant and child development and the psychology of infancy and childhood. More surprising to the foreign observer is the apparent fact that there seems to be little sharing of research and practical experience between the East Europeans and the U.S.S.R.

Ideological presumptions are clearly imposed on child-care practices and on the character of scientific research. This is interestingly clear where a conflict arises in the nursery organization concerning individual versus collective property. In both East Germany and Hungary, toys and play materials have been made relatively abundantly available to individual infants and collectives of small children. Institutionally reared children, in particular, have been prone to destroy their playthings. It has become a problem, of sorts, for the child-care specialist in the Communist world to review with his policy- and decision-making colleagues the chronology of dialectic materialism in the nursery. In effect, there is a present argument of considerable scientific persuasion that babies and toddlers cannot readily value collective possessions until they have had possessions of their own, possessions which they can learn to value out of innate egocentric beginnings. Experiences such as the destruction of toys or minimal retardation are forcing child-development specialists to look much more closely at their progeny. Failures of child-rearing practices (e.g., expectations of collective responsibility at too early an age) dramatize inconsistencies between ideology and innate limits of childhood adaptability.

PEDIATRIC VERSUS EDUCATIONAL EMPHASIS

In contrast with the U.S.S.R., the administrative responsibility for staff selection and programming continues under the respective ministries of health. This may reflect unique circumstances in which the East Europeans have been required to give greater attention to health considerations than either the United States or the U.S.S.R. would find necessary. Tubercular infections of dairy herds of Eastern Europe add to medical problems, and the limited availability of medical and nursing staff and pharmaceutical supplies has lent weight to the argument that epidemics could spread rapidly to the populations in day-care centers.

Many child-care researchers insist that a medical orientation is intrinsically limiting and potentially damaging in the care of the well baby. In Czechoslovakia, however, the pedagogical approach was considered even more constricted and institutionalized than the medical orientation. Some of the institutions in Eastern Europe clearly evidence the untoward isolation of children from both staff and one another. Such isolation is intensified by staff ratios of one adult to ten or fifteen children. The mobility and turnover of staff further exacerbates this problem. Children in some institutions showed clear and dramatic evidence of severe motor and cognitive retardation in the first and second years and attendant social promiscuity in the older toddlers. But even in the well-run day-care facilities, there appeared to be a high percentage of minimal or marginal retardation among children placed there during their first weeks or months.

Central control is continued via ministries and their agencies, yet the actual personnel holding key administrative positions in different centers seem to be of particular significance in determining the actual program. In centers where pediatrician administrators were oriented to the needs of *well* babies, there was much less emphasis on stereotyped, institutionalized forms. Throughout all the countries the basic emphasis was that of insuring good physical health. Yet, too frequently, there was only limited understanding or programming directed toward meeting the normal maturational and adaptational needs of well babies. It should be emphasized that none of the three countries was basically satisfied that its programs approximated their ideals.

CONVENTIONS OF DAY-CARE AND INSTITUTIONAL SERVICES

Working parents have constantly pressed for an increase in the availability of day-care and institutional service. The limited availability of placements necessitates a screening procedure and priority system to assess which babies are to be accepted. The well-being of the child and the needs of the parents are predominent considerations. Priority is given if the mother is unmarried or home care is lacking. In East Germany, the only East European Communist nation where abortion is illegal, nominally humorous reference was made to the priority given the child born out of wedlock when some couples refuse to marry until the unwed mother is assured of day-care placement for her baby.

Newborn babies may be accepted for day care at one or two weeks of age. More typically, however, the working mother may save her vacation time to add to her maternity leave, with the result that her baby will be in day care about the second month. The child remains in a facility supervised by the ministry of health until age three, when he is transferred to a preschool nursery administered by the ministry of education.

These programs are available in both urban and rural areas. Typically, there are geographic subdivisions in which regional representatives of the particular ministry provide supervisory and consultative functions for the local administration of the day-care centers. The centers may be established in cooperative farm units, in the factories where there are large numbers of working mothers, or separately in either urban or residential communities. The farm cooperative or the factory workers union may finance part of the nursery care, but the state is usually responsible for costs, with a minimal, sliding fee charged to the parents. It would appear that the total cost per child for the day-care center roughly approximates one-third of the income of an average working parent. Where more than two children from the same family are in day care, the cost to the state of having the mother work would seem almost prohibitive. The cost of day care then approximates the mother's earned income.

Construction, furnishings, and physical facilities of these day-care centers are expensive and advanced by Western standards. The units are intended to house twenty babies per unit, with approximately 100 infants in a center. Recognizing the depressing impact of massive centers, efforts are directed toward maintaining small and psychologically intimate units. The problems of new construction are apparent, however, since the dispersion of small units throughout a highly congested urban area necessitates the construction of a very large number of facilities.

Immediate admininstrative direction is usually under a day-care expert, often a teacher or a nurse who has had special training in both well-baby care and administrative procedure. Her staff will include one adult caretaker for each ten—the ideal number— or fifteen babies. The official workday is eight hours; and the work week, six days. Because of the considerable overlapping of parental work shifts, the baby center must have staff available for approximately twelve hours, e.g. from 6 A.M. to 6 P.M. By overlapping the caretaker's shifts at midday, the ratio of adults to babies is higher at such peak times as the afternoon meal, rest period and playtime. Moreover, for both the earliest and latest hours of the day, there are as few as two or four babies per adult because of variations in arrivals and departures.

Depending on parental choice, the baby may be bathed and fed his first meal at home. If so, this information is given to the caretaker when the baby is brought in the morning. It is not atypical for the father to bring the child very early in the morning. The child is taken into a receiving room where the parent undresses him and places his clothes in an assigned locker. A caretaker then accepts the child from the parent, who leaves for work. The baby is taken into a second receiving room, where he is either bathed or dressed in garments belonging to the day-care center, usually an informal uniform. The baby may take a nap at that point, with feeding later.

The parents are not permitted to bring a sick baby to a day-care center. Children are sent home if they are feverish or look ill on arrival in the morning. Should a baby fall ill during the day, he is placed in an isolation unit within the center where he may be seen by the pediatrician. The family is notified that evening. The child is not permitted to re-enter the center without consent of the family's pediatrician. Medical records are extensive, continuing from the time a baby is first accepted at a center. They contain notes on immunizations, which are procedural, and daily and weekly notations about health, diet, etc. This comprehensive medical record will follow the child into his primary school. Each of the day-care centers has a pediatrician who makes daily visits and is available for emergency calls. The medical responsibilities are limited and clear. The staff plans the daily activities, menus, etc., for the well babies.

PROBLEMS IN PROGRAMMING

The day-care staff are obviously troubled, in even the best of East European facilities, in their attempts to cope with *individual* needs of such a large number of infants and small children. Their adverse staff ratios, the necessity for staff sick leave, holidays, etc., put many of the babies into the hands of substitute caretakers. There is considerable evidence of depersonalization, because of the staff's inability or failure to recognize special problems with particular children. This seems an inevitable consequence of both the high infant-staff ratios and the interchangeability where four or more adults may be responsible for the same child in any one week.

To improve communication between home and the day-care center, several procedures have been devised. In the receiving rooms of the centers, attractively if sometimes aseptically furnished, the menu of the week is clearly posted so that the parents will be familiar with their child's diet.* To cope with problems and identification of individual needs, various records are maintained by the day-care staff. One is an open record in which staff observations of the babies are shared with the parents. The records may be taken home for closer parental study. Parents are asked to add anything they consider significant about their baby's characteristics or reactions. A second set of professional records which touch on idiosyncratic problems germane to the families' adequacies or difficulties in coping with the baby, medical problems, etc., are maintained as semiconfidential documents.

The observer concludes that day-care staff have extremely little time and little opportunity to either observe effectively or to record their observations appropriately, except for patently distressed or ill babies. On a global basis, where problems are extended, such records

---

* The East European pediatricians and caretakers do not find that their babies have feeding problems or food fads under this regime. One suspects that the babies cannot afford such luxuries.

are undoubtedly of importance. But for use as research data, the records are less than adequate.

The National Methodological Institute for Child Education and Research in Budapest makes exceptional use of its records. Day-to-day, detailed reports of the children are consistently maintained, even though staff ratios are one adult to ten babies. The research orientation of this institute has provided a seemingly excellent motivation for sustaining a very high investment of the staff via their observation of individual differences in respective babies. A group of approximately nine babies has three caretakers assigned to it, with one caretaker on duty at a time. Each of these caretakers has "primary" responsibility for one-third of the babies in the group, yet she cares for the others when on duty. Scheduling is carefully adhered to and each caretaker records events of the day, particularly those adaptational capacities that emerge in her three "special" children. Since the institute's staff of pediatricians and psychologists are constantly working with research projects, the in-staff training alerts the child caretakers to developmental research questions (Peter-Pikler, 1964). This may lead them to overreport or to inadvertently stimulate certain types of behavior, yet whatever untoward research consequences might derive from this practice, the recording and research alerts and sustains the child caretakers' interest in the differences and responses of their babies. Intellectual dedication to research recording is used to help the staff sustain an involvement and current knowledge of each baby.

As a residential facility, where babies are accepted from birth through age three, this institute's programming and staffing provide continuous twenty-four-hour coverage. The Hungarian workday is officially eight hours; six workdays a week. Yet, by a special exception, the caretakers in this institute work a twelve-hour day for four days a week. However fatiguing the twelve-hour day must be for these women, the arrangement provides a continuity of care that is otherwise impossible. The institute has no difficulty in finding a staff, since a three-day weekly holiday is an exceptional luxury in Hungary. This method of staffing seems directly related to the Budapest institute's study of the adverse impact on the adaptational and cognitive capacities of the babies when changes in child caretakers occur, even under planned, optimal conditions (Tardos, 1964).

The conventional East European day-care center has a wide variety of housekeeping responsibilities. The caretakers are customarily freed, however, from laundry, cooking, cleaning, gardening, etc., and given express responsibility for the immediate needs of the babies, that is, feeding, bathing, dressing, and supervising free and directed play periods, group activities, and others. Some centers have attempted to use collective housekeeping services, but more typically such functions as washing and cooking remain the responsibility of each center. There are obvious technological and economic housekeeping problems which should be remedied in time, not the least of these being severe diaper rashes related to inadequate laundry facilities, although infrequent diaper changes may also be at fault.

BUILT-IN PROBLEMS IN PHYSICAL PLANTS

However effectively these day-care centers are organized, elementary problems, such as the physical construction, remain. Each country has modified and improved its architectural designs, permitting ever greater amounts of space and light and with attempts to decrease the number of occasions when babies or toddlers are visually separated from the caretaker or the number of unnecessary steps the day-care staff must walk, etc. The more recent construction in East Germany perpetuates a two-story construction, a recognized error. Even though more economical, the two-story building presents problems to the caretakers of babies or younger children. When one caretaker carries two babies downstairs and outside, she leaves behind another caretaker who for that moment must be responsible for her own ten to fifteen babies plus the eight to thirteen infants of the temporarily absent caretaker—a total of eighteen to twenty-eight babies!

The Hungarians have moved toward an H-shaped, single-story building, where all rooms for babies are immediately accessible to play space outdoors. The children can move or be moved out of the living space into play space without neglecting the safety of children left behind. Such a design also permits the separation of some indispensable adult functions—cooking, cleaning, etc.—from the immediate vicinity of the children. This serves the dual purpose of protecting nap time as well as permitting the staff some respite from responsibility. The medical isolation unit and bathing areas have been carefully designed in the newer constructions so that all babies remain in the full sight of the caretaker. Where two-story structures are used, large balconies seem preferred throughout Europe, so that babies may have crawling and walking space in the sunlight and may be placed outside for naps. One of the consistent practices of the three countries which is shared by the U.S.S.R. echoes a pediatric view of the 1920s, but with a more sophisticated, contemporary overtone—children should sleep in the open air and be exposed to cool temperatures in sleep. Thus, it is felt, babies sleep more deeply and therefore awaken with more verve and freshness for eating, responding, and learning (Shchelovanova and Aksarina, 1960).

With over a decade of experience with enormous populations of babies, the East Europeans have concluded that the infants' needs for space and variability in institutional care proves of enormous importance to both the babies and the staff. The spaciousness of day-care centers, particularly the most recently designed, affords the children of each age group two separate rooms plus an available yard. As a compromise for the caretakers who might thus be exposed to excessive distances, doors and windows are carefully located (Egeszsegugyi Miniszterium, 1957). Only a few of the elegant but impractical, monolithically spacious institutions built in the early 1900s still remain in use. Their isolation offers mute testimony of a prior generation's blindness to the basic needs of children for continuous human contact.

SELECTION AND TRAINING OF CHILD CARETAKERS

Low salaries, poorly defined "professional position" and status, and lack of related training have combined to make the recruitment of the child caretaker a problem. One may also conjecture that deliberate political devaluation of the "middle-class professional" tends to undermine securement of a well-trained and adequate staff. The emphasis on the social value of industrial productivity may also indirectly serve to subvert efforts to improve professionalization and status of the caretaker. There is also a parallel attitude in Eastern Europe that compounds naïveté with condescension, namely, that since almost anyone can care for a child, their overworked and fatigued child caretakers should be able to cope with "only" ten to fifteen children under the age of three.

The practical necessity of filling vacant positions at the centers seems to leave little discretion in staff selection. Especially in the rural areas characterized by rural-to-urban migration, staff selections seem based on the interests of the applicant and less on an assessment of the personality characteristics or educability of the trainee herself. The East German programs seem representative and merit comment.* Secondary education is a desired prerequisite for their child-care trainees. An equivalent of a junior college training pro-

* See Schmidt-Kolmer and Hecht (1964) and the publications cited in the bibliography issued by the Minister für Gesundheitswesen (1963a, 1963b, 1964).

gram has been newly initiated and attracts younger women. Unfortunately, this particular population has a high attrition rate, with many of the trainees moving to better paying positions or suspending work because of marriage.

Training programs have evolved pragmatically and vary considerably with each country, depending often on the availability of training centers, especially in rural areas. For the older caretakers, probably those women initially recruited for the centers when they opened, there are in-service training opportunities and courses equivalent to university extension service programs in the United States. Incentive pay increments are offered on completion of the courses. With eclectic variations of training, particularly in the initial selection of the staff, supervisory positions have been filled with professionals from other fields, usually pediatrics, nursing, or education.

While the child-caretaker positions seem ineffectively recruited in many instances, the administrative leadership at the centers seemed impressively knowledgeable, dedicated, and young. As with the observations made in the U.S.S.R. (Lourie, 1962), the senior staff appeared consistently hard working and dedicated. It was also apparent that some of the senior and knowledgeable staff did not make use of available day-care centers for their own children. Indeed, recent Czechoslovakian psychological research (Matejcek, 1962) has carried sufficient weight that the government, at least temporarily, has stopped construction of day-care facilities for the child under age one, and current Czechosovakian parent education includes the recommendation that the child remain at home until he is at least one year old.

Conceived in emergency and in difficult economic times, these programs have had to contend with potential damage to their children, with questions of incipient or minimal "hospitalism," which could develop under conditions less than ideal. The staff-training programs have an "enrichment" orientation, yet one that seems more aimed at prevention. Taking cognizance of the high turnover of caretakers and babies (through illness, vacations, or moving) and with a consequent limited familiarity of staff with individual babies, the trainee is introduced to the problems of excessive institutional-type stimuli on the one hand and emotional and maternal deprivations on the other.

The pervasiveness of such problems have led the Hungarians to the conclusion that the inevitable hurt and sorrow to the child is sufficient that day care for the younger child should be terminated as soon as national economic conditions permit—a view shared by some of the Czechoslovakian child-care specialists. The East Germans, however, seem more prepared to conclude that minimal motor and cognitive retardation related to the day-care program will prove to be reversible. In consequence, their training programs have perhaps laid greater emphasis on technical interventions and procedures that might reverse deprivational conditions, with programming not dissimilar to that in the U.S.S.R.

Training and emphasis on staff selection overlap, whether one trains for professional and technical orientations or for maximizing maternal, empathic, emotional responsiveness. The latter view is often considered quite incompatible with the extended emotional demands that a large number of babies make on any one caretaker.* Group care of well babies has necessitated a synthesis of professional knowledge and skills, of education (pedagogics), pediatrics, and nursing. This program development has been pragmatic, with less concern for a systematic study of program than an attempt at immediate solutions for clinically evident problems. The program directors in all of the countries continue to be concerned with the limited synthesis so far achieved in training and would like to look to the experience of their neighbors. We suspect that their major problems are less with the adequacy of their training and curricula than with the scarcity of staff and the excessive pressures which both the staff and babies must endure.

ACADEMIC RETARDATION AND CULTURAL
IMPLICATIONS †

Both Czechoslovakia and Hungary are troubled by sociocultural problems that are not unfamiliar in the United States. A Gypsy population that survived Nazi extermination comprises approximately 5 per cent of the population of Czechoslovakia and 2 to 3 per cent of the

---

* We are indebted to Dr. E. Peter-Pikler for August Eichorn's assessment of caretakers at the National Methodological Institute for Child Education and Research: maternally responsive women couldn't stand the tension of being unable to respond to the intense needs of ten babies at one time; you have selected child caretakers who are kindly, warm and responsive *paternalistic* women.

† Academic, or "pseudo," retardation needs to be conceptually differentiated from that of organic etiology. The U.S.S.R. defines the academic, or pseudo, retardate as being "inadequately educated." Their definition of oligophrenia (retardation) is explicitly concerned with organicity (Report of the Medical Exchange Mission to the U.S.S.R., 1960). We would stress that psychogenic damage to cognitive function may be irreversible when it has stemmed from inadequacies in earliest child care.

population of Hungary. The Gypsy's prior independent, itinerant existence, and his cultural self-isolation are becoming domesticated by requirements that they be employed in one locale and that their children be educated.

Social prejudices seem covertly yet clearly expressed with denigrating and invidious slurs about Gypsy manners, morality, fecundity, skin color, and the like. Of particular significance is the fact that the Gypsies provide approximately 50 per cent of all children in residential institutional care in both these countries.

The ready availability of residential institutions for infants has given rise to the fear that ongoing use of such care by a subcultural group, such as the Gypsy, will substitute "institutional" for "cultural" deprivation. The East Europeans, out of concern for hospitalism and pseudoretardation, seem fully prepared to consider the complex problems of ethnic cultural patterns that may impinge on and affect the developmental potentials of newborns and infants. The use of *residential* care is far less favored by the child-care specialist than is the day-care center. The latter is an intervention into cultural tradition and family education and it provides a new opportunity for modifying views that are tenaciously held by the Gypsy subgroup. Day care also offers a means of providing alternative, superior health and educational care for these populations. The East European problem, unlike that of the United States, however, has involved an ethnic population resistant to social integration.

SUMMARY

In such large programs, the possibilities for research are unique and potentially dramatically rewarding. Each of these countries maintains records containing (1) chronological age and date of placement of babies; (2) the type of care, whether residential full time or weekdays only; and (3) longitudinal information that continues into primary school. In consequence, they have a singular opportunity to assess profound questions pertaining to infant separation, multiple mothering, possible degree of retardation, etc.

Our impression remains that the care described has left a minimal retardation conceptually equivalent to the more severe, better-known hospitalism syndrome. However adequate the physical circumstances, the architecture, and the material commitments, the East Europeans have embarked on programs with staff ratios and limited training that seem clearly inadequate for their purpose.

Israel

Group child-rearing methods prevalent in only a small segment of the population of Israel have attracted international scientific and humanistic attention. Naturally occurring worldwide interest in a unique and highly idealistic social design has been greatly increased by the efforts of the responsible Israeli program planners to have their system evaluated and improved where possible.*

Approximately 4 per cent of the population of Israel live on collective farms, or kibbutzim. Here, in pursuit of philosophic equality between the sexes, for the practical need of labor to convert desert into farm land, and to protect their settlements against attack by hostile neighbors, women have left their traditional roles as mothers and housekeepers to become part of the labor and defensive force. Especially trained women (*metaplot*) share with parents the care of children born into the community. This multiple mothering, quite aside from economic necessity, is also believed to bring about a healthier child life (Segal, 1965 p. 4).

A young woman is selected by her kibbutz to receive training to become a metapelet after she has demonstrated interest and aptitude as a teen-ager by helping in the houses for children. If she still desires to become a metapelet after graduation from high school and completion of obligatory army service, she must serve a one year's apprenticeship. Her progress will be carefully observed by the experienced metaplot, as well as the rest of the community. Every member of the kibbutz has an interest in the selection, since in economic terms alone, her training is an expensive investment of precious kibbutz funds in a single individual. A more personal interest evolves from the possibility that one's own child may be cared for by this future metapelet. The completion of her training does not protect the metapelet from continued scrutiny by the community, which is free to discuss her performance in complete frankness at open meetings whenever dissatisfactions arise.

The newer metaplot have all received a three-month course given by the Seminar Hakibbutzim at Oranim. This organization provides

* Such confluence of interest was particularly clear in the Institute on Child Development in Kibbutzim jointly sponsored by Oranim Teacher's College in Haifa, Israel, and the Child Development Center in New York. See Neubauer (1965) for the proceedings of this conference of experts from the United States, Israel, and elsewhere. Acknowledgment is due especially to Dr. Peter Neubauer for arranging that one of the authors (A.E.M.) could attend and to Mordechai Segal for translating and sharing the curriculum for the Metapelet Training at Oranim.

both the teacher training and child-guidance clinic services for almost 97 per cent of the kibbutzim. The training is now being expanded to a one-year course. The curriculum concerns itself mainly with the process of child development and child-care practices in relation to both the developmental needs of the individual child and the need for cooperation with the parents of that child. Much time is also dedicated to further educating the trainees regarding the philosophy of the kibbutz movement. This serves to reinforce their own pre-existing attitudes as well as to guide them in rearing their charges according to kibbutz ideals. "These include strong ties to the land, pride in labor, and readiness to share one's life with one's fellow man" (Faians-Glueck, 1965, p. xvii). Another ideal, the linking of intellectual pursuit with productive manual labor, is also emphasized in the metapelet's training. Subjects of broad cultural interest are included for the individual's character building and the indirect effect this will have on the guidance she will give her babies.

Consultations with visiting psychologists are available to the metaplot. Regularly scheduled group discussions with the psychologist are also held. Additionally, refresher courses of three to six weeks at Oranim are available periodically for the older metaplot.

VARIATIONS IN CARE

There is no one "kibbutz method" of child rearing. Despite the common source of training (Seminar Hakibbutzim at Oranim) for most of the metaplot, there are great variations in practices among the kibbutzim and even within the same kibbutz. The latter reflects, among other factors, the individual personalities of the metaplot. The philosophical orientation, which varies among the kibbutzim, has its impact on the children's homes. For example, there are three major political parties which support the kibbutzim. Roughly speaking, these represent liberal, moderate, or more conservative viewpoints. Approximately 3 per cent of the kibbutzim are primarily religiously oriented and often follow traditional orthodox Jewish practices in the rearing of their children (for example, dresses and long hair for boys under three years of age).

During the first year of the child's life, the major portion of the feeding and care is provided by the infant's own mother, although the infant is usually housed in a cottage away from his parents' quarters in a group of four to eight (depending on the individual kibbutz). The mother gradually turns over more and more child-rearing duties to the metapelet in the latter part of the first year, as she returns to her regular job. However, close contact is maintained with the baby through evening periods and sabbaths spent together, in addition to unscheduled visits when work permits or when warranted by the child's needs as determined by the metapelet, the mother, or both. The fathers in this setting spend more time with their children than is common in Western families because of the proximity of work to home and the communal sharing of responsibilities which ordinarily take up the time of the head of the household. The sharing of the responsibility for a child's upbringing is seen theoretically by the program planners as a constructive opportunity for the metapelet to deal with the disagreeable tasks of training and discipline, while allowing a less conflicting relationship with natural parents, who are seen as sources of unambivalent love and pleasure.

The smaller groups of children are merged with other groups as they reach certain ages (e.g., ages one to one and one-half and three) and the ratio of children to metapelet increases. In adolescence, children live in compounds often separate from the rest of the settlement. In some kibbutzim, especially of the more liberal movement, sexes are mixed through adolescence. The trend is to allow separation of the sexes as *the children* request it, which almost inevitably occurs around seven years of age. Sexual promiscuity rarely obtains within a child's own cottage, apparently because of the siblinglike atmosphere and the taboo against what would seem to be incestuous acts.

Demonstrations of peer support in this group living situation are abundant (Marans, 1963). Children automatically hold each other's hands while waiting for their mothers after one of their group has been called for. Older children display benevolent attitudes and assume more responsibility for the younger children in the kibbutz than is commonly observed in Western society. The question is unanswered as to whether this reflects some dilution of attachment to the mother and, more significantly, whether there are latent depressive or sociopathic consequences in later years. In any event, it is demonstrable that particular attitudes evolve which better prepare the individual for collective living.

DISAGREEMENT OF EVALUATIVE STUDIES

Although the literature about the kibbutzim includes statements about "typical" personalities produced by the "intermittent mothering"—the combination of institutional and maternal care—there is disagreement as to the nature of the consequent personality and its cause. While some see the effects of earlier "maternal deprivation" producing an arrogant adolescent, Spiro (1935, 1956) describes the young adult who shies away from strangers and is quiet in the presence of his elders. While Bowlby (Lewin, 1965, p. 71) speaks of the optimal arrangements for adolescents overcoming the "bizarre" character of the caretaking methods of the earlier years, Rabin (1958) finds a different course of development. His results indicated that the infants raised in the "nuclear family" were superior to the kibbutz infants in tests involving social and interpersonal responsiveness, but the kibbutz ten-year-olds seemed to excel in ego and intellectual functions. The author poses the question, "What are the experiences which turn retardation to normalcy of advanced status?" Regarding the incidence of pathology, studies conducted by the Oranim Mental Hygiene Clinic (Kaffman, 1965, p. 263), which serves almost the entire population living in kibbutzim, demonstrate an incidence and distribution of emotional disorders in kibbutz children comparable to that found in urban centers of Israel as well as in Western literature.

The incidence of specific "behavior disturbances" has been reported by Kaffman (1961), for example, that 41 per cent of kibbutz children between the ages of two and nine years suck their thumbs. While this is thought to be at least two to three times the incidence in the United States, it should be noted that in the kibbutzim thumb sucking is commonly accepted as normal, and is given no external interference until around the age of nine. There is frequently a passive-permissive, as well as an active, encouragement of thumb sucking for the first two years. In one kibbutz, the incidence decreased from 30 to 16 per cent as a result of a less indulgent approach. Kaffman's studies indicate the same incidence of enuresis in kibbutz children as reported in Western cultures but with a different etiology. Before the age of six, enuresis is believed to be related to inconsistent training by the caretaker, who can produce an incidence of 50 per cent in her charges. After six, it is blamed on parental personality problems. However, in one kibbutz having an incidence of 13 per cent at three and one-half years of age, enuresis was practically eliminated when the child-care personnel were given professional help.

The majority of emotional problems in the children seem to develop when an obvious conflict exists between the metapelet and the parents. Of course, not all parents can share their children with others in such an intimate society (Gewirtz, 1966). Some mothers report that they are unable to work for fear their children will be improperly treated and some families have left the kibbutz because of their concern that multiple mothering will dilute ties to the biologic parents. In the few instances where analysis of childhood neurosis was carried out, however, the metapelet was presented as a shadowy figure with the usual picture of natural parents predominating in the child's thoughts. It has been suggested that this represents the ability of the ego to fuse these multiple maternal images.

On the plus side, it has been stated (Messinger, 1965, p. 196) that a disproportionate number of kibbutz-raised children are chosen for leadership positions during their compulsory two-year military service. Further studies are necessary to clarify the actual practice and results of child-rearing methods in kibbutzim.

FUTURE OF KIBBUTZ

Threats to the kibbutz way of life and child-rearing practices are seen in two recent trends. One is called the "familistic trend" (Gerson, 1965, pp. 235–36). In some kibbutzim, parents are seeking to have their children sleep in the parents' apartments where they would have more direct responsibility for the children's training. This has been thought to arise from the lack of gratification experienced by the women who, having failed to achieve true equality with men, are turning back to a more traditional source of satisfaction—child rearing.*

The other threat to the kibbutz movement has been labeled "careerism." As individuals seek higher education, professional, and personal achievement, the needs of their kibbutzim become a secondary consideration. This trend has been attributed to the lessening of the need for the self-sacrifices required of the earlier pioneering days and a reciprocal greater concern for personal comfort and achievement. Yet, other studies (Eisenberg, 1965, p. 11) suggest the contrary, finding that the present generation of young adults are even more committed to kibbutz values than their pioneering parents. Ninety per cent of the children of kibbutz parents choose to become members of the kibbutz when they reach young adulthood (Segal, 1965, p. 4).

* This may also suggest that when economic necessity decreases, instinctual, maternal tendencies re-emerge (Kugelmass, 1965, p. 290).

Metera Babies Center in Greece

Appalled by the conditions in the foundling homes in Greece after World War II, some prominent Greek citizens, including Queen Fredericka, decided that a new and different kind of home should be built.* They were aware that there were thousands of distressing places for orphans and children of unwed mothers elsewhere in Europe, as well as in America. They were told that experts had long been demanding reforms but that the cost in money and time to develop more appropriate settings was prohibitive. Undaunted, this powerful and determined group managed to divert money originally consigned to the purchase of military aircraft to begin the building of a new center for the care of homeless infants. Sizeable contributions came from Sweden, Holland, Venezuela, prominent Greek-Americans, and wealthy Greeks (Silverman, 1960). Metera (meaning "mother" in Greek) Babies Center accepted its first babies in 1955.

Metera now stands as a model for the institutional care of homeless infants. It is not typical of Greece or of similar facilities of any other country. From the outset Metera has been engaged in the attempt to develop an interim home for motherless babies, where from birth to two years of age they could be raised to achieve their full developmental potential despite the institutional setting.

An extraordinary well-baby nursing training program and excellent administrative and supervisory methods have been produced which are outstanding when compared with most other child-rearing institutions in the world.

The predominantly happy and healthy babies at Metera provide a clear contrast to the classic picture of maternally deprived and often marasmic babies found in other infant institutions.† Yet babies who remain in the Metera Babies Center beyond eight months of age do not continue to demonstrate consistent, optimum developmental progress. Metera is eager to identify the causal factors and institute preventive measures against the lesser degree of impaired development that does occur as their babies enter the toddler stage. Research is contemplated which will also permit the opportunity to study

---

* Especially important in this reform were Miss Litsa Alexandraki, Special Advisor on Child Care to Greek Ministry of Social Welfare, and Mr. M. Goutos, Secretary General of the Greek Ministry of Social Welfare.

† Evidence of retarded development and personality malformation can often be found as early as three months of age in other institutions.

both cultural determinants of, and institutional innovations in, child-rearing practices and their effect on early child development.*

Metera is also concerned with the protection of unwed mothers and the care and eventual placement of infants born to mothers unable to care for them, most frequently due to the illegitimacy of the birth. In some cases, adoption is arranged; in others, return to the biologic mother. Foster-home or institutional placement is used if necessary. Metera accepts for residence a limited number of selected unwed mothers from all over Greece, usually in the last month of their pregnancy.† The babies are transferred to a pavilion for newborns at Metera from the hospitals where they are born and are assigned to one of eight pavilions after completion of routine admission studies.

There are approximately 110 babies at Metera, ranging in age from birth up to two or more years. For many reasons, some technical and legal, an increased proportion of babies over eight months of age have remained despite the desire to arrange for earlier adoptive placement. Adoption as soon after three months of age as possible is considered desirable.

Four graduate well-baby nurses live on a permanent basis in each pavilion for twelve children. Three levels or classes of student well-baby nurses assist to varying degrees on the pavilions. The attempt is made to keep a baby-staff ratio of 1 to 1 per twenty-four hours. Four pediatricians make daily rounds on each of the pavilions. Social workers aid the rehabilitation of the mothers and work toward the adoption of the child into a stable and loving home.

---

* The Aghia Sophia Children's Hospital of Athens, Greece, through its research arm, the Queen Anna-Maria Institute of Child Health, is collaborating in research with the Children's Hospital of the District of Columbia. Their research concerning environmentally and culturally determined developmental retardation, will be centered at the Metera Babies Center. Dr. Spyros Doxiadis, the co-founder (with Miss Alexandraki), original and present Medical Director of Metera, is also the Medical Director of the Aghia Sophia Children's Hospital and the Chairman of the Queen Anna-Maria Institute of Child Health. (See Chapter 11.)

† If a rural village girl in Greece becomes pregnant and then has not married because of lack of interest on the part of the girl or her lover, or because of an insufficient dowry, she becomes a family disgrace. Such an event has been dealt with in the past by a brother's being assigned to kill her or the villagers' stoning her to death. The Greek Social Welfare Service has an "underground network" constantly on the alert in every city and large village to detect such unfortunate situations. They attempt to contact the girl early in her pregnancy in order to help her plan for her safety and the baby's future. Otherwise, these girls often flee to the large cities and turn to prostitution for support. Their children end up in overcrowded orphanages where they soon become retarded and unsuitable for adoption.

SELECTION AND TRAINING OF THE CARETAKERS

The well-baby nursing school of the Metera Babies Center offers a three-year program for unmarried girls who are high school graduates between the ages of eighteen and twenty-five. Married girls are not accepted for training, and few trained nurses are retained when they marry because it is felt that divided loyalty will divert attention from the babies. Applicants apply twice a year and number two or three times the student positions available. Selection is made on the basis of written materials (autobiographical sketch, general knowledge test and essay), one week of personal interview, and a medical examination. Final selection is made after careful assessment during the first five months of training. The didactic training is exceptional and includes language, art, music, dancing, personal hygiene, and ethics in an effort to elevate the cultural level of the students during their training. More traditional nursing subjects include anatomy, physiology, microbiology, obstetrics, general psychology, social welfare, child development, and baby care. Well-defined routines for every aspect of baby care are carefully taught. Efficient management and sensitive, gentle handling of the child in the performance of every task is stressed.

Students are gradually permitted in the pavilions after three months of course work. They are allowed no actual responsibility for the babies' care (even under supervision) until the second year of their training. When assigned to a pavilion they share in the responsibility for the entire pavilion with particular assignment to a cubicle, or "box," containing three children. Ideally they are always assigned the same "box." The student's work on the pavilions is carefully supervised by the graduate well-baby nurses in each pavilion, as well as by the nursing director and her assistants to be certain that classroom-learned techniques are practiced and become natural patterns of work. Lectures and class discussions continue through the second and third years, accompanied by increasing time spent in the pavilions and at nursery schools, day-care centers, and the Maternity Hospital of Athens (where second-year students gain obstetrical and neonatal-care experience during four-week assignments).

Although the majority of the babies receive much warm attention, especially strong love attachments may develop between a nurse and one of her babies. Often nurses experience a kind of mourning period after their favorite babies leave. Adoptive parents must spend a month getting to know their baby by daily visits to Metera and it is the baby's nurse who must pronounce the baby and parents ready to leave the institution.* The investment of the nurse in "her" baby may provide a rigorous test for judging the suitability and readiness of the adoptive parents for this step. The active participation of a well-baby nurse in this decision helps to raise her professional status. The social worker sometimes has to help reassure the nurse that the prospective parents really are worthy of a favorite baby.

RESEARCH PROPOSALS

Of course, there are some babies who do not have the qualities that attract the love of the nurse to whom they are assigned. Studies could consider these babies and determine means of making them more "attachable." In the meantime, comparison of their development with that of their more fortunate peers would be expected to demonstrate less healthy trends. Another possibility that presents itself is that even in the most attractive babies, "love" of the variety available to them may not be enough. The babies seem to make a spurt developmentally during the preadoptive visiting periods when they are receiving the undivided attention of two warm, interested and (very soon) loving people on a daily basis. It would be worth checking to see if a comparable dramatic spurt in development and social ability would occur if pairs of nurses were assigned to two babies for a three-week period during which they have twenty-four-hour contact with the babies on a one to one, "mother-child" basis.

Various conjectures have been made on the elements in the environment which are missing for these babies as they reach six months. One possibility is an inadequacy of sensorimotor stimulation in the baby's environment in spite of nominally "adequate" object relationships. Despite the presence of toys and animation in the pavilions, there may be a lack of contingency of these stimuli to the developmental needs of the babies, which precludes development-promoting responses.† The development of autonomous

---

* Because of peculiarities in Greek adoption and inheritance laws, namely, that adoptive parents must be over fifty years of age, a large per cent of the Metera adoptions are made by persons living outside Greece. Many Metera babies are in the United States and Holland, though it is obviously an expensive undertaking for the potential parents to travel to Greece and spend at least a month getting to know the baby selected for them. The adoption laws are currently being liberalized as a result of the efforts of members of the Metera staff and other progressive leaders in Greece.

† Suggested by film studies and visiting consultants, including Drs. Caroline Chandler, Lois and Gardner Murphy, Reginald S. Lourie, Richmond Paine, and L. Joseph Stone.

functioning may be disturbed by restricted opportunity and/or encouragement for the babies to play on the floor alone and explore. Age-appropriate toys are not available in adequate amount and are often inaccessible to the babies while they are lying alone in their cribs or sitting unattended in high chairs. A warm, loving environment is provided, but it may be inadequately attuned to the specific and differing needs of individual babies.

Along with the studies at Metera itself, the babies adopted from Metera who are being raised in Greece, the United States, and perhaps also Holland provide the sample for further cross-cultural investigations. Another study could compare child-rearing patterns among Greek families of several socioeconomic groups.

It should be re-emphasized that although there are apparently deficiencies at Metera in the care provided for babies over six to eight months of age that interfere with optimal development, a large majority of the babies raised there fare quite well and do not show the severe effects of institutionalization still rampant in other baby homes of this size throughout the world.

France *

The economic circumstances of Paris have for many years required the full-time employment of both parents for the majority of families in the lower socioeconomic groups. In response to the obvious need for child-care facilities, day-care programs—*creches*—for babies from two months to three years of age have been in existence for over fifty years. In 1963, there were over 180 such creches established or supervised by the Paris Administration of Public Assistance (Centre International, 1960).

There are creches in most urban neighborhoods, each with a long waiting list. Some have over 300 babies waiting. Most new suburban-housing developers build a creche, the management of which is usually turned over to the Administration of Public Assistance. In older neighborhoods, a variety of physical structures have been converted to creches of varying degrees of adequacy. In some of the poorest neighborhoods, the buildings used often provide inadequate indoor space and little opportunity for any outdoor activities. Yet

* The authors are indebted to Dr. F. Davidson, Chief Medical Inspector of Health of the Paris Medical-Social Service for National and Infant Protection, and her staff (especially Mme. Hermant, Chief of Social Service, and Dr. Clair Vesin, Creche Pediatrician) for opening the doors of their creches so wide.

there are many conversions which afford almost ideal circumstances, for example, sun balconies for the smaller babies from eight weeks of age and large yards with sandboxes and flower gardens for toddlers and children up to three years. The Public Assistance officials welcome the opportunity for advanced architectural planning of the new creches in suburbs where space limitations are less critical.

The public creches are open only to babies of mothers who work, except when specific social problems provide an urgent indication. The mothers pay according to their means, but all pay something for their babies' care. The French government gives an allotment to working mothers (2.3 per cent of salary) to help offset this expense (Davidson, 1962) when necessary.

The creches are open from 7 A.M. to 7 P.M., six days a week. The average creche accommodates forty to sixty babies. The quality of care varies considerably from one creche to another, depending partially on physical limitations but more so on the attitudes of the staff. In one poor neighborhood, where both crowded conditions and adverse attitudes were in evidence, babies were kept all day, except for feedings, in the bassinetlike cribs, side by side, with crib covers occluding observation of anything but ceilings and few hanging toys. The nurses could not be induced by the doctors to put the babies on their abdomens at any time because of the fear they might suffocate. Moreover, the nurses were afraid to handle the babies because they might accidentally become bruised and the parents would complain. They were afraid to let the babies play on the floor for the same reason, although the limited floor space was inadequate for babies to learn to crawl.

The majority of the creches are in stark contrast to this distressing picture. More typically, they are roomy, bright, and cheerful and provide space indoors and outdoors for uncrowded activities of the entire group. The newer nurses are more familiar with the psychological implications of the care they provide. The Administration of Public Assistance is optimistic that there will continue to be improvement in all the creches.

THE DIRECTOR

More and more of the creches are directed by graduate nurses who have completed postgraduate training at L'Ecole de Puericulture in Paris. Yet their one-year course is oriented more to the care of sick than well children. All students rotate through the department for premature babies, the outpatient clinic for sick children, all the pediatric specialty clinics, as well as studying bacteriology and other laboratory subjects. They are also taught about and participate in welfare programs. In addition, those nurses who are preparing to work in a creche instead of a hospital have a one-month course in the administration of a creche. The level of training at L'Ecole de Puericulture is relatively high, the same courses being used for preparing medical doctors to specialize in pediatric practice.

The director of the creche is crucial. She has an apartment in the creche for herself and her family. If she has small children, they will attend the creche. She selects equipment from the assortment made available by the Administration of Public Assistance. She is in charge of the finances of the creche, including the selection and purchase of food from the neighborhood stores for the meals served the babies. The only restrictions are that she must buy the best food available and that her budget must not consistently exceed that of creches of comparable size.

The director has many other administrative responsibilities, yet she rarely has secretarial help to relieve the burden. She must decide if a child is too sick to remain in a creche for the day. There are isolation units available for mild diseases. She must be certain that her children have been taken by their parents to the well-baby clinics and have received their immunizations. She must check certifications of good health for every baby brought back to the creche after any illness. She must be in contact with welfare agencies and specialty clinics to which she may refer some of her charges. She must receive each mother weekly to collect the fee for care which they have agreed upon. This visit, of course, affords the director the opportunity to answer questions about the child's care, to deal with problems of the family related to the child, to share with the mother the staff's experience with her baby, and by all this to strengthen the cooperative relationship between family and creche. The director must also select and supervise kitchen and cleaning help and the nursing assistants.

Nursing assistants, the child caretakers, are women who have achieved an academic certificate at age fourteen (equivalent to completion of junior high school) and have then received two years of additional vocational training (at the high school level) for the position of assistant child nurse (*auxilliary puericulturist*). The behavior of the caretakers usually reflects the attitudes of their director, but they are usually allowed to function fairly autonomously. In general, they appear warm and gentle with the babies and obviously skilled in techniques of feeding, bathing, and initiating games and songs with the older children. They appreciate babies' individual differences to a certain degree and try to modify their care patterns accordingly. In general, one is impressed that the creche staffs seem to prefer the active, aggressive, and more independent child.

The ratio of actual caretakers to children ranges from one caretaker for every six or ten children. With so many children, the nursing assistants and certainly the director find little time for relaxed kinds of involvement, education, or play with the individual babies. They make the attempt to individualize but most often have to deal with the child as a member of a group.

The babies themselves "adjust" and accommodate amazingly well to the systems they encounter. For example, when the mother brings her baby in the morning, undresses him, hands him to the nursing assistant, and leaves, there is rarely any sign of separation concern in the baby unless the mother "hangs around" until the reaction comes to "reassure him." The babies are hugged and then placed on a potty by the nursing assistant when they are received from the mother. A few years ago, despite strict regulations prohibiting such premature attempts, the caretakers in some creches started a baby on the potty as early as three months of age, tying his shirt to a pole to support him in a semisitting position. Babies under a year may sit complacently on the potty for ten to twenty minutes having been given a cookie or toy to hold their attention until their turn to be bathed or dressed in clothing provided by the creche. They are then given permission to play in another room.

CURRENT RESEARCH

Toys are well designed and well utilized by the staff with the toddler and older groups in the better creches. But even in the best creches there seems to be relatively little attempt to provide infants with stimulation in the form of suitable toys and visually attractive objects, such as mobiles. Experimental programs of stimulation are being evaluated by research psychologists (Lezine, 1962), but no broadly applicable program has yet been developed.

Studies of nurse-infant interactions have been sensitively carried out by psychiatrists and psychologists (David and Appell, 1963) in an attempt to understand better this unique relationship. Child psychiatrists and psychoanalysts (David and Soule, 1963) have been teaching at L'Ecole de Puericulture in an attempt to enhance further the psychological awareness of the future directors. Seminars on creches have been conducted at the Paris International Center for Children (Centre International, 1960) in which internationally renowned experts have participated.

The Administration of Public Assistance is not satisfied with the present state of care in the creches, although they do recognize the tremendous gains in the past five years. They are hampered by staff shortages, possibly a reflection of the demanding nature of the roles as well as the low salary scale. The need for training that is more specifically directed to the care of well babies in creches, rather than sick children in hospitals and clinics, is also appreciated. The administration's low budget allows for less variety and quantity of toys than they would like to have available. The rate of construction of adequate facilities cannot keep pace with the growing need for more creches, much less replace those which are so limiting to the potential functioning of the staff and the babies.

Conclusions

Any appraisal of the value and significance of programs in other countries faces a particular handicap, since philosophical and ideological issues may prejudice the viewer. Nevertheless, our review of child-care practices abroad permits several conclusions relevant to American research and program development.

Extended experience, over several decades in some of the countries, has led each toward an eclectic integration of skills and professions. Pediatrics, education, and psychology have proved of particular importance for the programming of *group* care for the *well* baby. Moreover, increasing social (and governmental) awareness and willingness to finance programs and research in child care have been matched by varying degrees of scientific curiosity addressed to the problem of more adequately meeting urgent contemporary social problems. Broad social and cultural changes have had a common impact in mobilizing and sometimes fragmenting traditional family bases of child care. Changing social and economic circumstances require new, if not better, solutions to age-old problems.

Communist or Socialist "collectivistic" programs are fascinating to the researcher. The reputed effectiveness of such programs has titillated the interest of the lay public, particularly after U.S.S.R.

space technology dramatically emphasized that country's educational advances. It seems clearly evident that the extensive child-care experimentation of the U.S.S.R., pragmatic as it is, affords valuable extensions of methods and program possibilities for those children who must inevitably spend some portion of their life in institutional-type arrangements.

It is dramatically clear, both in the United States and abroad, that enormous improvements in institutional programs have almost eradicated the most severe forms of marasmatic hospitalism. Staff training and social services have been sufficiently improved in the United States that we rarely find much more than "minimal" retardation in the institutionalized infant or social promiscuity in the institutionalized preschool child (Provence and Lipton, 1962). In fact, the mock sociability of the institutional toddler leaves the lay public ill-prepared to see the latent damage to such children's cognitive capacities or their social and emotional mental health.

American methodological knowledgeability and ingenuity in research have been paralleled by significant advances in theoretical, often eclectic, understanding of infant-child development and maturation. Since such American advances are relative, one has need to contrast them with research elsewhere in the world. Those specialists who best understand the considerable limitations of American research may hope to find, and may optimistically overvalue, research abroad. A careful review of international research in child development, however, readily demonstrates the naïveté of such a view. However limited it may be, American research in child development seems unequaled anywhere in the world. Yet research in infant development or in the application of research to child-care programs in the United States falls far short of work elsewhere.

One may particularly regret the relative apathy and disinterest of the American public in implementing appropriate programs for children, particularly those from deprived circumstances. The mid-1940s probably saw the peak of change in American programs, with the last wave of evacuation of small children and infants from residential institutions. Certainly many babies have remained in varied types of institutional care, but emphasis has been given to placement in a foster home. Recently, professional disillusionment with the inadequacies of some types of foster-home programs, as they are typically envisioned and financed, has brought a swing of the pendulum and a questioning of the possible, positive virtues of reconstituted institutional care. This development has undoubtedly been compounded by the inability of social agencies to obtain either a sufficient number or adequate foster homes for children of minority races.

At a time when scientific achievements seem to offer ever better solutions, reports from other nations, particularly Israel and the U.S.S.R., lend credence to the view that historical conventions of "mothering" and child care might be less significant or consequential. Child care by "experts" has become too readily accepted. A further misconception that "science" can rectify unexpected or untoward side effects of substitute child-care systems compounds an apparent public illusion. We doubt that anyone knows enough about either childhood developmental lags and retardation, or potentials for reversibility of retardation, to justify such expectations (Bloom, Davis, and Hess, 1965; Escalona, 1950; Escalona and Heider, 1959; Escalona and Leitch, 1952; Hunt, 1964).

From a scientific vantage point, the researcher in the United States can only regret most wholeheartedly that the mass care programs of other countries have thus far failed to research the longitudinal consequences of their own innovations. The risks in developing mass programs seem enormous, given the proportions of the child populations that are presently placed in day and residential care. At a time in our scientific history when clinical and theoretical understanding of such profound pathologies as borderline schizophrenia, psychopathy, and sociopathy is still fragmentary, a most conservative and cautious assessment of child-care programs and research in other countries seems an essential prerequisite to the extension of programs here at home.

THE DIFFICULTY OF DIRECT COMPARISONS

The authors feel that there are three fundamental differences that separate the behavioral research scientist in the United States and his social community from that of "collectivistic" orientations: (1) differing assessments of infant vulnerability and individual differences, (2) differing social and philosophic goals for the children, and (3) differences in willingness to provide the staff needed for large-scale child-care programs.

The issue of infant vulnerability is controversial even within the United States. We are not prepared, as are many persons of the Communist scientific community, to hypothesize that the mode of infant and child care is irrelevant to psychopathology in later life.

On the contrary, extended clinical experience here has led many scientists to an opposite conclusion: The infant's vulnerability and the specific significance of these tender years is inextricably related to subsequent emotional and cognitive well-being.

We do not doubt that contemporary science has discovered techniques and interventions for institutionally reared children that may stimulate precocious cognitive and motor development in early childhood. But at what price? The Russians, for example, are reputed to pay an exorbitant economic investment for this achievement (Bronfenbrenner, 1964). We suspect, moreover, that they may pay an even greater price in damage to personality and mental health of the children concerned. We are left with the tentative conclusion that Soviet programs have led to a de-emphasis of the significance of personality factors without controlled scientific exploration of the impact of training and child-care practices on the future of their own children.

While our review has primarily been concerned with the child under the age of three, we would extend our comments to the preschool child of three and four. A prevalent vogue in the United States has led to a too-ready acceptance of reports that the preschool child can invariably accept placement in preschool situations where he might benefit from precocious learning. This point of view does not seem unique to the United States; we have found such attitudes in the major technological societies of East and West Europe as well. Even where day care or residential care for the infant or toddler may be rejected as damaging or traumatizing, as in Czechoslovakia and Hungary, placement of the three- to five-year-old in preschool day care seems increasingly acceptable and unquestioned. Yet this practice, as a matter of choice, is anything but noncontroversial and clinical experts strongly question the advisability of early separation from the mother, particularly when the alternative is placement in a group. Because of the known vulnerability of the preschool child, we do not recommend day care *except* under carefully controlled conditions with respect to the age of the child, the staff ratios involved, the length of time in care each day, etc.*

The issue of infant and childhood vulnerability is obviously one where alternatives must be evaluated. What is the potential damage to a small child in his own home if the parent is disturbed or distraught or if the parent is ill or overworked? We share with the Hungarian, Czechoslovakian and Israeli child-research specialists the view that immediate social and economic needs are directly relevant

* See L. Murphy, Chapters 5 and 6.

to child-care practices and programs. They justify substitute child care when alternatives are patently more trying and damaging. Current United States research has focused on the devastating effect of particular social and cultural conditions that prevail in many economically impoverished (usually minority) groups of the community (Pavenstedt and Bandler, 1965). We have concluded that infant day care for this population could provide a breakthrough in a viciously self-propagating set of social tragedies. Day-care programs might provide a much-needed and immediate crutch for those ethnic groups crippled by social and economic disadvantage.*

Regarding our second difference from "collectivistic" societies, we suggest that there is neither the philosophical orientation or economic need (except relatively) which would necessitate vast programs of institutionalized child rearing, such as those of the Israeli kibbutzim or the collectives of the U.S.S.R. The social goals and aspirations of collectivistic societies are manifestly different from the philosophic ideals of contemporary America. The aims of inculcation of collectivistic identity in the Soviet child contrast markedly with the independent self-sufficiency aspired to in the American philosophy of child rearing. Beyond such global differences, however, we doubt that there are fundamental differences in the general cultural aspirations that all people hold for their children with respect to such attributes as honesty, sincerity, social consciousness, capacity for love, intellectual vigor, etc. The scientific disagreement has more to do with the age at which social and cultural values may be appropriately introduced to the child without damage to his mental well-being or his relative autonomy to make decisions. Although it remains the appropriate province of the political philosopher to assess the desirability of particular social ideals, science has its unique contribution in the search for answers to questions of fact. Can particular ideals ever be effectively inculcated or transmitted in infancy? What is the price in inhibitions, repressions, and related fears that certain ideals or aspirations impose on the vulnerable mental life of the child? At what age may social values be directly or indirectly introduced to the infant and child without damage to his mental capacities?

Our third difference from collectivistic orientations concerns the

* We have not attempted a review of more direct long-term remedies for basic social and political problems. We should also add that "poverty" as defined in the United States constitutes an invidious, highly relative evaluation. The "impoverished" populations of the United States have annual incomes as great as the working class of countries such as Great Britain (£600 = $1,440 per year).

readiness of a community to provide sufficient and adequate staff to implement those social and educational goals we desire for our children. The pervasive social and economic support of the child caretaker in the U.S.S.R. and the kibbutzim in the collectivistic societies is relatively unique on the international scene. These countries have been prepared to recruit, maintain and reward staff of relatively exceptional talent and intensive dedication to child care. The Soviet goal in child rearing, clearly specified as "the creation of the New Communist Man," is matched by a national dedication in both social attitude and economic investment for this purpose.

East European preparedness to implement programs, not unlike the less well-developed programs of France, reflects primary economic motivations, and only secondary concern with philosophic goals. The American goals have been far less articulated and publicized, with a laissez-faire attitude that the American family should independently nurture and shape the child's emerging personality attributes and attitudes.

DOES THE UNITED STATES REALLY CARE?

Differences in cultural, social, and political orientations inevitably influence both the caretaker's dedication to the nurture of the child and her style of care. We have described those factors which bear on the selection and training of child caretakers abroad. Without doubt, the task of the caretaker in day-care or residential programs is extremely arduous, demanding, and complex. In those nations or communities where the child and his caretaker are afforded high value, high status, and support, the chances of recruiting effective adults and providing for their training are greatly enhanced. These conditions, we believe regretfully, do not prevail in contemporary America. Although the American community provides ever increasing material advantages for its children, the intrinsic significance and value of early maternal child care seems implicitly devalued in large segments of the population in the United States. While we have become renowned for scientific and educational advances and for our psychological and sociological orientations, cultural trends in the United States seem myopically to disavow, if not deprecate, the typical child caretaker, the much discussed and abused mother. Indeed American research has yet to clarify such elemental definitions as "adequate" or "inadequate" maternal care, particularly in our own underprivileged populations.

The evidence from every major city in the United States gives stark testimony to the severity of the problem of child care in a significantly large segment of the population. The juvenile courts constantly deal with more cases of delinquency and neglect. Lack of adoptive and foster homes, particularly for children of racial minorities, has led to crowded institutions. The population with the greatest vulnerability to injury in early childhood has the least access to services that might mitigate some of the potential damage. While economic inequities are a direct and relevant issue, the psychological impoverishment is related more to the damaged family and its cultural malaise.

Contemporary clinical and research efforts in the United States have been directed toward the study of impairments of cognitive and emotional capacities of children that may derive from cultural conditions in which the children are reared. Experimental, educational interventions in the United States have also focused on the range of "individual differences" between children. This may appear as a significant difference of orientation when contrasted with Soviet theoretical views of genetic equality. This difference is theoretically important, yet in practice Soviet staff and researchers are most explicit in their "individualizing" approaches to child care. In the United States, research is presently attempting to assess the reversibility-irreversibility of damage to cognitive functioning of the "older child," the child of age four or more (Deutsch, 1965). Research on enrichment programs should afford increasing insight to the degree and type of damage to cognitive and intellectual functioning. We remain skeptical, however, as to the effectiveness of corrective, enrichment-type interventions that are attempted as late as the third or fourth year of childhood, particularly where there may be minimal, related psychopathology.

Disadvantaged ethnic groups undoubtedly produce gifted as well as impaired children—and sometimes the two are not readily differentiated. We suspect that there is a considerable percentage of children in this population who are only nominally damaged, nominally retarded—the "pseudo-retardate" who functions effectively everywhere but in school. But the clinical experience of the psychiatric clinic, of the educator and juvenile court staffs also suggests that the vulnerability of this population includes an unduly high proportion of cognitive dysfunction that is comparable to that of the hospitalism syndrome. A nomenclature for classifying the nature of these "disorders" is limited and inadequate (Freud, 1965).

Gross deprivational institutional experience has its direct parallel in the isolation of infants in the homes of very deprived families (or in the relative isolation of inadequate day-care centers). Yet other children from the same ethnic and cultural groups may also be exposed to an extreme range of *excessive* stimuli, such as too frequent changes in living circumstances, divorce, changes in caretakers, or exposure to needless violence. Not unlike the child deprived of stimuli, this latter group also evidences a syndrome of minimal disturbance and retardation.

Our review permits only limited conclusions, since the issues tend to be ambiguous and elusive. Yet the issues are not simply "relativistic." On the national level, there are both social and scientific opportunities in such programs as day care if research accompanies the intervention. Sharing research in child development on an international basis has become feasible and potentially fruitful.

REFERENCES

Administration Génerale de l'Assistance Publique à Paris, Department de la Seine, *Nouvelles Realisations de Protection Maternelle et Infantile*, 1956–60.
Barkóczi, I. Development of Infants' Manipulative Activity. *Pszichologiai Tanulmanyok*, 6: 65–80, 1964.
———. Comparative Analysis of Investigative-Manipulative Conduct of Infants and Monkeys [Csecsemók és majmok kutató-manipulációs viselkedésének összehasonlitó elemzése]. *Magyar Pszichologiai Szemle* 22: 343–354, 1965 (text in Hungarian).
Bloom, B. S., A. Davis, and R. Hess. *Compensatory Education for Cultural Deprivation*. New York: Holt, 1965.
Bowlby, J. Editorial Comment on Child Rearing in Kibbutzim, *Manchester Guardian*, July, 1963.
Bronfenbrenner, U. The Making of the New Soviet Man: A Report of Institutional Upbringing in the U.S.S.R. Ithaca, N.Y.: Cornell University, 1963. (Mimeographed.)
———. In Colloquium on Maternal Deprivation, II, Excerpta Medica Foundation, New York, 1964.
———. Soviet Methods for Character Education: Some Implications for Research. Ithaca, N.Y.: Cornell University, 1963. (Mimeographed.)
Centre International de L'Enfance, Paris. *Seminaire sur les Crêches*, 1960.
David, M., and M. Appell. A Study of Nursing Care and Nurse-Infant Interaction. In B. M. Foss (Ed.), *Determinants of Infant Behavior*, vol. 1. New York: Wiley, 1961, pp. 121–135.
———, and M. Soule. Personal communication, 1963.
Davidson, F. Day-care Centers in Paris and Its Suburbs. Working Paper No. 13, World Health Organization. Joint UN/WHO Committee on the Care of Well Children in Day-care Centers and Institutions, Geneva, 1962.
Deutsch, M. Proposed Center for the Study of the Relationship of Environment to Development and School Performance. Unpublished, 1965.
Egeszsegugyi Miniszterium, Budapest. *Egeszsegugyi Tipusepuletek Tervgyujtemenye*, EM Kozepule Hervezo Vallalat, 1957.

Eisenberg, L. Discussion. In P. Neubauer (Ed.), Children in Collectives, Springfield, Ill.: Charles C Thomas, 1965.

Escalona, S. K. The Use of Infant Tests for Predicted Purposes. Bulletin of Menninger Clinic, 14: 117–128, 1950.

———, and G. Heider. Prediction and Outcome. New York: Basic Books, 1959.

———, and M. Leitch. Earliest Phases of Personality Development: A Nonnormative Study of Infant Behavior. Monographs of the Society for Research in Child Development, vol. 17 (serial no. 54), No. 1. Evanston, Ill.: Child Development Publications, 1952.

Faians-Glueck, S. Introduction. In P. Neubauer (Ed.), Children in Collectives, Springfield, Ill.: Charles C Thomas, 1965.

Falk, J. The Role of Child Care in the Cure of Dysplasia Coxae [A gondozási feltételek szerepe a csípőizületi dysplasiák gyógyulásában]. Orvosi Hetilap, 106: 2143–2146, 1965 (text in Hungarian).

Freud, A. Normalcy and Pathology of Childhood, Assessment of Development. New York: International Universities Press, 1965.

Gerson, M. Family Problems in the Kibbutz. In P. Neubauer (Ed.), Children in Collectives, Springfield, Ill.: Charles C Thomas, 1965, pp. 233–237.

Gewirtz, J. Personal communication, 1966.

Hunt, J. McV. How Children Develop Intellectually. Children, 11 (3): 83–91, May–June, 1964.

Kaffman, M. Inquiry into the Behavior of 403 Kibbutz Children. American Journal of Psychiatry, 117: 732–738, 1961.

———. Comparative Psychopathology of Kibbutz and Urban Children. In P. Neubauer (Ed.), Children in Collectives. Springfield, Ill.: Charles C Thomas, 1965, pp. 261–269.

Kugelmass, S. Discussion. In P. Neubauer (Ed.), Children in Collectives. Springfield, Ill.: Charles C Thomas, 1965.

Langmeier, J. New Observations on Psychological Deprivation in Institutional Children in Czechoslovakia. Unpublished, 1965.

———, and A. Matejcek. Physical Deprivation in Childhood. Prague: Státní Zdravotnické Nakladatelstvi, 1963.

Lewin, G. Infancy in Collective Education. In P. Neubauer (Ed.), Children in Collectives, Springfield, Ill.: Charles C Thomas, 1965, pp. 69–73.

Lezine, I. The Role of Toys and Games in the Day-care Center. Working Paper No. 9. World Health Organization. Joint UN/WHO Committee on the Care of Well Children in Day-care Centers and Institutions, Geneva, 1962.

Lourie, R. S. Report from the Viewpoint of Child Psychiatry on Mission to U.S.S.R. for the President's Panel on Mental Retardation. Unpublished, 1962.

Makarenko, A. S. A Book for Parents. Moscow: Foreign Languages Publishing House, 1954.

Marans, A. E. Personal Observations, 1963.

Matejcek, Z. Investigation of the Mental Development of Institutionalized Children by a Children's Psychiatric Service in Central Bohemia, Ceskolovenska Pediatrie, 17(7–8): 621–27, 1962.

Messinger, J. Discussion. In P. Neubauer, (Ed.) Children in Collectives. Springfield, Ill.: Charles C Thomas, 1965.

Ministerium für Gesundheitswesen, Kinderpflegerin. Ausbildungsunterlagen für die sozialistische Berufsausbildung, Berlin, August, 1963(a).

———. Rahmenlehrpläne für die Ausbildung der Werktätigen Qualifizierungsabschnitt, A 1–A 5, Fachrichtung Kinderpflege, Berlin, September, 1963(b).

———. Arbeitsordnung für Kinderkippen, May, 1964.

Neubauer, P. B. (Ed.) Children in Collectives. Springfield, Ill.: Charles C Thomas, 1965.

Pavenstedt, E., and B. Bandler. The Educational Needs in Preschool-aged Disadvantaged Children. Boston: South End Family Program. Unpublished, 1965.

Peter-Pikler, E. Some Principles Concerning Supervision of Creches and Residential Nurseries. *Nepegeszsegugy*, 46: 33–36, 1964.

Provence, S., and R. C. Lipton. *Infants in Institutions.* New York: International Universities Press, 1962.

Rabin, A. I. Infants and Children under Conditions of Intermittent Mothering in the Kibbutz. *American Journal of Orthopsychiatry*, 28: 577, 1958.

Report of the Medical Exchange Mission to the U.S.S.R. *Maternal and Child Care.* U.S. Department of Health, Education and Welfare, Public Health Service Publication No. 954. Washington, D.C.: Government Printing Office, 1962.

Robinson, H. B. Day Care for Infants and Young Children in Russia. Working Paper presented at Conference on Early Child Care Re-examined, National Institute of Mental Health, Bethesda, Maryland, 1965.

Schmidt-Kolmer, E., and S. Hecht. Die Entwicklung 1– bis 6– jähriger Kinder in gemischten Gruppen im Vollheim. *Pädagogische Forschung*, Wissenschaftliche Nachrichten des Deutschen Pädagogischen Zentralinstituts, Jahrgang, 1964, No. 2.

Segal, M. Theory and Aims of Kibbutz Education. In P. Neubauer (Ed.), *Children in Collectives.* Springfield, Ill.: Charles C Thomas, 1965, pp. 3–5.

Shchelovanova, N. M. Studies in the Development and Physiology of the Central Nervous System from Birth through Three Years of Age. Described in personal communication from A. V. Zaporozhets, 1964.

————, and N. M. Aksarina. *The Upbringing of Young Children in Children's Establishments.* 4th ed. Moscow: Medgiz, 1960. Translation of this work has been done by the Center for Studies on Children and Youth, National Institute of Mental Health, Bethesda, Maryland. Page numbers refer to this English translation.

Silverman, M. The Happy Orphans of Metera. *Saturday Evening Post*, March 19, 1960.

Spiro, M. E. Education in a Communal Village in Israel, *American Journal of Orthopsychiatry*, 5: 283, 1935.

————. *Kibbutz: Venture in Utopia.* Cambridge, Mass.: Harvard University Press, 1956.

Tardos, A. Effect of Environmental Change on Infants' Play Activity, *Pszichologiai Tanulmanyok*, 6: 273–287, 1964.

The President's Panel on Mental Retardation, *Report of the Mission to the U.S.S.R.*, August 1962. Washington, D.C.: Government Printing Office, 1964.

Tur, A. F. *The Care of the Young Infant*, Leningrad: Medgiz, 1954.

Zaporozhets, A. V. Research in Child Development and Its Application in the U.S.S.R. Address presented at Children's Hospital of Washington, Washington, D.C., 1964.

PART IV

New Research in the Prevention of Culturally Determined Retardation

This part is composed of reports on four longitudinal researches. These reports are presented as examples of work designed to test certain limited aspects of the larger problem—the care of the very young child. No one attempts to solve the whole problem, yet each illustrates some of the difficulties of doing research in this area of human development. Each involves rather long periods of observation and demonstrates how challenging it is to design and carry out a study based on the best knowledge available and controlling for as many of the variables as possible.

The need for research is generally accepted, but it becomes more pressing as the United States begins to undertake service programs for very young children on a more massive scale. Rather than allowing programs to proliferate in a kind of mindless reproduction of old patterns, the research must undertake careful assessment of alternatives.

The four researches reported here are unusual in that there is planned collaboration among them, in itself a by-product of the conferences reported in this book. Although each program shares research aims and hopes to keep findings comparable, quite different strategies are employed. Each, however, is an outgrowth of "the times." As Halbert B. Robinson, director of the study at North Carolina, has written:

> The plight of the culturally deprived child, often subnormal, apathetic and doomed to repeat his parents' history of poverty and despair, has captured the sympathy of the nation. Numerous projects of many kinds are being rushed into existence; child development specialists and educators are being pressed into devising and guiding programs of intervention designed to combat the socioeconomic and emotional hardships endured by the children of marginal families in our society.
>
> The dramatic needs of these children, the lure of large amounts of money for such programs, and the immediacy of the demands being made, all encourage interested workers to take an active role of leadership, to put into action our favorite hypotheses about optimum childhood development. The facts are, however, that we really know very little about the effects of programs of intervention upon the intellectual and emotional development of children, particularly infants and preschool children. The pressures to which we are presently subjected must not blind us to the fact that our knowledge about very young children is sketchy and vague. The great bulk of what we do know, moreover, has been acquired from studies in university nurseries

of highly select children whose probable endowment and whose home environs are quite different from those of the children with whom we are being asked to work.

The four studies that follow will be presented in apparently reverse order—the first three reporting research still on the "drawing boards" and the last a study at the Children's Center in Syracuse, New York, which has been in progress for several years. As is the nature of longitudinal studies, this ongoing program has been accelerating with the passage of time.

◆§ 11 §◆

The Children's Hospital in Washington, D.C.

ALLEN E. MARANS,
DALE R. MEERS, and
DOROTHY S. HUNTINGTON

It has become increasingly evident that a disproportionate incidence of developmental retardation and distortions occurs among children growing up under slum conditions. Furthermore, these handicaps persist into adult life and are perpetuated from generation to generation to such a degree as to constitute a cultural pattern. "In some slum areas, 10 to 30 per cent of the school children are mentally retarded. . . . Evidence gathered . . . shows a major causative role for adverse social, economic, and cultural factors" (Kennedy, 1964). Of at least equal concern is the finding that although the majority of slum children are not severely retarded, they most often place in the range of low average or borderline retarded when measured by common standards. Usually, these children are adjudged retarded—

The authors gratefully acknowledge the suggestions made by Dr. Lois Barclay Murphy.

or, more frequently, borderline—on the basis of their school performance and the findings of psychological tests. The tests often demonstrate an inadequate development of such skills required for academic success as verbal facility, abstract reasoning ability, frustration tolerance, and motivation for success, as well as a deficiency in the accumulation of stored knowledge, which reflects an inadequate exposure to the world outside their immediate environment. Although these children have learned to survive in the difficult circumstances of a slum neighborhood, they are ill-equipped to contend with the demands of formal schooling.

It is postulated that the child-rearing patterns to which the slum child has been exposed are largely responsible for the kinds of cognitive and emotional handicaps that are reflected on tests and in school performance. It is further postulated that these handicaps which persist through adult life become established in the first months and years of life and are not readily amenable to amelioration after even three years of age.

As one way to intervene in this cycle which perpetuates retardation, the possibility of taking babies into small groups for care during the day has begun to receive attention. If this is done on a large scale, society could provide a good start toward achieving the inborn potential of vast numbers of children. The apparent success of group care for infants in various parts of the world (see Chapter 10) has led people in the United States to investigate the possibilities here.

Up to the present, group care for children, particularly for children under three years of age, has not been a method of choice in the United States, except in emergency situations, such as the day-care centers at defense plants during World War II. Both professional and lay opinions have been profoundly influenced by the results of studies of inadequate institutions for homeless babies. Severe distortion of physical, cognitive, and emotional development and even death have been the seemingly inevitable outcomes of some types of group care for motherless babies (Bakwin, 1949; Bowlby, 1951; Brenneman, 1932; Chapin, 1908). The early pediatric and psychiatric conclusions about the adverse effect of group care for babies have been matched by particular philosophical ideals in the United States concerning "the rights of infants" (Ribble, 1943). The infant's need for and right to a mother's attention and the concomitant concern with the preservation of the "nuclear family" continue as barriers to any popular acceptance of group care. The concept of a nuclear family, however, seems more an ideal and a fiction than a reality for a large portion of the economically and culturally disadvantaged families of America. Yet the conclusion has long persisted that any family, no matter how bad, is better than any institution, no matter how adequate, for the nurture and care of babies particularly during their first three years (Wolins, 1963).

However, several things have caused professional attitudes to change in recent years: (1) the recognition that the arrangements working mothers make for their children are often casual and shifting, even if non-"institutional"; (2) a growing dissatisfaction, if not disenchantment, with foster-home placement because of difficulties in securing adequate numbers of appropriate foster homes, the inability to provide sufficient professional supervision, and the frequent shifts in placement usually encountered by a child who requires care for a prolonged period of time; (3) a growing conviction that the patterns of child rearing practiced by some segments of the population perpetuate physical, emotional, and intellectual handicaps from generation to generation; (4) a nationwide concern about such conditions which has stimulated a demand for preventive programs to interrupt and bypass the apparent circularity in which one generation of deprived parents impairs the next; and (5) the demonstration that other technological societies continue to be enthusiastic about the apparent results of group care for infants undertaken in bold social experiments on a massive scale.

The World Health Organization (1964) convened a committee of child-care experts to discuss institutional and day care and to amass clinical data that might stimulate the countries of the world to provide more adequate "substitute mothering," with all that this is now known to imply. Bowlby's statement still rings true: "The proper care of children deprived of a normal home life can now be seen to be not merely an act of common humanity but to be essential to the mental and social welfare of a community. For when their care has been neglected, as happens in every country in the Western world today, they grow up to reproduce themselves" (Bowlby, 1951, Preface).

The Present Situation in the United States

It has been proposed that day-care programs on a large scale might be the most feasible of the possible methods to provide a preventive approach to the problem of culturally determined retardation, while at the same time creating a solution to the dilemma of the working mother. This does not in any way diminish the need for a resolution of the economic and sociological ills which perpetuate the conditions in which developmental retardation and distortions occur so disproportionately. And it is not being recommended, of course, that all children be separated from their mothers or removed from apparently inadequate home conditions. What is being contemplated is that enrichment and special attention to individual needs be supplied from the outside via day care. This care would supplement that which the families do provide to the maximum of their capacities.

In response to requests from the various states, Congress in 1962 authorized up to 10 million dollars annually for the provision of day-care services and facilities for group care to be licensed by the states. Legislators at the national and state level have requested guidelines from experts for the implementation of such programs. The experts consulted have been able to utilize their knowledge and experience for recommendations regarding group care for children from three to five years old.* But they have counseled the legislators that programs intervening in the first three years of life would be maximally preventive. Yet such expert consultation must acknowledge that there is little experience and only limited knowledge on which to base recommendations for an ideal large-scale program appropriate to the United States for the day care of children from birth to three years of age. The preponderance of research and the related theoretical hypotheses have been concerned with life in the nuclear family, and there is little evidence that material gleaned from a family setting can be directly translated to group care. In order to achieve maximum success in enhancing early growth and development, and thus to prevent the culturally and environmentally determined impaired development manifest throughout the country, logically conceived and tested bases for such programs in the first years of life must be further developed. Research methodologies must be made available so that a continuous process of evaluation can provide the means of constantly improving present and future programs.

---

* The American Public Health Association, through the Day Care Committee of its Maternal and Child Health Section, has prepared *Children in Day Care with Focus on Health*, published by the Children's Bureau of the Department of Health, Education, and Welfare in 1967. The Child Welfare League of America, the Children's Bureau, and the Bureau of Family Assistance of the Department of Health, Education, and Welfare have also been involved in developing standards for day care.

In addition to day-care centers, residential care of small children also needs restudy. For various social and health reasons beyond the scope of this analysis, it is obvious that it will be necessary to provide full-time care for many children under three years old for many years to come. Some residential care programs capitalize on present knowledge to ameliorate or to prevent the effects of institutionalization which have been so well described in the literature. But many institutions, aside from acquiring modern buildings and equipment and despite the best of intentions, find themselves still confined to traditional programs, often with grossly undesirable results. The "institutionalization syndrome" has far less to do with physical facilities than with sterility of human relationships. The prevention of developmental retardations and distortions in children under group care urgently requires research focused on the development of more appropriate programs, staff training, and organization.

The Research Plan

Motivated by the awareness of such needs, the Department of Psychiatry of the Children's Hospital in Washington, D.C., has initiated a child-rearing research project, titled "The Prevention of Culturally Determined Retardation," which is supported by the Edgar Stern Family Fund and U.S. Public Health Service, National Institute of Mental Health (Grant #10421). The project is still in its planning stage. Basic hypotheses have been formulated, staff members are being selected, and specific methodologies are being developed. The research design is primarily concerned with the study of children from their birth to three years of age who come from disadvantaged backgrounds. The major goal is the development of a method for the *prevention* of culturally determined retardation and dysfunction in cognitive, motivational, personality, and social spheres.

It is proposed that several groups of children be raised from birth to age three in one of the following groups, according to the needs of the children, their families, and the project:

1. A twenty-four-hour residential care unit for sixteen children whose legal guardianship has been assumed by the District of Columbia Department of Welfare and/or the Pierce-Warwick Adoption Service of the Washington Home for Foundlings.

2. At least one day-care unit operating five days a week, twelve hours per day, for sixteen children whose families will also be seen

by neighborhood aides who will work intensively with the mothers to offer social supports, to teach them to understand and facilitate their child's development, to deal with social problems, and the like. These mothers will be encouraged to spend time with their children in the day-care unit, and some mothers may, if this proves appropriate, be hired as auxiliary care workers. In these groups, attempts would be made to maximize the effects of differential experience by working intensively and extensively with the children and their families.

3. At least one day-care unit operating five days a week, twelve hours per day, for sixteen children whose families will *not* receive additional attention (only the children will have the supplementary care of the unit).

4. At least one group of sixteen families whose parents will receive the supplementary help: trained neighborhood aides to demonstrate principles of child care, to instruct the mothers in working with the children, to help with social problems, etc., but whose children will be seen only for routine developmental testing. The effect of optimal social supports for the mothers will be the variable to be researched.

5. At least one group of sixteen families who match the experimental groups on a set of social and demographic characteristics who will receive no supplementary aid but whose children will be examined periodically to follow their development.

6. At least one group of sixteen families who come from a socioeconomic group markedly different from the experimental groups, whose children will be examined periodically to follow their development.

Comparisons of the development of the children in these different groups will at least begin to answer questions relating to the efficacy of the proposed programs. It will also provide data relating to numerous other questions, such as:

How may one most effectively assess vulnerabilities of children at birth in order to prescribe assistance for their optimal development?

How may one most effectively assess developmental differences in babies and their consequent environmental requirements?

How may one best meet the requirements of well infants who are kept in hospital nurseries because there is no other place for them?

How may new, more creative methods of dealing with children by adoption agencies better meet the needs of society?

How may "poverty" families be best helped themselves to meet the needs of their children?

In addition, attention will be given to what change in family structure is brought about by involving one member of the family unit in the project and what changes are brought about in the personal integration and effectiveness of those adult members of the community who are trained to work in this project and who thereby stimulate further growth in the adult population; it will also be noted which personality and character patterns get in the way of such integration.

The development of the children in the different groups will be assessed and compared through the use of standardized tests of physical, neurological, and psychological development. The choice of the specific tests will be made on the basis of work during the past and projected completion of the pilot phase of investigation. The characteristics to be used as the bases for sample selection and population matching will be examined during the pilot phase. All relevant demographic data on the geographic area involved will be integrated, in order to describe most effectively the population involved, to make decisions concerning the social characteristics of the families to be included in the sample, and to make decisions involving the geographic location of the day-care units, if it is necessary that they be "spotted" away from the neighborhood of Children's Hospital in order to have an appropriate sample. To be investigated are such factors as how many women in the area have prenatal care; their characteristics of age, education, income, etc.; the heterogeneity of the community, how transient the economic level, family stability, racial composition, etc. These data will be obtained from previous studies done at the Children's Hospital, by the United Planning Organization, George Washington University, Georgetown University, Howard University, and the District of Columbia Board of Education, Police Department, Health and Welfare Council, and Department of Public Health.

One of the major issues involved in sample selection is the choice of the babies. In the small numbers planned for the different care units, it is important at the outset to exclude babies with evidence of serious congenital deviation. Since these infants are coming from a group known to have high incidence of neurological difficulties, we will screen the neonates very carefully. Those children with abnormalities appearing at later stages will be retained in the sample, since they will be representative of the population being studied.

The subjects will be as representative as possible of the disadvantaged population which has been described. However, to evaluate properly the effects of environmental intervention separately from the effects of physical impairment on the development of these "high-risk babies," it will be necessary to exercise reasonable selection with regard to the perinatal condition of potential subjects. The appropriateness of the following criteria will be further explored and specific guidelines developed during the pilot period:

1. The subjects shall be full-term infants with birth weights of 2500 grams or above who are the product of a normal pregnancy and spontaneous or low forceps delivery (Scott, Jenkins, and Crawford, 1950). In view of the demonstrated relationship between medication during labor and diminished visual attention during the first four days of life, which raises the possibility of other detrimental effects, an attempt will be made to obtain infants whose mothers received little or no analgesic agents during delivery.

2. Normal condition at birth as indicated by an Apgar rating of 7 or above.

3. Normal pediatric and neurological examination and neonatal course.

In return for their participation in any aspect of the program, free health care will be provided to all the children of the families, and social service consultation will be made readily available. Methods which have been developed through experience with this population in other contexts of their relationship with the hospital will be of value in maintaining the cooperation of the families.* Liaison between the project and the test community will be further reinforced through the indigenous workers hired for this purpose.

The full-time residential babies will be selected from those whose parents cannot or will not care for them. They will come from the same kind of background as those from the selected geographic area. The project will be apprised of their availability by the welfare department, the juvenile court, or by direct application by the mother

---

* Experience in maintaining a continual relationship with families has been gained by personnel in the Well Baby Clinic, Chronic Disease Follow-up Clinic, Department of Psychiatry Out-patient Clinic, and research projects such as the Pica Study and Iron Deficiency Anemia Etiology Study reported elsewhere, and a preliminary anthropological study of disadvantaged family life patterns.

through a cooperating independent social agency. These are babies who cannot be accepted for adoptive placement. Often, their family histories render them ineligible for adoptive consideration; in addition, there is a dearth of available adoptive parents. As a rule, such babies are placed in transient care in ad hoc hospital settings, in group infant foster care, in a succession of foster homes, or in such institutional facilities as Junior Village in Washington, D.C., theoretically a temporary shelter for homeless children but often, in practice, a more or less permanent placement.

The major responsibility for the implementation of the programs of intervention with the babies will belong to the trained child-care workers and neighborhood aides. This role will become a new and urgently needed discipline in the United States if large-scale offensives against developmental disturbances early in life are to be undertaken. The selection and training of these women will be based largely on knowledge gained from programs in other countries (see Chapter 10) modified by theoretical orientation of the project and the differences in national goals. The selection process will seek to identify the qualities in women (such as fondness for babies, an inherent sensitivity to the various needs of babies, a sense of self-value, a capacity for autonomous functioning, and a flexibility that allows for further learning) which would best qualify them for "mothering" a small group of babies who are not their own. Their training, followed by group and individual supervision, will strive to enhance their awareness of the individual needs of babies at different stages of development. Their repertoire of responses will be specifically augmented so that the effects of certain different practices can be compared. But of primary concern will be the reinforcement of the autonomous functioning of the child-care workers and aides.

Plans are being made for the construction of day-care and residential nurseries, accommodating approximately sixteen children in each. These buildings will be adjacent to the Children's Hospital and the local elementary school and therefore be central to the area to be served. Advanced architectural thinking is being enlisted in the attempt to provide a physical environment which will afford and facilitate "mothering" for a small group of babies. Flexibility in physical arrangements is a critical need if the varying needs of individual babies as well as the differing styles of the child-care workers are to be considered. Ease of access to the outdoors and the selection of textures and design of interior surfaces are all important. The floor plans should allow the babies to have access to work areas, such as kitchens and laundries, as well as to furnished "living rooms" where child-care workers will chat and rest with their children.

An additional requirement of the architectural design is that unobtrusive observation be possible at any time and almost any place in the nurseries. Audio and visual recording of events or time samples will supplement direct structured and unstructured observations. Observation in the selected homes will duplicate that in the special facilities as closely as physical conditions there will permit. Periodic assessments of physical, intellectual and emotional development will be conducted on all of the infant groups in a standardized manner. The cooperation of the medical and neurological departments of Children's Hospital will provide close supervision of physical health and development, as well as consultation services whenever the occasion demands.

Information will be exchanged with the staffs of the comparable research projects described in the next three chapters. By this means, the effects of the different research strategies in the four projects can be compared. Where possible, common methods of observation and assessment will be attempted. Collaboration is being established also with the Queen Anna Maria Institute for Child Health of Athens, Greece, which is responsible for research conducted at the Metera Babies Center.* It is anticipated that the addition of a cross-cultural perspective will serve to underscore the cultural origin of patterns and their effects within the local test population. Child-rearing patterns as taught and practiced at the Metera Babies Center will be compared with those in the Greek villages from which the nursing students come in an attempt to differentiate those patterns which can be learned by young adults from those which are culturally determined. The current phase of this collaboration is establishing a baseline understanding of relationship patterns and rates of development of the babies at Metera. Also, an exchange of personnel between the Children's Hospital of Washington and the Metera Babies Center is creating a mutual awareness of theoretical orientations, a sharing of respective skills, and consideration of mutually feasible research goals and methodologies.

---

* See Chapter 10. The project, titled "Collaborative Cross-cultural Child Rearing Study" (Public Health Service, NIMH Grant 09228) is presently in its initial phase.

Theoretical Assumptions

While the design of the study acknowledges the "high risk" of genetic impediments or "constitutional" vulnerabilities that derive from limited prenatal and postnatal care, those in the project are also convinced that the retardation under study is affected by the interaction of high-risk organic conditions with cultural, social, and psychological processes. Psychology has not yet produced a theoretical model accounting for the derivation of a characteristic style of functioning for each individual which results from the constitutional givens interacting with experientially influenced proclivities for the use of sensory and motor modalities.

Therefore, the most essential theoretical premises of this project should be stated:

1. Ego "structure" derives from an interaction between the infant's biological capacities and the environment which nurtures, demands, and presses.

2. The "structure" of ego processes begins to be crystallized in earliest infancy, and early structuring may be irreversible where either organic or environmental pressures are seriously inappropriate (or traumatic) to the developmental needs at that time.

3. The infant's capacities to perceive, integrate, and make use of past experience (memory) are premised on relative freedom from crippling stress, whether of organic, environmental or structural origins.

4. Development of tolerance for anxiety and frustration requires some minimum of maternal support in struggling with the inevitable stresses of infancy as a precondition for the child's steps in adaptation.

5. Learning is motivated by either—and frequently both—the child's delight in exploration (and mastery) of his environment and his attempt to master his fears and anxiety.

6. Intellectual capacity may be impaired either in its entirety or in particular functions or subject matters.

7. Parental modes and ideals are understood, however primitively, and are internalized in the course of preverbal development.

8. Motivations may be "realistically" (but in the wider world, maladaptively) limited when goals seem unreachable because of limited opportunity or where emotional conflict is an impediment.

One of the most culturally disadvantaged populations in the community will be studied because of the apparent magnitude of developmental retardation and limitations of function. The primary, experimental intervention is via the infant day-care center and the residential center where the psychological nutriments of infant life may be supplemented. A day-care center is enormously complex; the personalities of the caretakers are of particular relevance to the style and richness of nurture and stimulation provided. The nursery environment is designed to meet the needs of healthy babies, who are cared for in groups of four. Each group has one primary caretaker. In so far as possible, the ratio of babies to caretakers will be determined by the individual needs of infants. The day-care center provides a type of supplementary care which should complement the infant's nurture in his own home. This study then entails the evaluation of the maturation and pattern of the infants, the contributions of the parents and home environment, and the characteristics of the nurturing, staff-care methods of our own facility.

The general statement concerning management of the day-care nursery approximates the aims of the staff for the residential unit as well. As we have earlier discussed, a confluence of historic and social circumstances has led to an increasing need for group care for children in the United States. Influential segments of some foreign countries, for example Israel and the U.S.S.R., have looked toward nursery care as a means of enriching the lives of both children and parents. But there are, of course, problems which continue to be inherent in residential care where the infants are deprived of a primary, biologically reinforced maternal relationship. If the residential research nursery is to approximate the ideals of its staff, it might well look and be organized like a comfortable middle-class home. A fundamental question is how well children can be raised in an ideal residential setting.

Staff Selection and Training

The obviously critical nature of the characteristics of the staff dictates intensive consideration of their selection and training for the success of the infant-care programs. Experience, plus review of the literature, leads to the conclusion that it is essential to screen potential staff very carefully and then to build into the program sufficient sustenance that caretakers do not need to excessively defend against emotional involvement with their babies. An assessment of screening procedures and the development of criteria for selection of caretaking staff are required. In effect, selection processes are aimed at identifying those qualities in women which would best qualify them to "mother" babies who are not their own and which would best sustain their investment in the babies.

The related training program will need to take into consideration the dilution of time, affection, and interest that the child-care worker suffers in any group or residential setting. The training and subsequent supervision will need to provide specific support and direction of her "repertoire of responses" plus a heightened interest in the babies that may compensate for any lack of intuitive awareness. Such awareness of each infant's needs should facilitate an increased degree of autonomous functioning of the caretaker, a sense of her own contribution to the baby's maturation.

As structured child-rearing practices, procedures, and schedules are evolved in the study, assessment of the personality characteristics of the caretaker who is best able to use such over-all directions can occur simultaneously. Although a certain minimum of intelligence is essential, those selecting staff believe that this work is more intuitive and empathic than explicit and lean toward "natural mothering" rather than toward the well-trained "master's degree" candidate. Both caretakers and infants obviously will vary considerably. We have found it interesting that even the U.S.S.R., which minimizes genetic explanations in psychological differences, makes considerable use of programing to accommodate the differences in maturational development of babies. It is demonstrable that programs can be written in obsessive detail as to how children "ought" to be cared for. Yet, analogous with the game of chess, while rules can be explicit, they may be quite ineffectual unless they are flexibly used in the unique circumstances of each interchange. A monograph outlining and discussing essential minimums of programing and staffing will be prepared as a basic text.

A review of the international literature regarding child-care centers suggests that rather broad and general outlines can be completed but that they *must* be adaptable to the uniqueness of each center: to the uniqueness of its staff, to the individual differences of the children, and even to the differences in geographic and physical circumstances.

Concluding Remarks

Retardation—its severity, magnitude, and apparent cultural origins—is the focus of the study. The major research problem involves an intervention aimed at reversing the potentials for retardation that exist, a preventive, rather than a corrective, intervention. Conventional enrichment programs apparently have questionable potency to reverse already established (academic) retardation, and it is our provisional conclusion that interventions to effectively preclude pathognomonic results in capacity must begin in infancy. One research approach is based on a day-care center; the other is full-time residential care for infants up to the age of three years.

It is not posited that a single "intervention" will be of significant value or, moreover, that a single intervention is technically possible. There are innumerable activities geared to the functioning of a day-care or residential center, any one or any group of which may have relevance to the children under study and therefore constitute an intervention. The very fact that a family would consent to and participate in a longitudinal study of its child and of itself is a research intervention of considerable magnitude. If the sum total of "intervention" is successful, the major difficulty will be in isolating the specific relevance of a vast range of complex and interrelated behaviors of the subjects and the staff.

Further, it is not posited that there is one, and only one, method of child rearing. Doubtless there are many methods; or, more accurately, there are many aspects of child care which are not only senseless and tedious, but also self-defeating. It is our position that the child-care research specialist presently is clinically and intellectually prepared to develop programming that will avoid particularly obvious limitations frequently inherent in residential care. The proposed research will seek additionally to define some of the basic components for large-scale programs of infant group care that can meet the needs and facilitate the development of individual babies who come from disadvantaged families as well as those without families. It is hoped that society might be able to utilize such programs toward the prevention of culturally determined retardation.

REFERENCES

Bakwin, H. Emotional Deprivation in Infants. *Journal of Pediatrics*, 35: 512–521, 1949.

Bowlby, J. *Maternal Care and Mental Health*. World Health Organization Monograph Number 2. Geneva: World Health Organization, 1951.

Brenneman, J. The Infant Ward. *American Journal of Diseases of Children*, 43: 577–581, 1932.

Chapin, H. D. A Plan for Dealing with Atrophic Infants and Children. *Archives of Pediatrics*, 25: 491–496, 1908.

Hoffman, G. L. New Dimensions for Day-care Services. Address presented to National Conference on Social Welfare, Cleveland, Ohio, 1963.

Kennedy, J. F. Message from the President of the United States Relative to Mental Illness and Mental Retardation. Reprinted in *American Journal of Psychiatry*, 120: 729–737, 1964.

Provence, S. A., and R. C. Lipton. *Infants in Institutions*. New York: International Universities Press, 1962.

Ribble, M. A. *The Rights of Infants*. New York: Columbia University Press, 1943.

Scott, R. B., M. E. Jenkins, and R. P. Crawford. Growth and Development of Negro Infants: I. Analysis of Birth Weights of 11,818 Newly Born Infants. *Pediatrics*, 6: 425–431, 1950.

Wolins, M. Some Theory and Practice in Child Care: A Cross-cultural View. *Child Welfare*, 42: 369–377, 1963.

World Health Organization. *Care of Children in Day Centres*. Geneva: World Health Organization, 1964.

❧ 12 ❧

The Frank Porter Graham
Child Development Center

HALBERT B. ROBINSON

The Frank Porter Graham Child Development Project is designed to provide a setting in which active intervention in the lives of culturally deprived children can take place. Careful longitudinal studies will parallel these efforts, evaluating and modifying them as new knowledge and skills accumulate. The center will provide a program covering the first twelve years of life, including both a day-care facility for infants and young children of working mothers and an elementary school for older children.

Chapel Hill, the setting for this center, is a community of about 35,000 people, encompassing both an "intellectual" element, comprised of university students and faculty, and the population which has grown up around the university to provide service to it. Part of the impetus for the center comes from active community concern for the culturally deprived children of the service group, brought dramatically into focus by efforts to handle children of both segments of the community in the same schools. Typically, the children of faculty and professional families far exceed in school performance those from less fortunate families. This problem was highlighted by efforts at racial integration of the schools, although citizens soon became aware that the problems of the culturally deprived were by no means limited to children of Negro families. As citizens became more fully aware of the depth of the deprivation existing in this apparently well-to-do and intellectually stimulating environment, a number of action-oriented programs were initiated, including projects designed to aid the school dropout, the adult semiliterate, the unemployed and underemployed, and a preschool summer project, later replaced by a federally financed Head Start program.

Meanwhile, many citizens and members of the university faculty became convinced that the most effective approach would probably be through the provision of stimulating and enhancing efforts beginning perhaps as early as infancy, programs of prevention rather than treatment. Surveys of the actual care of culturally deprived children, particularly the day care available for children of working mothers, strengthened the suspicion that the apathetic, passive, and intellectually handicapped children seen in the schools were a natural outcome of their earlier experiences. The center thus grew as a cooperative venture, sparked both by professionals within a number of university departments and by members of the community who were seeking an answer to the real problems they were facing.

Along with this impetus to intervene in the cycle of poverty, there was the strong realization of a basic need for research dealing both with normal childhood development and with the effects of various programs of intervention. The center was thus conceived by all as a research program, and most important, as a longitudinal research program. Children both in and out of the center are to be followed closely throughout the first twelve years of life.

Organization of the Center

As proposed, the Frank Porter Graham Child Development Center will consist of two basic divisions, a day-care facility for 240 infants and children of working mothers and a school for 550 primary and elementary level children, those in both divisions chosen to be representative of all segments of the diverse community.

THE DAY-CARE FACILITY

Central to the plans for the day-care facility is the concept of the "family unit," of which there will be twenty. Each of the family units will have twelve children, ranging in age from early infancy through the kindergarten years. Children who "graduate" from this facility into the elementary school will also retain some contact with their original family unit, as, for example, during the hours before and after the school program; but in the main, each family unit will consist of approximately two children at each year level from birth through five years. Two or three child-care workers will be the main staff of the units, assisted by preschool, kindergarten, and other teachers for the older children. In each unit, provision will be made for eating, sleeping, group and solitary play; each child will have his own "cubbyhole" in which he can find privacy and some semblance of solitude. The organization of the center around the family unit, rather than by age group, was conceived to serve several purposes. First, the child is provided the opportunity for long-term relationships with important adults, relationships which furnish continuity and support as he moves into widening circles of experience. Second, this arrangement makes possible the placing of all siblings from a given family in a single unit, enhancing their relationships as in the ordinary family setting. Third, this arrangement enables the child-care workers to solidify long-term relationships with the parents of the children, hopefully encouraging a close and meaningful cooperation in the child's best interests. Fourth, the presence of children of several ages is seen as stimulating to all, perhaps especially to the younger ones who have the opportunity to interact with stimulating older children and to observe more adequate models for language and play than if they were isolated with many other infants and toddlers at their own level of mastery. Finally, the staff in such an arrangement should find it more natural to treat each child as an individual than if he were one of many children of the same age.

The infants and toddlers will spend the major portion of each day in the family unit. The two-year-olds will be away from the unit, engaged in special classes and recreation programs, for one or two hours in the morning and one hour in the afternoon. The three-, four-, and five-year-olds will spend progressively more time away from "home" as they become increasingly involved in educational and recreational activities. Special playrooms and kindergarten classrooms are provided in the center for such activities. In addition, every effort will be made to enlarge the experience of the children outside the center, to escape the doldrums of a single environment, through field trips and volunteer services. As examples of the latter, women in the community will be encouraged to "borrow" children for a few hours for trips to the grocery store or their homes.

Tuition for day-care services will be charged on a sliding scale. The center will be open from approximately 7 A.M. to 6 P.M., five days per week, with the possibility of more limited services on Saturdays. However, any individual child's schedule will be shorter than this, coinciding with his mother's hours of work.

THE ELEMENTARY SCHOOL

In collaboration with the Chapel Hill Board of Education, which has provided part of the building funds and will furnish part of the operational funds, a twenty-four-room elementary school will accommodate children who have experienced the day-care program, a large number of the children in the control group to be described later, and as space permits, other community children. This school will provide an opportunity not only to follow closely the children of the longitudinal study, but also to furnish individualized attention, experimental curricula, and enrichment programs. Afterschool and summer programs, both academic and recreational, will continue to provide full-day supervision of children of working mothers, as well as providing a concerted effort to maintain the expected gains made in the earlier years. Previous studies have tended to show that children who have profited from preschool programs accelerated at their entrance to school, fail to maintain this advantage unless concerted efforts are made to combat the effects of their culturally deprived nonschool environments. With the close cooperation of the School of Education of the university, the school can to some extent serve the purposes of a laboratory school, providing training and demonstration to prospective and experienced teachers.

PERSONNEL

A multifaceted program is planned that will draw on the talents and interests of many departments of the university. Organized as an independent institute of child development within the university, a number of members of the senior staff will hold joint appointments between their own departments and schools, and the institute. In addition, there will be employed a large staff of child-care workers, teachers, and other persons involved in direct care of the children as well as in more research-oriented aspects of the program. It is anticipated that the entire staff, from directors to janitors, will number some 170. As recruitment policy, every effort will be made to involve as many male workers in all positions as possible, since many of the children come from homes in which the fathers are either absent or play a subsidiary role to the mothers. Each family unit will have assigned to it at least one male staff member, part of whose responsibility it will be to spend a significant amount of each day in interaction with children in that unit.

The Program

The purposes of the center, as pointed out previously, will be concentrated in two broad areas: (1) to help break the cycles of retardation, poverty, and disease which exist in sizable segments of the community by providing an opportunity for optimum development during the crucial formative years; and (2) to develop an understanding of the antecedents of a wide variety of behavior patterns pertinent to educational achievement and mental and physical health. Thus, it is essential that every facet of the center be flexible, stimulating to the children, and attuned to the research needs as well as to the service and demonstration aims of the enterprise. It cannot be a "typical" institution in which the needs of the child risk subordination to the needs of institutional routine.

STIMULATION

The usual experience of the typical culturally deprived child is a drab, routinized, unstimulating succession of predictable, largely empty, hours and days. Every effort will be made in the center to provide novelty, varied experience, and a steady, moderate flow of input into the child's perceived world built upon a basic and supportive routine. Not only will the physical environment provide a wide variety of toys and interesting spectacles, but also the program itself will be geared, in both its formal and informal aspects, to enrich the experience of the child and to involve him actively in play and learning. Child-care workers will be trained to engage the children in frequent conversation; preschool, kindergarten, and elementary school programs will be carefully formulated to provide verbal and nonverbal experiences of increasing complexity; volunteers and staff will provide frequent opportunities to explore the world outside the center. Moreover, efforts will be made to provide an opportunity for independent exploration in its semirural setting and a chance to escape the "groupness" of the typical day-care and school facility.

ACHIEVEMENT MOTIVATION

Recent studies have begun to show the importance of an internal motivational system, which is a generalized impetus to be productive, to achieve some standard of excellence and to gain rewards in the pride of doing one's best. Apparently, children from deprived environments develop very low levels of achievement motivation. This drive does differ among children but has striking effects on their development. Children with a high degree of achievement motivation, for example, become brighter as they grow older; those with a more passive outlook tend to fall behind their developmental potential. It is understandable that the marginal family, crowded, discouraged, and often overworked, values the passive child; yet the passive child is precisely the one whose chances to escape the cycle of poverty are greatly reduced.

A number of longitudinal studies have shown that children whose achievement motivation is high have experienced from earliest infancy somewhat "pushy" parents who have maintained high standards for behavior but at the same time have given ample rewards and warm responsiveness for mastery and independence. As a vital part of the program, members of the staff will attempt to emulate this pattern, providing for the children high expectations, aid in achieving goals, and genuine approval for mastery. The evidence is clear that motivation for achievement must begin long before the child can conceive of distant rewards or punishments. Furthermore, he must learn it from the people who are important to him in his immediate surroundings. The role of the staff of the center is thus clearly a crucial one.

RELATIONSHIPS WITH ADULTS

The relationships that a child develops with important adults are regarded as vital for his emotional security and for his healthy psychological growth. It is thus essential that the adults in the center provide continuity of experience, that they be affectionate and accepting, and that they provide appropriate models by which the child can develop adequate patterns of behavior. Careful selection of personnel will thus emphasize thorough evaluation and probationary periods of employment. For all the programs, special efforts will be made to employ only individuals who are likely to remain in the community for a protracted period. In-service training, as well as pre-employment selection, will be designed to encourage healthy child-rearing practices, a balance of permission for activity within firmly defined limits, and, in general, the "democratic" environment which numerous studies have identified as conducive to the growth of emotionally healthy, outgoing, internally controlled young children.

WORK WITH FAMILIES

Extensive work with families of the children in both divisions is seen as an essential part of the program. Probably children enrolled in the center will become very different from the families from which they come. It is anticipated that they will be intellectually brighter, more active, and striving, and that they will possess a greater awareness of their personal worth, strength, and effectiveness. If so, the center's program may engender substantial anxieties and stresses in many of the families, particularly those of marginal socioeconomic status. Studies show that most of these families discourage the asking of "how" and "why" questions by their children; they frequently cannot tolerate the slightest manifestation of verbal or physical aggression directed toward them by their children; they expect their children to endure hours of inactivity; and so on. It is important, therefore, to alleviate as much as possible the inevitable conflicts within the parents as they relate to their children and the center, not only out of concern for the mental health of these families but because it is essential that the parents understand and support the program itself. Efforts to achieve this aim will be given a high priority.

The child-care workers, teachers, research and administrative staff will endeavor to establish meaningful and positive relationships with the children's parents. Parents will have the staff of a single family unit with whom to relate concerning all their children, and the child-care workers will be given auxiliary help during the hours when children are delivered and picked up in order to interact freely with the parents. Evening and weekend sessions in which the programs and aims of the center are explained and dramatized will occur regularly; it is hoped that the center will provide a facility which the parents can use regularly for themselves, for recreation, continued schooling, and so on. A public health nurse and a social worker will be employed to keep in touch with the families and to help solve or ameliorate the problems they face, not only with regard to their children's behavior but in other areas as well. Close contact will be maintained with other helping agencies in the community.

MEDICAL AND DENTAL CARE

As an integral part of the program, comprehensive health care of high quality will be rendered to each child in the demonstration center, and pediatric care will be offered to children in the control group who are not attending the center. In-staff pediatricians, dentists, and nurses will provide regular surveillance of the children's health and development and special care in case of illness. Infirmary facilities will accommodate children well enough to leave their homes but needing more intensive or specialized care than can be provided in the family units; they will also provide isolation in order to control the spread of infection. Research into the most effective ways to provide such care will constitute part of the medical program.

As with the Children's Hospital project in Washington, D.C., initial contacts with the families of most of the children will be made during the mother's pregnancy. Careful records will be kept of prenatal as well as postnatal health data. Although clinical facilities are presently available to the families of the culturally deprived group, they are routinely used by most families for emergency care only, not for preventive health services. As a rule, continuing or close relationships with the child's physician are not maintained. On the whole, the medical and dental care planned by the center will be clearly superior to that the children would receive if they were not enrolled.

Child Population and Control Groups

Children will be admitted to the center *before* birth, that is, during the mother's pregnancy. They will actually enter the day-care facility at whatever age during infancy the mother returns to work, possibly as early as two weeks for some babies. For infants whose mothers do not intend to resume working for several months, introductory part-time care in the center from an early age will permit an easy transition when the mother does begin working and will enable the staff to provide medical care and observe the infants during the early months. Children will be chosen to be representative of the entire community, but it is expected that there will be an emphasis on children of low socioeconomic families, since these families most need the services of the center. In order to qualify for admission, a child must be of the appropriate age; his mother must be working or otherwise absent from the home during the day on a regular basis. The family must intend to keep the child in the center day-care and elementary school programs as long as he is of the appropriate age and must, therefore, expect to remain in the vicinity. This policy will exclude children whose fathers are students at the university. Families will be encouraged to enroll all their children in the center, including subsequent babies in future years.

When the center is in full operation, approximately fifty babies will be admitted each year. Since applications will probably exceed available places, a random selection of applying families will be made, except that all families already having a child in the center will be accepted. The children who are not accepted into the program, who are expected to be equivalent in background to the center population, will constitute the primary control group. The child-rearing practices of their parents will be investigated and contrasted with those of the parents of center children. Their development will be observed at frequent intervals, parallel to observations being made of center children. In addition, they will be encouraged to enroll in the center's elementary school program when they become eligible for school. Medical services will be offered to these families in order to enlist their cooperation and to ensure that it is the psychological aspects of the program, not primarily the medical aspects, which are responsible for any superior development of the center children.

A secondary control group is also planned, outside the community altogether. It is predicted that the center's program will have some impact within the community, even on children not enrolled, and therefore it is deemed necessary to follow an equivalent group who is not exposed to the same cultural milieu.

Research Programs

As has been indicated, the center will provide an opportunity for research in many aspects of child development, with a population somewhat more representative of "typical" children than has usually been the case for such studies. Primary in the research efforts will be a longitudinal study of the children involved in the program, including careful collation of data from the prenatal period through at least the elementary school years. Frequent psychological testing and observation, medical surveillance, linguistic analyses, family visits, testing and interviews with parents, and other data will form important aspects of the longitudinal study.

In addition to the longitudinal study, a great many short-term studies will be carried out in the center by investigators from many departments within the university. Because of the size of the center, it is possible to accommodate matched experimental and control groups for a number of subprojects. Moreover, the large number of small family units will permit the introduction of divergent programs in different units, with subsequent evaluation of their effects. For example, it would be possible to introduce instruction in a second language into different family units and to compare the children's progress in the second language with their progress in English.

The various focused, experimental, and descriptive studies which are planned at present are too numerous to describe in detail here. It is planned to conduct research into cognitive and perceptual development of young children; to study the effects of various formal programs of instruction (e.g., reading and foreign-language learning) at different ages; to follow the development of children along the dimensions suggested by Jean Piaget and to attempt to influence the ages at which children reach the stages of intellectual development he describes, etc. Medical studies of infectious diseases, regimes of health supervision, metabolism, biochemistry, etc., will take place. Other studies will be related to social and exploratory infant behavior, to relationships between various experimental variations in child-rearing practices and children's behavior (e.g., the effect of permitting or forbidding aggression toward parent-figures), to the improvement of primary mental abilities of children, and to a wide variety of educational practices at the elementary school level. Studies are also planned by specialists in the fields of psycholinguistics, sociology, genetics, psychiatry, social work, public health, and others.

In summary, the Frank Porter Graham Child Development Center is conceived as a facility encompassing a broad-gauged program of intervention and investigation. Its intention is to learn how to provide for the optimum growth and health of the infant, preschool, and elementary school child, and to see what effects such care can bring about. At this point, enthusiasm and hopes for success in helping parents to raise bright, active, emotionally stable children are high, but it is clear that the effort must be accompanied by careful design and by hard-headed research into the many aspects of child development.

✑ 13 ✑

The Yale Child Study Center Project

SALLY PROVENCE

In this chapter a program of research that reflects the mutual interests of a government agency and a university Child Development Center is described. The program is a response to increasing concern about the development of infants without families and those who are reared in other situations of inadequate care.

Statement of the Problem

Thousands of infants and children who live in environments characterized by emotional deprivation, intellectual poverty, and family instability present this country with one of its most urgent problems because of their limited development, restricted horizons, and wasted or seriously troubled lives. The significance of the program of inter-

313

vention and study to be described is that it addresses itself to the characteristics and needs of some of the disadvantaged children in our society. The research aims to provide data that will lead to development of more effective methods of preventing or alleviating the intellectual and personality damage sustained in situations of inadequate or adverse care in the earliest years. The high cost and often disappointing results of programs designed for those who have suffered such damage testify to the necessity for more intensive efforts in infancy and the preschool years. Prevention, early diagnosis, and early intervention are obligatory if we are to improve the current situation. Much is known about how to prevent, diagnose, and intervene which has not been effectively translated into programs of care. We must learn more about how to deliver the needed services.

There are also many areas that are unknown or insufficiently explored. We have, for example, hypotheses, speculations, assumptions derived from past work about the ways in which the infant comes to recognize, be attached to, and trust his mother, and grow in his relationship with her and with other significant people and factors in his environment. But without minute and careful studies of many real babies and their mothers in a variety of relationships and circumstances, we cannot substantiate existing hypotheses. Nor can we know in detail what is involved in mothering that can maximize optimal development, what impedes it, and what may cause irrevocable damage. To cite but one specific example: A sharper definition of the normal child's need for continuity of mothering would have obvious practical implications for the staffing policies of day-care centers and institutions.

Similarly, we have hypotheses about certain ego functions that begin to show themselves in earliest infancy and change and mature with the growing child. These ego functions (defenses, ways of actively mastering the environment, abilities to learn and apply knowledge about people and ideas) are of crucial importance in the child's later successful or unsuccessful adaptation to his world. We must study closely the ways in which such ego functions develop in the maturing infant and child; what factors in his physical makeup, his interpersonal relationships and his social environment help to determine his adaptation. Until we can answer such questions more precisely, we cannot know with enough specificity the kinds of interventions that would foster optimal development for a specific child, or what kinds of rehabilitative measures would correct faulty development.

The problem we face, then, is threefold and reflects the state of the children's field at this time: we must find ways to alleviate the intellectual and personality damage suffered by the disadvantaged; we must learn more about how to deliver the necessary preventive and therapeutic services; we must advance our scientific understanding of the necessary and sufficient conditions for optimal child development. As we begin to master the third task, we can more confidently recommend and apply specific techniques of prevention, diagnosis, and intervention.

Objectives of the Research Project

We propose to study three groups of children, from early infancy to age seven, who are homeless or otherwise disadvantaged:

    a. a group in their own families

    b. a group in foster families

    c. a group in a congregate living situation.

The project involves a program of active support and intervention in each group. The major objectives are:

1. To provide advice, support, and casework treatment to foster parents and natural parents aimed at improving the care of their children; to provide a program of day care and education and health supervision for the children; to assess these interventions by comparing these two groups of children with two groups in which there has been no intensive intervention.

2. To design a program of group residential care for infants and children up to seven years of age and to describe it in detail—its characteristics, strengths and shortcomings; to determine whether such a program has merit as a model for providing services to homeless children; to compare the development of these children with the control group of children in an existing institution.

3. To design a day program of care and education for the three groups of intensively studied infants and young children in accordance with the best current knowledge about their developmental needs; to describe the care and the environment in great detail; to make judgments about the merits of the program as a model for day care from infancy onward.

4. To develop a training program for a variety of people who will provide services to children in families. In particular we are concerned with child-care personnel in residential and day-care settings, social workers, teachers, and aides who work in child welfare programs.

5. To increase knowledge about children from the disadvantaged segment of society with emphasis upon the developmental process they share with other children.

6. To compare the development of the three "intervention" groups of children from infancy through seven years of age in various dimensions. This comparison will be related to the three environments (own family, foster family, and group home) and will focus upon developmental progress (quantitative) in various areas, personality development, and problems in behavior and development.

7. To delineate more sound and effective guidelines for providing services in the interests of the child, his individual family, and the wider society.

8. To study in depth individual children in the three environments indicated. We expect the rich biographical portraits we will obtain to be of special value in the development of hypotheses.

9. To derive hypotheses about several crucial aspects of child development that will enrich scientific understanding of this field. Particularly we hope to increase our understanding of the complex interactions between the child's individual endowment and potentialities, his particular environment, and his particular phase of development. Much of the data we will use in the derivation of our hypotheses will come from the above-mentioned studies in depth of individual children in their individual environments and the comparisons of the three groups.

Our study will focus on certain issues. A few of these will be enumerated here as examples. In regard to *maternal attachment*, some of the important questions might be: At what age does the infant have the cognitive and affective capacity to form a special and specific attachment to a maternal figure? Given this basic capacity, what happens to the infant if this attachment is disrupted? Does temporary disruption affect children from different backgrounds and at different ages in different ways? Insofar as this disruption is deleterious to emotional and cognitive development, are there ways its effect can be mitigated by the provision of certain kinds of continuous care or relatively constant and stable mothering figures? What is the effect of multiple "good" mothers? At what point in the life of an infant does complete separation from a mothering figure produce emotional and cognitive decline? Is it possible that for some children with a poor and inconsistent relationship, such separation with the substitution of more stable and constant figures actually promotes development?

Another example might be in the area of *identification:* At what point do infants begin to identify with, to take on and begin to internalize characteristics of the most significant people in their environment? How do these first identifications show themselves? Are there ways to intervene so that these first identifications and the rudimentary images of self which are based on them are facilitating and supportive to development rather than impeding and damaging? Do children from different environments form these basic identifications at different times and in different ways? What are the relationships of identification to the constancy and exclusive aspects of the human object?

In the area of certain aspects of ego development: When does the infant begin to use his innate ego potentials to cope, to adapt, to synthesize and deal with experiences, with people, and with things in a positive and mastering way? How can we help him, through providing good interpersonal relationships, to cope and overcome rather than to reject, withdraw, or destroy?

In the realm of *body image* development: At what age can the infant conceive of, recognize, and use his own body as a willed, autonomous, and positively valued entity to move in space, to manipulate things, to move toward and away from people? When can he actually comprehend that his body is a unique, whole, special, and separate object which exists in—but apart from—the world and is capable of dealing successfully with the world? What produces the kinds of disruptions in body-image development that leave the child confused about himself, his own separateness and intactness, and his relation to other objects and people in his environment?

Finally, how do such issues as those mentioned of maternal attachment, identification, ego development, and body image influence and interact with one another at each stage of development? How are the many issues discussed above affected by interactions with parents with their individual personalities, intellectual aspirations, "life styles," cultural characteristics, feelings about the child, socioeconomic status, and with other crucial figures in the environment of the child?

General Design and Some Methodological Considerations

The proposed research is a longitudinal study of development in infancy and early childhood utilizing a multidisciplinary approach in a service-centered investigation. The major dimension is the environment, ranging from own home to foster home to institution. Children will be studied in these three settings as well as in a day program for children, the pediatric care setting and individual testing and play sessions. The investigators come from the fields of medicine (pediatrics and psychiatry), child development, psychoanalysis, social work, early childhood education, psychology, and nursing. All of the senior members of the staff have had extensive experience in their respective fields and have participated previously in multidisciplinary clinical teams or research projects. The basic approach may be called clinical research of human development. We emphasize the clinical dimension because we agree with Shakow (1959) that "training and skill in therapy add to the effectiveness of the research-minded person" and that "the sensitivities developed by the clinical approach to the nuances of behavior, the central concern with personality manifestations, the persistent recognition of the home in influencing development" are particularly relevant to the problems we wish to study.

Data are to be collected by investigators who are participant and nonparticipant observers. The participant observers (family teams) are those who have direct contact with the children and parents and who will usually be rendering a service—for example, a social worker who makes home visits, the pediatrician who gives medical care, the child development specialists who conduct the developmental examinations, the teachers and child-care staff who are responsible for the education and care of children in the Center, and so on. The participant observers thus will have a service-related contact with the child or family in accordance with sound clinical and educational practices. Support, child-care advice, health care, and education are to be provided to the best of our ability. Thus the study itself and the roles of the participant observers are service-centered. Although certain methodological problems are inherent in this approach, we believe that they can be adequately solved and that this approach is the one most likely to have access to the relevant data and achieve the goals of the study. The use of people from several disciplines concerned with child development and family life guards against a narrow approach. Moreover, the fact that parents and children are seen by several observers provides a system of checks which minimizes the tendency to bias and uniformity in the material. At the same time it is expected that there will be areas of agreement in the observations of the various investigators from which validity can be inferred. The senior members of the group come from the clinical and research experiences in which they are accustomed to be aware of the influence of their own actions and reactions upon the patient or study subject and the effect this has on the patient's behavior and on the data being gathered. In much of their work they also will be observed by others. Thus they will operate within the field of observation and the interaction becomes part of the data.

The advantages of a service-centered approach derive mainly from the fact that responding to the needs of parent and child (advising, supporting, and attempting to alleviate suffering) usually leads to a steadily if slowly increasing trust on the part of the parents in various members of the research team. This gives access to relevant information about themselves and their children which would otherwise be difficult or impossible to obtain. We also consider it to be an advantage that we can collect the data on the child in the natural setting of his home, in a day program geared to children, and in other situations that are not artificial or contrived. The medical examination is one example, which is a part of the "stuff of life." Various crises may occur, and these, too, can provide data. In this way ecological realities are incorporated into the clinical assessments of the study.

Nonparticipant observers will differ from participant observers in function but not in the disciplines represented. They will observe the child and parents through the use of a one-way mirror and at a distance. Data will be collected around (1) the child's behavior in such settings as the school, the developmental test, and the medical examination; (2) other child and staff/child interaction in various situations; (3) parental behavior in respect to staff, other parents, other children, and so on; (4) the quasi-experimental situations such as the individual play session.

The study design takes into account that methods of data collection and, to a certain extent, the focus on content areas will have to be modified with the growth of the child. A situation that is favorable for making relevant observations of a six-month-old infant will often be inadequate to approach the complexity of a three-year-old. Moreover, content areas will encompass data that vary in significance during different developmental phases. The adaptation of the investigation to the growth of the child is reflected in (1) The nature of the program of education and care of the children at different ages, which is geared to developmental needs; (2) The major settings in which observations are made—for example, more observations will be made at home in infancy and at school as the child grows older; (3) The selection of natural and quasi-experimental situations appropriate to the age and developmental phase. This adaptation is reflected in our awareness that parenthood, too, is a developmental process and that parents will be experiencing satisfactions, crises, and changing attitudes in relation to growth and change in the child. These changes will be taken into account in the contact with parents.

This study will employ prediction as a methodological tool for approaching some of the complexities of child development, especially personality development. Prediction about the course of an illness, the likelihood of a response to certain kinds of treatment or interpretation, and the significance of a certain symptom are an essential part, implicit or explicit, of every clinical contact and involve a process of assessment of past and present. Moreover, planning of curricula in child-care programs based upon accumulated experience "predicts" that children's development is likely to be supported by specific measures or impeded by others. Experiences in the formal use of prediction in the study of personality development have been extensively described especially by Benjamin (1959), by Escalona and Heider (1959), and by members of the staff of the Yale Child Study Center's longitudinal study of personality development (E. Kris, 1950; Coleman, Kris, and Provence, 1953; M. Kris, 1957). This approach of prediction is based upon the demonstrated usefulness of a body of theory and tested knowledge about human behavior and child development from psychoanalysis, pediatrics, academic psychology, education, the social sciences, and other disciplines. It is useful, moreover, because it does not exclude concepts of maturation, continuity of development, phase-specific characteristics, the impact of certain types of events that have been found to be clinically sound as propositions for understanding development. Thus it is a tool that is appropriate to the phenomena being studied, the complexity of their interrelationships, and the multiple dimensions of the field. Expectations about the course of various aspects of development—for example, intellectual functioning, areas of conflict, adaptive abilities—emerge from the application of theory to knowledge about the present situation and about the prehistory of a specific child. Experiential variables considered in the context of a specific child's individual endowment and his phase of development can be linked predictively to possible or probable specific effects upon development. The examination of outcome makes possible the re-evaluation of prediction.

The Study Population

The seventy-five infants to be studied in the program of intervention will be obtained primarily through the cooperation of state and local departments of welfare, the obstetrical and pediatric departments of the Yale–New Haven Medical Center, and other local agencies. It would of course be extremely difficult or perhaps impossible to conduct this kind of research in the absence of such cooperative agencies and departments. It is expected, for example, that the twenty-five children who live in their own families will come mainly from families receiving public assistance. This is also likely to be the source of the twenty-five infants who will live in foster families. The twenty-five children in the residential group will live in a setting designed by us. Some of the principles that will govern the setting up of this residential program have been spelled out in A Guide to the Care of Infants in Groups written by the author (1967). Children who are placed in the residential setting will be those for whom the welfare department has no other plan—that is, no possibility of a foster home or of remaining in their own homes with adequate support. While people concerned with child welfare in Connecticut have been making strong efforts to find homes for infants, there are always some for whom this is not possible. Some loss of children from the study is expected through the usual moves or a family's unwillingness to continue. In addition, because we are committed to putting the best interests of the child first, we will lose some of the children—especially those in the residential program—through our support of plans for placing them in adoption or in stable foster homes. With that probability in mind, we will expect to take more infants into the groups in order that we can maintain a sample of at least twenty-five children who can be followed over a long period. Control groups will be selected for each of the three "intervention" groups.

Functions of Staff

Some of the functions of the various members of the interdisciplinary research staff will be delineated:

Social Work Participation. The social worker's main function will be to make observations of various aspects of the study child's home environment, using the term in the broadest sense, and to provide whatever support, child-rearing advice, and psychological help may be appropriate in each situation. The social worker will also be responsible, together with other staff members, for observations of parent-child interaction and parental functioning in situations other than the home, such as the developmental examination, the regular health examination, or the school program. To accomplish these functions, the social worker will make home visits regularly. While the ultimate purpose of all social work contacts with study families will be to collect relevant data, the social worker will have a more immediate goal without which the over-all purpose of the study cannot be accomplished: The social worker will use casework skills to develop with each study family the kind of relationship that will permit the most fruitful collaboration. More than any other members of the research staff, the social worker will be the family's "person," the one who will not focus most attention and interest on the child but will attempt to communicate to the parents her concern for their welfare, her interest in their thoughts, feelings, aspirations, and problems. Experience in an earlier longitudinal study leads us to expect that as the casework relationship develops, significant information about each parent's life experience will emerge with increasing richness and clarity. Such information, together with observations of current parental behavior and attitudes in other aspects of the study, should allow us to formulate working hypotheses concerning the personality structure of each parent and the dynamics of family interaction. Our hypotheses, in turn, should allow us to make predictions about probable areas of conflict between parents and/or between parent and child, and about areas of probable strength in supporting a child's development. Such predictions should allow us to be alert to developing problems and perhaps to help before crises develop. As a derivative, the continuity of the study will be protected and the "demonstration" purpose will be advanced.

The Educational Program For Children. The importance of providing an environment that supports learning and assists the child in mastering a succession of developmental tasks is generally accepted. One such environment is the intact, well-functioning family in which parents are at least reasonably adequate and derive some pleasure in their nurturing roles and in their ability to cope with the demands of everyday existence. Another such environment is that of the school for young children in which learning proceeds in the context of meaningful relationships with teachers and peers in a setting geared to the children's interests and developmental needs. Whereas the school can support the learning of young children of all classes, it may have a crucially important place in the lives of the children who live in impoverished environments. There is a wealth of knowledge supporting the proposition that the teachers of young children must be more than warm, friendly people who like children, though these qualities are enormously valuable. The professional competence of the teachers is of added significance with the disadvantaged children, for whom recognition of deficits in functioning and supplying appropriate types and varieties of learning experiences is particularly important.

In our program of intervention the teaching staff and their aides will carry the main responsibility for the daily care and education of the children. The staff will include persons with several levels of professional sophistication: the educational director, a group of professionally qualified teachers, and a group of people devoted to children who will serve as child-care and teaching aides. In collecting data on the children under their care the teachers' primary goal will be to build a rich and comprehensive picture of each child. In order to approach and deal with a variety and quantity of data which confront them, the teachers will formulate priorities of observation. That is, without blinding themselves to or discarding relevant data, they will focus their attention and their recorded observations on certain aspects of group life, on particular transitional situations during the day, on specific kinds of interactions between children, between child and adult, and so on. Any systematic organization of behavioral data within categories must inevitably lose some of the individual qualities of the child. Thus an additional important component of the teachers' observations and recordings concerns the qualitative factors that cannot be "caught" in a categorization system.

Developmental Examinations. Members of the staff who will be administering developmental and psychological tests are trained in developmental diagnosis and are themselves a multidisciplinary group of pediatricians, psychologists, and child psychiatrists. In addition to standardized developmental tests from which a quantitative score and a developmental profile can be computed there will be an analysis of specific functions measured on the test and gleaned from other observations including, for example, such factors as perception, memory, imitation, development of object constancy, abilities to solve specific tasks presented. Most of these observations are conceived as being dynamically interrelated and help supply the basis for formulation of predominant personality factors. The developmental examiners and possibly other staff members familiar with the children will also conduct individual play sessions with the children to facilitate the study of play as it reveals some of the child's approaches to developmental tasks, as it expresses vulnerabilities, phase-specific anxieties, and conflicts.

Health Supervision. Three pediatricians and a nurse will devote part of their time on the project to health supervision and care of the children. Pediatric care will be given in the center in the form of periodic evaluations of health and growth. The medical and nursing contacts for the child in the child health conference setup will include a thorough medical and developmental history, examinations, growth records, periodic diagnostic screening, and dental examinations.

Other Observations. The designation "nonparticipant observers" indicates those members of the study staff whose function at the time of observation does not include a direct relationship with child or family. Their observations are crucial in increasing the richness and objectivity of the data. The observation mirror setup planned for the examining rooms will be the setting for observation of the physical examination of well and sick children, developmental and psychological tests, and individual play sessions. Other observations will be done in the school rooms and yard devoted to the day-care program and in the group residence later when it becomes available. The documents produced will include narratives of the behavior of mother and child in which the object is to record as much as possible of what goes on in a given time; it will include records that focus upon specific *forms* of behavior; it will include behavior recorded in many specific situations such as separation from parent, response to tasks imposed by the adult, mealtime, nap time, physical examination, and so on.

It is beyond the scope of this presentation to discuss methods of recording data and of data reduction. It is apparent, however, that an enormously important aspect of this interdisciplinary, longitudinal study is a continuous attention to maintaining the quality of the observations, periodic summaries and syntheses of data, development and examination of hypotheses, and so on. We are not unaware of the danger that longitudinal studies may become longitudinal forever and we are committed to the tasks of making our results available to others as soon as possible. From this study, with the opportunity that it offers, there are several kinds of research reports that can emerge. Each of these has many elaborations and obviously others will suggest themselves as the study proceeds.

1. Recommendations based upon research findings for practice in the child welfare field.

   a. Methods of supporting family life
   b. Modes for day care
   c. Guidelines for decision-making in regard, for example, to removal of a child from one living situation to another.

2. The influence of specific styles and methods of child care upon the development of children.

3. Description and evaluation of interventive efforts.

4. Individual case studies.

5. Description and evaluation of training program for child-care workers.

The first phase of data collection began in October 1967 with the opening of the day-care center and the admission of twenty-two children in a pilot group. Our expectation is that the longitudinal study beginning with neonates will be started in the late spring or early summer of 1968.

REFERENCES

Benjamin, J. D. Prediction and Psychopathological Theory. In Jessner, L., and E. Pavenstedt (Eds.), *Dynamic Psychopathology in Childhood*. New York: Grune & Stratton, 1959.
Coleman, R. W., E. Kris, and S. Provence. The Study of Variations of Early Parental Attitudes. In *The Psychoanalytic Study of the Child*, vol. 8. New York: International Universities Press, 1953.
Escalona, S. K., and G. M. Heider. *Prediction and Outcome*. New York: Basic Books, 1959.
Kris, E. Notes on the Development and on Some Current Problems of Psychoanalytic Child Psychology. In *The Psychoanalytic Study of the Child*, vol. 5. New York: International Universities Press, 1950.
Kris, M. The Use of Prediction in a Longitudinal Study. In *The Psychoanalytic Study of the Child*, vol. 12. New York: International Universities Press, 1957.
Provence, S. A Guide to the Care of Infants in Groups. New York: Child Welfare League of America, 1967.
Shakow, D. Research in Child Development: A Case Illustration of the Psychologist's Dilemma. *American Journal of Orthopsychiatry*, 29: 45–59, 1959.

✎§ 14 §✎

The Children's Center in
Syracuse, New York

BETTYE M. CALDWELL and
JULIUS B. RICHMOND

The task of chronicling the development of the Children's Center
is not unlike that of the hero of 1984 whose assignment was to rewrite history daily. In the present instance, a constant rewrite is
necessary, not to bring past action into line with current policy, but
rather to describe the rapid evolution of both policy and procedure
in a project whose scope was only partially realized by its founders.
In the two years since the launching of the program,* many important
changes have been made. For example, the program was originally
intended for children from six months to three years of age. It now
extends to five-year-olds. The original goal was to run a small pilot
project for twenty-five children; there are now seventy-eight enrolled

* The authors' work is supported by Grant No. D-156, Children's Bureau,
Division of Social and Rehabilitation Services, Department of Health, Education,
and Welfare, and Grant No. MH-07649, National Institute of Mental Health,
United States Public Health Service.

(with additional children being processed for intake weekly up to a maximum of eighty-five within present staff and space limitations). While not limited to the disadvantaged at the outset, it was anticipated that most of the children would come from low-income families in which the mother was working. Now, however, a wide range of economic and social backgrounds are represented, and the mother need not be employed. The program was originally housed in an antiquated and dilapidated converted duplex; it has since been moved into the educational building of a local church where all rooms are spacious, clean, and bright. Originally, all participating children remained for the full day; now half-day attendance is permitted and encouraged.

To some extent there has even been a change in the authors' conceptualization of the task of any day-care center.* Obviously the unique feature of this project was its concentration on the child under three in group care. To quote from a section of the original proposal submitted to the Children's Bureau:

> The basic hypothesis to be tested by this demonstration unit is that an appropriate environment can be created which can offset any developmental detriment associated with maternal separation and possibly add a degree of environmental enrichment frequently not available in families of limited social, economic, and cultural resources.

Key terms in that statement were "offset detriment" and "possibly add environmental enrichment"—a somewhat negative and decidedly conservative statement of goals. After two years experience, evaluation of our data leads us less to concern about avoiding detriment and more to an unabashed awareness of the potential offered by the program. It is a pleasure to rewrite our brief history to bring it in line with this new orientation.

In spite of the changes in format and conceptualization, there has been no change in the intent to develop a *research* and *demonstration* day-care center for very young children. Every attempt has

---

* In referring to their program, the authors reflect a certain semantic confusion regarding its appropriate designation. Originally it was called a day-care center, which it is. It is also a nursery school, especially since a half-day group was added. The verbal children refer to the center as their "school"; the parents tell their children that they are going to school, and the teachers like to think of themselves as teaching in a nursery school. Therefore, it is generally called a nursery school, although occasionally referred to as a day-care center. Whatever the terminology, the authors are talking about the same program, which is formally titled the Children's Center and is technically an enrichment program.

been made to see that neither role is slighted. Nor has there been any change incompatible with the original goal of the project and with the hypothesis which led to its inception:

> The program is based on the proposition that, while environmental supplements for deprived children may be beneficial at any age, sensitivity to enrichment declines with age. Thus the program is geared to the very young and is designed to provide whatever environmental supplements are needed to decrease the subsequent visibility of underprivileged children—to forestall the verbal and motivational deficit which can be observed on the first day of formal schooling and which all too frequently remains like a symbolic scarlet letter about their necks until the frequently premature termination of their school careers (Caldwell and Richmond, 1964, pp. 481–482).

As the Children's Center is still very young, the authors feel somewhat reluctant to offer a guideline for other groups wishing to develop programs. However, since this book concentrates on the very young child, this chapter will describe aspects of the program for the child under three for the reader to use in whatever way might be of value. Some early evaluations of our data after the first year of operation will also be presented.

Program Statistics

LOCATION AND PHYSICAL PLANT

Since September of 1966 the center has had a somewhat schizophrenic physical identity. The administrative offices, medical examining room, and major research labs are still housed in the original building, a ramshackle collection of rooms, barely habitable. The building did meet fire and health department codes with a minimum of remodeling, however, and its availability made it possible for the study to begin when more comfortable space was, as is generally the case, simply nonexistent.*

The children are now housed in the educational building of the University Methodist Church, approximately five blocks away. In addition to eight classrooms and two offices, the church also permits

---

* After the selection of a possible site, anyone wishing to begin a similar program must consult officials of the local fire and health departments regarding site suitability. To qualify for a license, a day-care facility must meet state standards. In some states, the department of education will have additional requirements for staffing and program.

use of a modern kitchen and dining area and a large gymnasium where the children can engage in vigorous indoor play in bad weather.

Although the aesthetic contrast between the new quarters and the old is great, the arrangement has certain limitations. Each Friday afernoon the educational program is largely shelved while all teaching personnel ready the classrooms for church use on Sunday. Some of the rooms do not require this, but others need virtually a complete changeover of equipment. In the infant group, for example, all cribs, playpens, and feeding chairs have to be carried out and those belonging to the church restored to their regular places. The simple fact that the staff is willing to perform these extra labors attests to the general morale and to their conviction about the importance of their work. Outdoor play space is limited, but again the community has helped. Adjacent to the church is the National Guard Armory, which owns a wide cement driveway and parking area between the two buildings. Arrangements were made to fence off this driveway to make an outdoor area for tricycle riding. There is still little space for other outdoor activities, and from time to time small groups of children are carried up to the yard of the administration building to play or to a small city playground three blocks away.

THE SAMPLE

Table 1 presents a summary of certain characteristics of the children enrolled as of November 1, 1966. This current sample represents a significant expansion from the original twenty-five children under three years of age. In view of the authors' basic hypothesis that the optimal time for beginning an enrichment program was prior to age three, one might legitimately inquire why the age limit was raised. The answer would come under the category of "natural history" in the area of social welfare. Within a year, there were several "graduates" of the program. Although the community had day-care facilities for children over three, all had long waiting lists. No matter how valuable the enrichment of the year might have been for our "graduates," development is not static; the children could not be expected to sustain any gains they might have made had they returned to their own homes or to a probably less than optimal neighborhood baby sitter. The decision to keep them in the center is an example of the way in which service and research function symbiotically; in this project they have always complemented one another to the mutual advantage of both. Of course, such an expansion could not be

Table 1. *Description of sample of families and children in the Children's Center observation and enrichment samples (Data as of November, 1966)*

	Sex		Ethnicity		Age in Years					Socioeconomic Class			
	Boys	Girls	White	Negro	Under 1	1–2	2–3	3–4	4–5	Lower[a]	Middle[b]	Upper[c]	
Longitudinal Study Group	24	37	42	19	17	39	5			14	43	4	61 children
			38	18						13	39	4	56 families
Enrichment Group	37	41	46	32	11	14	17	17	19	17	27	34	78 children
			39	20						11	22	26	59 families
Waiting List for Enrichment Group	21	21	21	21	3	4	7	17	11	4	22	16	42 children
			20	16						3	17	16	36 families
Total	81	92	104	69	28	53	29	34	29	30	88	55	173 children[d]
			97	54						27	78	46	151 families[e]

[a] Consistently lower class in six occupation-education groupings; essentially both parents unskilled, neither a high school graduate.

[b] The "middle" class here was a group rated as lower class on some scales and middle class on others; mainly semiskilled and skilled workers.

[c] Consistently middle class on the ratings. Father is a white-collar worker (or mother is white-collar worker in mother-only families) and both parents are high school graduates.

[d] Includes eight children who are in both the longitudinal and enrichment groups.

[e] Includes seven families who are in both the longitudinal and enrichment groups and two families in both the longitudinal group and waiting list.

accomplished without additional funds and space. Both require considerable time to attain, and actually a full year elapsed before expansion into three- and four-year-old groups became a reality.

At this time too a half-day group was added. Originally, the authors wished to offer part-time care to accommodate mothers who did not work full time. The few attempts made along these lines did not work out too well, however, and the practice was discontinued temporarily. The part-time employment of the mothers usually involved two full days and one half-day spread out erratically through the week. Perhaps by chance, the children involved in such arrangements were among the youngest in the sample, and it was the judgment of most personnel that these part-time babies did not adjust as well as the others. It was felt that perhaps the infants lacked the internal cognitive resources with which to organize temporal events so that the experience of being at home some days and at the center on others led to feelings of uncertainty. Therefore, perhaps erroneously and perhaps prematurely with too small a sample, the practice was discontinued. With the recent expansion, all the children dropped from the program for any reason were given top priority. One of the part-time babies came back as a two-year-old. She is still a somewhat irritable child who cries more than other children in her present group. Thus, our judgment about the ill effects of an erratic part-time program, while logical enough, may have been more influenced by temperamental characteristics of one child than should have been the case. Since the fall of 1966, part-time attendance is not only permitted, but also encouraged; but it must occur on the same part (usually half) of every day. Thus, if a child attends five half-days per week, he comes either mornings or afternoons, not a morning one day and an afternoon the next.

It is the conviction of the authors that a part-time program is extremely important. For one reason, the personal and societal values of part-time work for women are such that this pattern deserves encouragement, necessitating part-time day care. But there are other reasons for our interest in part-time care. Although the dangers of maternal separation were probably overstressed for a decade or so and although the consensus of scientific opinion at present is that major difficulty can be avoided if certain emotional safeguards are provided, no one—certainly not the present authors—wishes to disrupt the child's primary family relationships. Yet at the same time, there are families whose inadequacies deny a child the opportunity to develop his full potential. If having certain experiences during the first few years of life is indeed crucial for such optimization, then it may be necessary to plan for environmental supplements beginning within the first few weeks or months of life. If this is ever done on a large scale, and we believe that it will, it is vital to have information about the precise quantity of enrichment needed to prime the child's cognitive development without in any way disrupting his primary family relationships. The simple fact that infants and young children sleep for a large part of the day lends credibility to the assumption that full-day enrichment is not necessary. And, certainly, costs are reduced. Twice as many part-time children can receive the benefits of such a program.

Although it was our intent to enroll fully half the children on a half-time schedule, many families have pressing need for full-day care. Currently, approximately two-thirds of the children attend all day. In fact, among the older children at least, there appears to be a degree of status associated with all-day attendance, possibly because the all-day children have lunch at the center. However, mothers sometimes make subtle or direct requests to have their children remain all day, pleading that "He so wants to take his nap with the other children," or "Could he just eat lunch with the other children some day when another child is absent?"

Another change associated with the current expansion is the deliberate inclusion of middle-class children. Actually there have always been a fair number of middle-class families (as determined by education and *potential* income) involved in the program. But at the outset, almost all had some type of family pathology, severe marital discord, divorce or separation, spouse in mental hospital, alcoholism, etc. They were all accepted on a *pro tem* basis, with the explanation that the program had been established primarily to serve disadvantaged families but that their child could participate in the program for six months, by which time it was assumed that community agencies would have discovered and accepted the center and would refer appropriate families. This did indeed occur, but at the time the middle-class children were taken out of the program, several parents denied receiving any such warning. One mother, protesting the unfairness of such a policy, asserted dramatically that she would sell all her books in order to keep her child in the program!

The policy was in effect unfair, but still another factor prompted the move to include middle-class children. In the previous decade, major progress had been made in racial and economic integration of the local schools. Quite apart from moral and ethical considerations, it is generally accepted that in integrated schools the horizontal diffusion effects of language styles, motivation, work habits, and attitudes toward education make substantial contributions to the educability of the underprivileged child. Thus, it did not seem wise to deny the children in our program the opportunity of experiencing such pacer contacts during their early years any more than it would later. While the center had always been racially balanced, when funds and space became available for an expansion, by policy middle-class children were admitted.

One final point should be made in reference to the sample as described in Table 1. It will be noted that acquisition of control cases has tended to lag behind the intake of children into the enrichment program. To those familiar with the problems inherent in doing such research this lag will come as no surprise. At present, a control group for the two older groups has not been assembled because all research effort has been directed to an initial evaluation of the children recently admitted. A control group for the older children will soon be available. In comparable research, a time-lag control group, while less than optimal, is nevertheless permissible and has been used by a number of investigators (Goldstein, 1965; Gray, 1965). Unfortunately such an arrangement has been necessary from the beginning in the project for fairly complex reasons which will be described in detail in other publications.

STAFF

As such programs are so new on the American scene, standard staffing patterns are not established. The Children's Center staff is described not as a model but merely as one that has worked for us. The major requirement of any staff member is that he or she be interested in the welfare of young children and families and have some knowledge about child development. Many academic and professional sequences offer training in human development, and therefore representatives of many fields have contributions to make. In the present study, the two principal investigators represent the areas of developmental psychology and pediatrics; research and service personnel are trained in child development, education, social work, experimental and developmental psychology, pediatrics, nursing, or sociology.

We are frequently asked about the total number of persons needed in a program of this size, a question which is always surprisingly difficult to answer. Part-time work is encouraged, and thus at one time there may be more people on the premises than at another time. At the present, there are forty-four people on the staff, representing thirty-two full-time equivalents. They fill the following assignments: one director, two educational supervisors, one research coordinator, two medical staff, (one pediatrican and one nurse), one and one-half social workers, four and one-half research staff, fourteen caretaking positions, two secretaries, and four supportive personnel (kitchen, maintenance, chauffeuring). All are paid except three Neighborhood Youth Corps Aides in training.

Lest the reader hasten to the conclusion that there is one adult for approximately every three children in the program, reference is made to the data presented in Table I. A large number of children and families are participating in the basic longitudinal study but not in the enrichment program, and a substantial proportion of staff time goes to them. Those in the longitudinal study only receive well child care from the center's medical staff; casework as needed is offered by the social workers; and the children and families are frequently assessed by one of the learning procedures used in the study. From the standpoint of the number of persons necessary for caretaking alone, our experience would suggest that for a comfortable program a 1 to 4 ratio of staff to children must prevail during all waking hours for the children under three, a ratio of 1 to 5 or 1 to 6 for the three-year-olds, and 1 to 6 or 1 to 7 for the four-year-olds. Obviously the number of adults needed will vary with the situation and with the type of activity carried out at any particular time.

Although all these people are needed to make the program live, there is no question but that the teachers and caretakers occupy a special role. The program cannot possibly work unless each one fully understands the purposes and the strategy behind each activity and unless each is in sympathy with and dedicated to its operating principles. Unfortunately, training alone does not produce persons with these qualifications. Furthermore, there is probably no academic training that will simultaneously give students the knowledge they need about human development and specific educational techniques, the zeal for participation in social action programs, and will prepare them for the amount of time they will spend changing diapers, pulling boots off and pushing them on, comforting and rocking, carrying and lifting. Fortunately, however, many persons who have the necessary qualifications are available. When discovered, they can be given whatever on-the-job training is necessary. And, to be sure, a constant training program for all our staff—including the director—is in process. One of the complications of an all-day program, however, is that it is extremely difficult to find time for the staff to have formal meetings. As the staff is composed largely of women, most of whom have family responsibilities after work, evening meetings are difficult. The use of volunteers to relieve regular staff for meetings has been considered. The only logical point for such relief is during the nap period; yet, as children drift off to sleep, they want their "special" people, perhaps more than at any other time. Thus, the teachers are often involved in patting or rocking the last child to sleep just as the first one begins to awaken.

The physical demands of such a job are also not inconsiderable. Many jokes have been written about how impossible it is for an adult to duplicate all the movements of a two-year-old in a given day. Imagine then, the difficulty of keeping up with seventeen to twenty of them! It is partly because of the fatigue factor involved that part-time teaching assignments are favored. In addition, the center tries to make attractive positions available to women who otherwise would not be able to make a contribution to their fields. Initially it was felt that, at least in the younger groups, a single person must be available to the children throughout the day, even though other part-time personnel might come and go. Experience has shown that this is not necessary, however; the children get quite used to the "changing of the guard" and accept it willingly.

Since the summer of 1966, assistant teachers or teacher's aides have been included in each group. The assistants are given an intensive one-week training program prior to assignment, with on-going supervision provided thereafter. A training program for teaching assistants who will become available for positions in the community at large, not just in this program, is being developed.

FINANCIAL SUPPORT

Support for this program comes primarily from the U.S. Children's Bureau, Welfare Administration, Department of Health, Education, and Welfare. The longitudinal learning study has been supported by the National Institute of Mental Health, U.S. Public Health Service, Department of Health, Education, and Welfare. The approximate annual budget is $250,000, of which 90 per cent is for personnel. Obviously, to operate a program such as this, the main thing one needs is people.

Interested people are apt to be aghast at the budget and ask

"Couldn't you operate for a lot less money if it were not a research project?" This is actually a difficult question, but probably the best answer is: Not a great deal less. For example, until recently the director's salary came entirely from other research and academic funds; in a service program such an arrangement would not be likely. Furthermore, such research staff persons as the public health nurse spend hours in what would be considered service functions. One research person functions regularly as a substitute teacher, and all research staff interact a great deal with the children, often lending a helping hand when they happen to see that it is needed. One male research staff member devotes three hours a week to the three-year-old group, which seems to have an abundance of boys who need more contact with males. Also, because of the research and training orientation of the center, students are assigned to the project from the College of Home Economics, and placements are made for students in job-training programs. Thus, the research half of the research-and-demonstration assignment more than carries its weight in making a financial, albeit a somewhat invisible, contribution to the program.

Cost accounting for such a program is difficult to make and may not be applicable to other regions even if made accurately. For example, since 90 per cent of the operating budget goes for salaries, a key determinant in the cost of a program will be the salary schedule within any particular region. An estimate of the per capita cost of our program can be offered, however. If one subtracts $40,000 as the estimated cost of the research being conducted and assumes that, by streamlining certain supervisory and training functions, ninety children could be cared for (fifty full-day, forty half-day, representing seventy full-time equivalents), and further assumes that the ordinary child-care year is 260 days (five days per week for fifty-two weeks), one derives an estimated cost per capita per day of $11.54. If such programs can demonstrate their capacity to foster development and help prepare children for more adequate citizenship, the cost will appear to be trivial indeed.

Programs of the Center

Since we occasionally have referred somewhat grandiosely to the Center as a microcosmic health, education, and welfare unit, perhaps the best way of organizing a description of the on-going program would be in terms of these three components.

THE HEALTH PROGRAM

The health program of the center is carried out by a staff pediatrician who is available approximately half-time, by three second-year pediatric residents who see children regularly on a weekly basis throughout the year, and by four staff nurses. Two of the nurses function primarily as nurse-teachers; one is a public health nurse involved mainly in home visits, and one is regularly assigned to assist in the various well child clinics and in the daily health supervision of the children in the nursery school. In addition, many faculty members from the department of pediatrics attend conferences and help in the management of specific problems.

Although there are certain standard medical procedures carried out with all children and all staff, the routines differ for the four population subgroups. These are children who (1) participate in the longitudinal study; (2) transfer into the nursery school from the longitudinal study; (3) enroll in the nursery school with no previous participation in the longitudinal study and who have no private family physician; or (4) enroll in the nursery school with no previous longitudinal study participation and have a private family physician. Each of these will be described in turn.

Health program of the longitudinal study. It will be recalled that these children are participating in a study of infant learning as it relates to patterns of family care and that major controls for the enrichment program come from this group. Names are obtained from the birth registry maintained by the Syracuse Health Department. A letter and brochure are sent to parents who reside within the census tracts identified as low socioeconomic areas. One of the lures for participation in the study is the availability of free well child care. While free care has been available through many other resources in the community for many years, certain "extra" features are offered in the Children's Center program. For example, the parents are seen by the same pediatrician at each visit and can talk at much greater length than is usually otherwise possible; a staff social worker is available immediately if needed; free transportation is provided; a very friendly and informal atmosphere prevails. No more newborns are being added to the project via this pattern, but children already taken are still receiving care. Clinics are held six times per week, with usually only one or two children seen at any clinic period.

The medical routine for this group of children follows the pattern established in the main Pediatric Out-patient Clinic of the Upstate

Medical Center. Children are seen monthly for the first six months, bimonthly for the next six months, quarterly during the second year, and semiannually during the third year. No children in this group have as yet reached the age of three. This schedule is regarded locally as ideal for well child care, but in spite of all the physical and interpersonal supports offered to the families, attendance is often erratic. At each visit, the child is assessed on one of the learning procedures used in the longitudinal study or the mother may be interviewed regarding some aspect of the child's rearing. This arrangement gives the participating pediatric house officers an opportunity to observe developmental testing and some of the conditioning and learning procedures carried out with the children by the research staff. At the termination of each clinic, a short briefing session is held by all staff who participated to give different members of the unit an opportunity to compare notes, ask questions, and plan for future contacts with that family. No sick child care is provided unless, as is somehow often the case, the child is ill on the day of his well baby visit. However, the center social worker and staff pediatrician help acquaint the families with community health resources. These children are given top priority for all openings in the nursery school, but not all the families have needed or wanted day care. Since referrals are accepted from other community agencies and directly from parents, we have different amounts of information about pre-enrichment experience and early health and medical care.

The nursery school health program. The three remaining groups described above are included in the nursery school, but procedures vary somewhat according to the circumstances preceding enrollment. For those children who have participated in the longitudinal study, essentially no intake medical work-up is done; for all others, including those with private physicians, an initial history and physical examination is completed by the center staff pediatrician. Apart from daily screening and minor first aid treatment, no further routine medical procedures are done with the private group. However, the staff pediatrician usually attempts to establish rapport with the family physician, and requests for diagnostic work or treatment are made either through the parents or through direct consultation with the private physician.

Most of the children enrolled in the school are from homes where health standards and medical attention have been suboptimal. It is shocking and alarming to note how many families apply whose children have not had *any* consistent well child care or any standard immunizations. Therefore, the staff physician, nurses, social worker, and teachers make an earnest effort to provide and create opportunities for health education to occur. Every attempt is made to be flexible and accommodating, while at the same time not permitting the parents to abrogate their responsibilities.

As long as only twenty-five children were enrolled, brief rounds were made by the pediatrician daily. With eighty children, however, this is impossible. Therefore, an important function of the staff pediatrician is to help alert the teaching staff to symptoms that need medical attention. The head teacher now checks her children every morning. If there is anything unusual about a child's behavior or appearance, the principal of the nursery school arranges to have the child seen by one of the staff nurses. If needed, the staff physician sees the child as soon as possible. If the child appears seriously ill, the parent is asked to take him home. If the parent is not available or leaves at that time, the child is kept in a somewhat isolated space at the school until he can be sent home. Neither of our buildings has provided an isolation room, and the staff has had to work out all sorts of creative improvisations. It is surprising how often parents send really sick children to school—and this is true of the better-educated as well as the less-educated parents. Perhaps a mother who has to be at work constructs a perceptual defense against the signs of illness in her child. Aspirin is the sole medication given in the center (only if a child has been examined and the necessary tests made or if a child's private physician cannot see him for several hours) except for medications being administered as part of a pre-scribed therapeutic regimen. In the latter instance, the mother is expected to communicate with the nurse or teacher and to bring or send in the child's medicine. A record is kept of all medication given the children on the premises.

The management of accidents and injuries varies with the apparent severity. The teacher may handle minor ones (bumps, scratches, nosebleeds), washing the area with soap and water and possibly applying a bandaid for its psychological therapeutic effect. All such injuries are treated casually, however, in order to avoid giving the child too much secondary reward in the situation. For more serious mishaps (bumps on the head, falling and biting the lip, etc.) the same hierarchical screening procedure described above for illnesses—namely, teacher, principal, nurse, physician—is put into action. The many levels of communication may sound cumbersome but are essential if the necessary records are to be maintained. If all offices were housed in the same building, at least one step in the process could be eliminated.

Upon enrolling their children in the school, the parents sign a proxy statement authorizing the medical and administrative staff of the center to act in their behalf in the event of an emergency. Even so, every attempt is made to find one or both parents in the event of a serious injury, which fortunately has not occurred very often. The children are immediately transported, accompanied by a favorite teacher, a staff nurse, or pediatrician to the emergency room of State University Hospital, where any necessary diagnostic or treatment procedures are administered.

In addition to the prophylactic and therapeutic aspects of the medical program, the medical staff carries out many educational and consultative activities. For example, a yearly course in first aid is offered to all teaching and research staff. Supervision of employee health is provided, although actual diagnostic and/or therapeutic work is done elsewhere. Valuable suggestions for maintaining high safety standards are made. Dr. George A. Lamb, pediatrician on the Upstate Medical Center faculty, is studying the spread of viruses and infections in the children. His research has important implications for all group care for young children. In short, maintenance of a vital, dynamic medical program is essential to the success and continued growth of our work.

THE EDUCATIONAL PROGRAM

The most unique, ambitious, and controversial aspect of the total project has been an attempt to develop a logical and systematic educational program for children as young as six months. This effort stemmed from the basic hypothesis that the first three years of life represent a critical period for the priming of cognitive development and that the experiences of this period exert permanent influence upon the developing child. However, not all experiences can be assumed to be of equal value to the developing organism. Thus, in order to accomplish a fair test of the primary hypothesis, some sort of theoretical model of the way experience influences the developing organism is essential. In many respects, the basic hypothesis was in jeopardy unless a successful strategy could be devised for arranging the environment in such a way that growth-inducing events would indeed occur and that, furthermore, the child would partake of these events.

Guidelines for organizing an educational program for the child under three years were virtually nonexistent. During the years between 1930 and 1950, nursery schools for two-year-olds had been operated at child-development centers at Vassar, in California, and elsewhere. Most of these dropped such young children some time during the 1940s and 1950s. Furthermore, as the nursery school movement spread within this country and lost its early link with the child-development research centers, the field became less innovative and more conservative. Within the simultaneously developing day-care field, group programs for children under three were strongly discouraged and in some areas today they are illegal (Peters, 1964).

Such descriptive material as can be found about these early programs for two-year-olds tends to deal primarily with the social and emotional needs of the child, with a possible exception being the book by Isaacs (1930). In fact, it is not unfair to imply that during the late 1950s and early 1960s a sure path to ostracism in the field of early childhood education was to emphasize attendance at nursery school as an influence on intellectual development. Debunking the Iowa studies, which demonstrated intellectual gains associated with nursery school attendance, became a popular sport for writers of texts in the field (see the commentary by Watson, 1959, pp. 502–505), and the implication that such an experience could have lasting cognitive effects was subject to ridicule.

A dramatic reversal began with the publication of Hunt's monumental volume (1961), with the infectious spread of Bruner's dictum that any subject presented in an intellectually honest way could be taught to a child of any age (1960, p. 97), with the increased dissemination of the important theoretical and experimental work of Piaget (1952), and with the realization that something had to be done to improve the educability of the disadvantaged child (Riessman, 1962, p. 140). But while these (and many other) important formulations with implications for action were being introduced into the literature, all tended to stop short of planning the action, of designing specific experiences which would construct the bridge from abstraction to actual everyday events. The one notable exception is the Montessori method (1964), but in its generally disseminated form it is not intended for children under two. Possibly, the reincarnation of the Montessori movement in America is related to the same series of forces that gave rise to the re-examination of early child care described in this volume.

On the basis of such knowledge as exists about infant development and with the help of the above-described theories on the way experience is processed by the developing organism, a few general guidelines for translating theory into action were formulated. These guides make certain assumptions about factors that can be brought under the control of the social and experimental environment to foster optimal development. These assumptions represent different levels of generality and referent, but all have immediate implications for the planning of specific educational experiences. Before presenting them it should be stated that, from the standpoint of those who must create the daily environment, they still leave too much unsaid. However, they have been extremely useful in helping to provide a framework for the daily experimental program, and they are presented here in annotated form.

1. *The development of a young child is fostered by a relatively high frequency of adult contact involving a relatively small number of adults.* This assumption may appear to contraindicate any sort of group care program; however, even within a group situation it can be implemented. Thus, particularly for the youngest group of children, an attempt is made to assign most of the care of a child to the same staff member throughout the day and on consecutive days through the week. With rare exceptions, students (who might be on the premises only four to six hours per week) are not assigned to the youngest groups of children, and most of the major caretaking personnel work full-day rather than half-day shifts. For at least fifteen to thirty minutes per day, each infant is to be given the concentrated individual attention of one of the staff members, being taken out of the "baby fold" if possible. He may be held and rocked, read to, taken on a special errand in another part of the building, taken for a walk, play one of the carefully structured "learning games," and so forth. The teacher tries to make this a pleasant experience and is encouraged to respond to signs of waning interest or fatigue in the child. Each child is to be cared for upon awakening and to be either fed or supervised during mealtime by the same person daily.

In practice, the consistency implied by the above policies has never been achieved. Too many exigencies arise which apparently make it impossible for the daily one-to-one play session to occur or for the same person to be the primary caretaker throughout the day and from one day to the next. The authors, who admittedly do not have the responsibility of carrying it out, have never been convinced that the inability to bring this off is as much a function of time and schedule difficulty as it is lack of conviction by the staff that it is important for the child. Sometimes it appears that an almost alarming group-think mystique pervades the staff, a situation which is probably adaptive but nevertheless a little threatening to whatever degree of individualism one manages to retain. While some teachers must of necessity "float" from group to group as needed, most have specific assignments, except for the early morning or late afternoon periods when the children are regrouped to accommodate individual arrival and departure times.

2. *The development of a young child is fostered by the deliberate provision of a learning environment that is both stimulating and responsive.* The learning environment is conceptualized as encompassing the *interpersonal,* the *experiential,* and the *physical-spatial* aspects of the child's world. A much debated issue in the field of education, particularly the early childhood field, is the extent to which the learning environment should be merely a passive milieu or should attempt actively to bring about certain developmental changes. By and large, the conviction in the field of early childhood education has been on the milieu side of the debate. In our program, every attempt is made to strike a balance between the two. There is a great deal of clear and deliberate stimulation for learning; but at the same time, many opportunities are provided for the child to select experiences which he in some way needs or favors at any given moment. In practice this means that throughout the day there are alternating opportunities for child- and teacher-initiated choices of activity and materials. The teacher-initiated activities may be either group- or individual-oriented; but, whichever they are, they are carefully planned to provide experiences regarded as valuable for children of particular developmental levels. The range of teacher-initiated activities is very great: reading books, playing lotto games, carrying an infant around and labeling different objects, art activities, playing learning games which involve sensory discriminations (big-little, red-white, long-short, rough-smooth, etc.), singing, marching, playing group games (such as "London Bridge"), playing group word and attention games (such as "Simon Says"), etc. These are examples, a complete list would involve the complete teaching repertoire of nursery school teachers. The teaching staff has shown considerable creativity in adapting classical nursery school techniques and materials for children under three. One of the teachers wanted to see if the infants would enjoy finger painting but feared that there would be entirely too much tasting, even though the paints are nontoxic, and too much paint on the infants and their clothes. Her solution

was to tint beaten egg whites with a few drops of food coloring and to let the children spread this new art medium on the feeding table trays. Needless to say, the children loved both spreading and eating the paint!

On the responsive side, the teachers are trained to use their attention as a powerful social reinforcer. With the infants, the caretakers emit a pleasing vocal and affective response every time the infant vocalizes—insofar as this is practical. Obviously as the child gets older, the reinforcement ratio drops to a lower, although probably not entirely predictable, rate. Whenever the child carries out any form of approved behavior, the adult will try to respond with an approving glance, a smile, a nod, a pat, and especially with some remark. But social reinforcement also consists in giving bodily support (holding, snuggling, rocking, carrying) and in psychological availability. The child's need for such adult response does not appear to diminish significantly during the first three years or so.

3. *The development of a young child is fostered by an optimal level of need gratification.* Although one must conjecture what the optimal level of gratification is for any child, it is probably safe to assume that it is defined by sufficiently prompt attention to needs so that the young organism is not overwhelmed, but not such prompt or complete attention that budding attempts at self-gratification are extinguished. Teacher vigilance is probably the most critical element in identification of this level. Pacing is also important so that the child has enough time to permit his attention to any one activity to play itself out, but not so much that he becomes bored or disorganized. As a sensitive teacher comes to know a child, she becomes alert to signs of mounting fatigue and imminent crises and can learn to guide him through such situations and avert major episodes of disruptive behavior. Teacher training and supervisory programs devote a great deal of time and effort to the heightening of such perceptiveness.

4. *The development of a young child is fostered by a positive emotional climate in which the child learns to trust others and himself.* While we do not wish to make it sound like a fetish, a standard piece of equipment in each classroom is an adult rocker. This is perhaps symbolic of the value attributed to positive, nurturant, and supportive contact between the adults and the children. As new teachers come into the program they are reminded of their crucial role in shaping the child's earliest concept of what "school" will be like; the child must develop a trust in his teacher and his school as

but the first in a long line of successors to follow. The teacher's behavior and the total school atmosphere will be crucial in determining whether the child will come to trust the positions represented and will decidedly influence what he learns during his encounters with the school program.

5. *The development of a young child is fostered by an environment containing a minimum of unnecessary restrictions on his early exploratory attempts but a supply of natural restrictions that provide valuable feedback data helpful in refining movements and actions.* In order to create a safe environment for young children, many restrictions on freedom of movement are necessary. However, it is probably fair to claim that most environments go somewhat beyond the call of safety in maintaining such restrictions. Although it would be difficult to secure data to substantiate this contention, there is probably a class-biased and age-related pattern of restriction. That is, infants from low-income families probably are permitted more freedom of movement simply because cribs, chairs, and playpens cost a good deal of money. However, once a child begins to walk, the more people there are in the immediate environment and the more the house is crowded with objects (as tends to be the case when there are many people in a small amount of space), the more likely is interference with the child's freedom of movement. In the Children's Center environment, we are fortunate in having enough staff so that playpens are seldom needed, and the children are placed on the floor during most of their waking moments. All toys on low shelves are to be used by the child whenever he wishes; the few "untouchables" are either on high shelves or in storage cabinets outside the classroom. Chairs, stools, or big blocks are kept in obvious places to help the child realize how they can be used in problem solving and to provide kinesthetic feedback on his motor efforts.

6. *The development of a young child is fostered by the provision of rich and varied but interpretable cultural experiences.* The daily program offers a rich fare for cultural intake. People who function in various community roles visit the school to demonstrate in some way how they play their roles. During the year many field trips are made to worthwhile places in the community, particularly to places the disadvantaged children would not be likely to visit otherwise. Advance preparation for the visit is always made and discussion about the experience continues afterward, reinforced by books and phonograph records. Pictures of the event are shown and discussed or displayed later. On such visits, the child is accompanied by one or more

of the stable persons with whom he has an emotional relationship; it is assumed that, by their subtle valuation, the experience will be received by the child as one of value.

7. *The development of a young child is fostered by a physical environment that separates figure from ground and contains modulated amounts and varieties of sensory experience.* As is well known, inadequate sensory input during the early years is strongly implicated as one of the factors involved in the early learning deficit so often shown by the child who grows up in an environment of poverty. Thus, in our environmental planning we attempt to provide variety in intensities of sensory input, color, shape, texture, sound patterns, etc. We also try to make the surroundings aesthetically pleasant. Every now and then, the teachers move all the furniture in the room on the assumption that the new position will help the children to become aware of objects that had been in their perceptual field but essentially "taken for granted." Favorite play materials are removed from the rooms often enough to help keep the child's interest in them at a high level. Every mother of a toddler is familiar with the phenomenon of watching him work vigorously to throw two dozen or more toys from a toybox and then, when the array of toys is scattered all over the floor, he looks up dismayed as though to say, "I haven't a thing to play with." Also, as part of the regulation of sensory input through manipulation of the physical-spatial environment, the staff (with the help of the children) makes every effort to restore the room to order after vigorous activity that has involved "homogenizing" the equipment routinely kept in the room. It is felt that the maintenance of order is an essential aspect of the sensory environment and is crucial to help the child distinguish figure from background, particularly for the child whose home environment may be somewhat crowded or even chaotic.

8. *The development of a young child is fostered by access to certain kinds of play materials.* There are many excellent play materials available today. The Center program began at a time when scientists, educators, and manufacturers were combining forces to design play materials that would foster the development of eye-hand coordination, concept learning, language learning, motor skills, etc. Within the past five years, many delightful books for young children have been published, although there is still a shortage for children in the one to three age range. In addition to obtaining an impressive array of commercial play materials, we have attempted to develop some which do not cost a great deal of money but which will help

accomplish specific educational objectives. By this means we hope that parents with limited incomes will realize that valuable play materials are not necessarily expensive. Eye-hand coordination can be developed just as effectively with empty spools dropped into a small hole cut in the plastic top of a coffee can as with a toy that might sell for $2; size discrimination can be learned as readily with a set of measuring cups as with an expensive nesting toy. In addition, several staff members have written or illustrated books on topics being emphasized in the program. As indicated earlier, the creativity of the staff in devising new approaches to training and in the preparation of new materials has been a source of constant pleasure.

9. *The development of a young child is fostered by the introduction of new experiences that provide an appropriate match for the child's current level of cognitive organization.* Hunt (1964) has repeatedly emphasized this match as crucial for helping a child to move forward in his conceptual development. Learning experiences must not remain at the same level, nor can they afford to be too far ahead of the child's current cognitive organization. They must be enough ahead to motivate him but not so far as to be out of his reach. Making the environment live up to this principle requires great skill on the part of the instructors. It also requires, at the planning level, a recycling of learning experiences through the curriculum, always reintroducing them in such a way as to activate what has already been learned and to stimulate further learning and internal organization. Stated in the language of Piaget's theoretical system, a new experience will be assimilated only if it is initially similar to previous experiences. Accommodation to the differences in the experience can occur only if it is not too different; otherwise it will simply be rejected as an unassimilable encounter with the environment. To make this principle concrete in terms of the educational program, we constantly reintroduce the concept of the self at an ever more complex level. The infants learn to point to their own eyes, nose, hands, etc., and then to do the same things with a large doll or a picture. The next group, all of whom can make these identifications, learns to say these words and develops some awareness of the function of the body parts. The teacher might play a game in which she briefly puts her hand over a child's eyes and says, "If we *close* our *eyes,* we cannot *see.*" Then, upon removing her hands, "When we *open* our *eyes,* we *see.*" At the next level the body parts will be introduced with rudimentary awareness of number—"Simon says touch your eyes; Simon says touch your noses. Oh, that's right, we have only *one* nose but we

have *two* eyes." Such facts will be of little interest to the child who cannot identify eyes and the nose but will intrigue the child who can identify these parts and use his hands to point, but who may not have thought about body parts in different quantities. Probably in her skill at determining the proper "match" and maintaining it in her classroom activities the skilled teacher most readily identifies herself.

The simple schematic model presented as Table 2 has been found

Table 2. *A Schematic Model for Describing Developmental Goals and Types of Environmental Influence*

Area of Influence	Includes	Involves programming
1. Personal-social attributes	A sense of trust Positive self-concept Curiosity about environment Tolerance of delay of gratification Sense of mastery and competence Self-acceptance Acceptance of differences Persistence toward goals Independent behavior Social skills Consideration for others Joy of living Self-expression	The interpersonal environment The total learning atmosphere
2. Motor, perceptual, and cognitive functions	Balance Coordination Agility Intersensory integration Listening and hearing Looking and seeing Classifying Evaluating (counting, ordering) Coordinating and relating Conceptualizing Forming learning sets Remembering Interpreting language Producing language Graphic communication	The interpersonal environment The experiential environment The physical-spatial environment
3. Culturally relevant knowledge	Words Ideas Reservoir of solutions to representative problems	Content of developmental milieu Sequential assimilation and integration of age-appropriate experiences

helpful in directing attention to developmental goals and aspects of the growth-inducing environment which the caretaking staff can program. The developmental goals of such a program are conceptualized in three broad areas, each exemplified by a number of specific developmental attributes to be attained by the child. It is assumed that one can influence the emergence of these attributes by some arrangement of the interpersonal, the experiential (the actual teaching-learning events or exercises), or by the physical-spatial environment. Obviously, all attributes are to some extent influenced by all three aspects; however, by and large it is assumed that the socioemotional attributes are more influenced by features of the interpersonal environment; motor, perceptual, and cognitive attributes by the experiential and the physical-spatial environment; and culturally relevant knowledge perhaps equally by all three.

The planning of the total educational program is accomplished through meetings of the director with the staff. Responsibility for coordinating the educational program across all developmental levels falls to the curriculum coordinator, who meets regularly with the director and the principal to design specific activities to implement the curriculum model. "Quality control" of teaching is maintained by regular classroom observation done by either the director, the principal, or the curriculum coordinator. In addition to a fairly large number of planning conferences, the progress of individual children is discussed at biweekly conferences of the total staff. Originally, each child in the program was discussed at least twice a year; however, with the larger number enrolled this will no longer be possible. Smaller conferences of the persons directly involved are a necessary though less acceptable substitute. These conferences are essentially clinical in nature. Consultants from professional groups, such as pediatrics or clinical psychology, or from community agencies having some contact with the family are regularly invited to attend.

For those who would like to see these environmental guidelines translated into a schedule, representative activities of a typical "day" are presented in Appendix B. No pretense is made that the educational program is completely developed at this stage. The curriculum is constantly evolving as ideas which appear unworkable are discarded and replaced by new ones. At this stage we feel that we have the essentials for spelling out a program in great detail but choose to wait until more supportive data are available before stating anything more comprehensive than this general description.

THE WELFARE PROGRAM

The social work staff consists of one full-time and one three-fourths time worker. The services offered to the families are decidedly individualized. One of the workers does intake, interpreting the multiple functions of the center to any parent making an inquiry or application and providing information about approximate waiting periods, etc. All parents with a child participating in the longitudinal study are seen regularly for the dual purpose of obtaining research data and providing service to the families. This combination of roles has proved most attractive to the workers who have served on the staff. One research task involves a structured interview held periodically with the mother, the aim of which is to determine the strength of the infant's attachment to the mother and to other adults in the home. The social workers participate in the home-visiting program, which again serves the double purpose of securing information about the level of stimulation available to the children within the home and helping the mother in utilization of community resources, home planning, seeking and coordination of medical services, patterns of child care, and the like.

Social services to families with children enrolled in the nursery school are somewhat more varied, partly as a result of the diversity of their economic and educational backgrounds and the varying extent to which they are involved in other social agencies. Many families are referred to the Children's Center for day care only, while the referring agency continues all necessary social work with the family. Almost always, however, there is consultation between the center workers and those of the referring agency. The parents are nevertheless urged to participate in the center's group-oriented parent activities and to meet with either the school principal or the child's teacher for individual conferences. The social workers also participate in the individual child conferences and confer with teachers to facilitate a more coordinated parent-child service.

For the most part, the social-work activities with families are supportive rather than intensive. In several cases where intensive casework is obviously needed, the mother has refused to cooperate. On the whole, this has not occurred with extremely low-income families but with very young parents, usually students who are either divorced or separated, who resist any involvement in an examination of their behavior or child-rearing techniques. Some of the more successful social work has been with the more deprived families, with their child as the major entry. In at least one rather dramatic case, total family changes associated with social work activities centered around an infant enrolled in the Center have been almost like a reversal of the falling domino phenomenon.

Early Results

Two years is obviously too short a time in which to accumulate definitive data on the effectiveness of the enrichment program. A report (Caldwell et al., 1966) of the changes in performance on developmental tests is in press, so the results will be referred to only briefly here. Of twenty-nine children from approximately seven to forty-three months of age at the time of the first examination, all of whom participated in the enrichment program for at least three months (mean participation 7.5 months), only five showed a drop in score from the first to the second examination. The mean gain in developmental quotient was 5.6 points. Although some gain might be attributed to practice effects, it is not a likely explanation. In some instances the second examination occurred as much as thirteen months after the first, and for very young children there would not be any overlap in items introduced at the two sessions. Nor can the changes be attributed to familiarity with the examiners, for the children saw them infrequently and they were not members of the regular caretaking staff. All examinations were done in the center, however, and one could certainly implicate increased familiarity with the premises and with new procedures in general. Opposed to this explanation of the pattern of changes, however, is the often reported tendency of children from low-income homes to show a gradual drop in performance level after approximately eighteen to twenty-four months of age. The fact that the children showed any gain at all (which was significantly different from zero as indicated by a t test) is thus an indication of an effect.

There were wide individual differences in gain scores, ranging from -27 to $+26$ points. Only one of the negative change scores was greater than 10 points, whereas eight of the positive change scores were greater than 10 points. The distribution of change scores tended to be positively correlated with rated extent of deprivation experienced prior to being enrolled in the enrichment program (i.e., the most disadvantaged children tended to show the largest gains), but the coefficient was of insufficient magnitude to be considered statistically reliable. Contrary to advance expectations, there were no apparent differences in change scores as a function of age of child at the time of admission into the program.

For intermediate evaluations, it has not been possible to identify and follow a precisely matched control group at the same time intervals. Subjects from the on-going longitudinal study comprise the major control group, but these are all approximately one year younger than the youngest children enrolled in the original Children's Center group. However, the authors have been following another group of low-income children in a study of patterns of mother-child interaction as related to personal-social development, testing the children every six months (Caldwell and Hersher, 1964; Caldwell et al., 1963). This study draws from the same type of population (persons in attendance at a city-sponsored well baby clinic) as the current center group. Table 3 presents data from the three basic classes of the original center population and on this group of sixteen children who have been followed and observed (often by the same staff) but not enrolled in the enrichment program. The children included in the Children's Center curves have participated in the enrichment program for approximately one year. The children from the comparison group are those (out of twenty-five still active in the study) who had been examined on or near their first, second, and third birthdays. As can be seen in Table 3, the children from the nonintervention low-income sample showed a gradually dropping developmental curve. All three enrichment groups showed gains, although the slopes for the three groups are not identical. In contrast to the major hypothesis of the study, namely that the most advantageous time for beginning an enrichment program is early, it would appear that the three- to four-year-old group showed the most dramatic rate of rise and that the youngest group showed only insignificant gains. This may well be the case, but more time and more cohorts of children exposed to this or similar programs will be necessary before the question can be answered. The scatter in the initial means of the four groups illustrates the sampling error typical for such small groups and strengthens the need for larger and replicated groups.

To be sure, there were decided differences in characteristics of these three enrichment subgroups. For some reason, the two-year-old entering class was an unusually bright group of children, but instead of showing any sort of regression toward the mean, the average quotient in this group climbed slightly more than seven points. The relatively low initial score of the infant-enrichment group in relation to the relatively high one-year-old mean quotient for the control group is interesting and warrants explanation. The center had been in operation about six months when this group of infants was taken into the program, and by that time children in dire need of some kind of environmental support were being referred. One infant was the daughter of a severely mentally retarded woman who had one other retarded child; two of the children were referred by their mothers as being slow or retarded; one had been an under-three-pound premature baby who had (and still has) considerable muscular coordination problems. Whenever one of these children had to compete for an opening with a child who had no outstanding personal or family problems, the former would be given preference in the selection. As long as the center remains small, overweighting of the sample with problem-laden children is likely to continue. Application of statistical tests will be more appropriate when data are available from a larger number of such programs with samples obtained randomly instead

Table 3. Mean Quotients Earned by Three Groups of Children Participating in an Enrichment Program and One Control Group on Consecutive Yearly Evaluations

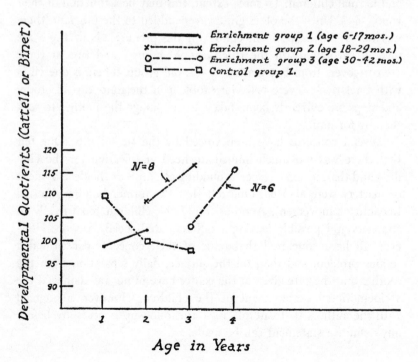

of on the basis of family need. To date, all assessment data related to intellectual progress are reassuring and there are grounds for continued optimism.

SOCIOEMOTIONAL DEVELOPMENT

Because criteria for normal, healthy socioemotional development are not as clearly established in our culture as are those for intellectual development and because most of the existing assessment techniques are not appropriate for children under three years of age, it is difficult to offer anything other than anecdotal evidence about the socioemotional development of the children. Furthermore, the staff may not be able to judge this area as well as the cognitive sphere. Accordingly, we have relied heavily upon consultants to appraise the social and emotional development of the children. Partly because of the novelty of the program and partly out of a need to reassure themselves, many of the nation's leading specialists in child development, child welfare, pediatrics, and child psychiatry have visited the center. In spite of the extreme social pathology in the homes from which many of the children come, the consultants find them to be refreshingly healthy and normal children. To some extent, this may be a function of their young ages. Until the older groups were added to the program, there was not a single "problem child" on the premises. Now there are several, particularly in the three-year-old groups, and two of these are carryovers from last year's two-year-old group. There is one child with a relatively severe behavior problem in the four-year-old group, and steps are currently being taken to encourage the mother to seek therapy for him.

Several concerns have been voiced by the consultants. One felt that there was too much immediate need gratification for the children and that, in some respects, budding attempts at the development of mastery were aborted. One felt that the former building limited freedom of movement. Another found the children too friendly to strangers and possibly lacking a differentiated social reaction. However, all have concurred that none of their concerns constituted a serious problem and that, on the surface, daily separation from the mother and the care given at the center have in no way damaged the socioemotional development of the children. However, all agreed with the authors that careful long-term follow-up is necessary before any definitive statement can be made.

PARENTAL REACTIONS

It is perhaps presumptuous to try to speak for the parents whose children are enrolled in the program; an entirely independent survey carried out by personnel with no affiliation with the center would be desirable. However, insofar as can be perceived from our vantage point, the parents are strongly supportive. Several have become staunch community advocates of the value of such programs and of the necessity for establishing them on a larger scale as part of community action against poverty. Three mothers, following their exposure to the center staff and philosophy, have enrolled in courses for teacher's aides and plan careers in the field. In general, we are heartened by the extent to which the parents have grasped the scope and purpose of the program.

But emotional support and participation are often different matters, and our success in involving parents in the educational program (except when it is a part of intensive casework) is limited. Reasons for this are not hard to find. The working mother of young children does not have a great deal of residual time or energy for home-school activities, most of which must be scheduled in the evening when fatigue is long and attention span is short. Some of the mothers have days off during the week rather than on weekends, and recently we have been attempting to arrange observations in the classroom or conferences with the teacher, the principal, or one of the social workers at these times. However, a day off during the week means work on the weekends, and household chores cannot be put off for too long.

Many of our evening parent interviews are held in the home rather than at the center. But in spite of the dedication of the staff and the identification with the needs and problems of our families, an occasional fragment of middle-class bias can be found. Recently one of the staff remarked to a person who was scheduling an evening home visit into a very poor neigborhood, "Aren't you scared to go there by yourself at night?" The young woman replied, "If they can live there all the time, I guess I can go there once in a while without harm." The solicitous inquirer was properly chastened.

Occasionally because of staff zeal about their work, a bit of pre-emptoriness toward the parents will creep in. For example, a group of teachers recently requested that parents be forbidden to bring their children after 9:30 in the morning. When a child is brought late, he often seems to feel that he has missed something and tries rather frantically to cram everything that he would ordinarily do in the full period into the time remaining. In addition, late arrivals often disrupt on-going activities and draw the teacher's attention away from the children who are busily engaged. After a discussion of the possible reasons why a mother might get her child there late (her failure to appreciate the importance of the program, her own fatigue, an habitually casual attitude toward time, delays caused by getting other children ready for public school, etc.) and our concern about keeping the children in attendance regularly, the teachers withdrew their request.

Some of the things parents do or fail to do can be frustrating to the teaching staff. For example, many parents ignore repeated reminders to send outdoor clothing. Although a few spares are always on hand, it is impossible to have well-fitting outer garments for all the children. If parents fail to provide the necessary clothes, all the children in a given group may be deprived of the opportunity to play outdoors. A few children come so dirty that they must be bathed by one of the teachers before the child can function in his group. As previously stated, some parents will send a seriously ill child into the center or else will fail to come and get one who becomes ill during the day. Although a small area has been set up as a sick bay, it is difficult to care for children who are really ill unless one person can be released from other assignments.

On the whole, however, the parents and teachers cooperate well with one another; the teachers respect the difficulties under which many of the parents have had to rear their children, and the parents respect the extra advantages that the teachers can give their children. In our experience, the low-income parent who is unconcerned with the education of his child is more a myth than a reality. One of the center's aims is to devise ways of translating that concern into effective action.

Summarizing Thoughts

By now, it is apparent that everyone connected with the center has unbridled enthusiasm for the project. Most crises have been manageable and fortunately minor, or at least they can be thus described after all the dust has cleared away. There have been no major health crises. Apart from one round of chicken pox and the chronic URI which is endemic in this part of the country during the winter months, there has been nothing to contraindicate having children in this type of group program. We recognize that without effective immunization for an ever greater number of childhood diseases, the values inherent in such a program might well not be worth the cost.

Staff morale has had its peaks and valleys. Until the summer of 1966, there were no changes in major caretaking personnel. Then, however, two head teachers moved from the city, and many new persons came in along with additional children. The center's move to new quarters brought its share of trauma. Even though the adult-child ratio remained constant, there seemed to be a new atmosphere associated with the new size. The noise level went up; the traffic flow intensified; and for a month or more a feeling of confusion possessed the staff. Like an adolescent who seemed to be growing too fast, we did not always know what to do with our hands and feet. No one was sorry when the new quarters proved not quite large enough for the contemplated 100 children and enrollment was stopped at 80. Now, with more experience in handling the larger number of children, we are ready to think once again of expanding to 100. When one considers the inevitable attrition rate and considers in addition that interim results (i.e., before all participating children reach some meaningful evaluation point such as first grade or third grade) must be evaluated separately for different age groups, even 100 children is a small sample. The authors hope that eventually it will be possible to pool our findings with those obtained in similar centers such as those described in Chapters 11, 12, and 13. Furthermore, it would be highly desirable to have evaluation teams from various communities exchange services from time to time, thus removing experimenter bias in any one program.

In many ways, the most challenging aspect has been the attempt to devise an optimal daily regimen for the children. To paraphrase Mark Twain, everyone has been talking about infancy but no one has been doing much about it. Furthermore, the cry for the launching of enrichment programs for young disadvantaged children has been so urgent that the term "enrichment" has been operationally defined in an all too casual way—"an enrichment program is a program that calls itself an enrichment program." But announcing that one *intends* to enrich and creating an atmosphere and a congeries of experiences which in truth *do* enrich the child are not necessarily the same things. There is still so much to be learned about creating growth-inducing conditions that we look now upon our own initial formulations as simpleminded and naive. Of course, until diverse programs are in operation, the most one can hope to do is demonstrate that *some* enrichment is associated with more of an effect than *no* enrichment. This is the first and most basic step.

We now see our project as an experiment in social action with the most profound implications. Of necessity, social welfare programs are, to a great extent, exercises in shoring up unstable structures. They are expensive and require extensive public tax support. The massive environmental modification produced by a program such as that of the Children's Center is also costly. Furthermore, it has limitations, as it cannot go beyond the environment and whatever powers for shaping development are inherent therein; the undoubtedly powerful genetic influences which also help to shape development cannot be touched. But the power of such programs to perform a truly preventive function, aimed toward anticipation rather than amelioration, deserves careful consideration in the current search for instrumentation of community supports for creative and effective social living.

REFERENCES

Bruner, J. S. *The Process of Education*. Cambridge, Mass.: Harvard University Press, 1960.
Caldwell, B. M., and L. Hersher. Mother-Infant Interaction During the First Year of Life. *Merrill-Palmer Quarterly*, 10: 119–128, 1964.
————, L. Hersher, E. L. Lipton, J. B. Richmond, et al. Mother-Infant Interaction in Monomatric and Polymatric Families. *American Journal of Orthopsychiatry*, 33: 653–664, 1963.
————, and J. B. Richmond. Programmed Day Care for the Very Young Child— A Preliminary Report. *Journal of Marriage and the Family*, 26: 481–488, 1964.
————, et al. An Intervention Program for Disadvantaged Infants and Young Children. Unpublished manuscript, 1966.
Goldstein, L. S. Evaluation of an Enrichment Program for Socially Disadvantaged Children. Unpublished manuscript, 1965.
Gray, S. W., and R. A. Klaus. An Experimental Preschool Program for Culturally Deprived Children. *Child Development*, 36: 887–898, 1965.
Hunt, J. McV. *Intelligence and Experience*. New York: Ronald, 1961.
————. The Psychological Basis for Using Pre-school Enrichment as an Antidote for Cultural Deprivation. *Merrill-Palmer Quarterly*, 10: 209–248, 1964.
Isaacs, S. *The Intellectual Growth in Young Children*. New York: Humanities Press, 1930.
Montessori, M. *The Montessori Method*. New York: Schocken, 1964.
Peters, A. D. Day Care. A Summary Report. *American Journal of Public Health*, 54(11): 1905–1912, 1964.
Piaget, J. *The Origins of Intelligence in Children* (M. Cook trans.). New York: International Universities Press, 1952.
Riessman, F. *The Culturally Deprived Child*. New York: Harper & Row, 1962.
Watson, R. I. *Psychology of the Child*. New York: Wiley, 1959.

Epilogue
Implications for Future Planning

REGINALD S. LOURIE

Underlying the conferences from which this book emerged was the conviction that enough new information about babies has become available that we should begin to apply it to new programs. Further, the conviction was shared by all the participants that the distortions in mental and personality development seen particularly in disadvantaged children have their roots in the earliest experiences, especially in the first three years of life.

Despite the successes of enrichment and stimulation undertaken recently for preschool children, it is apparent that they must often be remedial—undoing and making up for already well-established pathological development. Therefore, in future planning, particularly of preventive programs for children, it becomes logical to begin at the earliest possible ages. Preventive steps can rarely be taken in the prenatal period because we don't know where all the unborn

359

babies are. But at least we know, by law, when babies come into the world and preventive programs should start then.

In the past, many ideal programs for care of very young children have been envisioned. With these new dimensions, such dreams are now more possible to achieve. Even though we still have large gaps in our knowledge about babies, this volume offers in distilled form many of the usable components of the information we do have. With this body of knowledge, we can begin to examine the implications for future programs in infant and young-child rearing.

If we begin with the basic assumption that every child has the right to develop as normally as possible, certain obligations become clear:

Ideally, every child born in this country would be really known, not just as a birth statistic.

For each child, screening examinations would be given from which a profile could be developed in terms suggested by the vulnerability index described in Chapter 6. From these initial screening results, all children judged to be in a developmental high-risk category could be cataloged and periodically re-examined.

The environment of each child would be evaluated and similarly cataloged in terms which our authors indicate are possible.

A "prescription" outlining a program could then be developed for each child in terms of what constitutional hazards he might bring to the environment and what the environment itself should provide to make optimal development possible, with or without vulnerabilities.

When the environment contains distortions and disturbances which in turn become hazards to dealing appropriately with individual vulnerabilities, the community has a responsibility to provide assistance to the home environment and those in it, as well as provision of corrective environments outside the home in which there would be supplementary facilities to meet individual needs.

Continuity of care, long an ideal, would become an essential part of the total picture. As part of comprehensive child and family services, all children on the risk register would be periodically re-evaluated throughout the school years.

Implementation

Chapters 10 to 14 indicate that considerable experimentation is going on around the world in an attempt to apply our newer information about infants and young children. Before we are ready to mount an ideal program as outlined above on a communitywide scale, further experimentation and preparation will be necessary. Such basic steps as the following underlie sound program implementation.

METHODS FOR IDENTIFYING EACH CHILD

A continuing census will be required, particularly of the mobile segments in the lower socioeconomic areas of the population. Some cities have attempted to use the public health nurses for this task, but it seems more appropriate to use trained nonprofessionals as agents of the health and educational services. One possibility being explored is that of having an indigenous worker cover a city block or, in rural areas, a census tract.

Some states and other countries have begun to establish risk registers, notably in crippled children's programs, with the aid of computers. The experience gained could be extended to cover all children.

TRAINING THE WORKERS ON VARIOUS LEVELS

Appraisal of children and of their environment with tailored translation of the findings into programs will require training or retraining, of workers on various levels. For one, training still needs to be developed for professional workers currently involved with children and their subprofessional assistants to enable them to identify individual differences in babies and young children and determine what each needs in order to develop optimally.

Appraisal of the environment in which each child is to be raised would also require the development of new skills. At the moment, there is little protocol for just what is to be observed in a home, hospital nursery, or institution where babies are raised. With the help of the contributions in this volume, we have the thinking which makes such an inventory possible. The evaluation of the environment must, of course, include the parents, where present, or the persons providing the mothering. Training programs for those who will visit in the homes will require evaluation and integration of information from behavioral science (such as anthropological field studies), public health, nursing, and medicine.

Furthermore, training of personnel skilled in infant rearing would need to be initiated in order to staff the infant day-care programs properly. Such training is almost nonexistent in this country, but it is available in some other countries, notably Greece (Metera), the Soviet Union, France, and Israel.

Likewise, in this country almost nothing has been done to provide personnel to train for motherhood. A few small experimental efforts in this direction show that it is feasible and quite useful.*

Educators, too, will need to adopt new goals in training. The education programs of the community beginning with the earliest years of life would be carried out in relation to, if not actually in, child and family centers. One thinks of patterns of learning as beginning in the infant's attempts to deal with his body and his environment. It is logical to think of the educator as a participant in the development of useful styles of learning. If this is at all valid, a new concept of the educator's responsibility must be developed.

A NETWORK OF COMMUNITY CENTERS FOR CHILDREN AND PARENTS

These centers would coordinate the community's health, education, and welfare programs to eliminate the current fragmentation of services and make available a range of coordinated program facets to fill the "prescription" developed for each child in each living unit covered by the center.

Beginning with family planning and prenatal care, the center would provide a continuum of nurturing and preventive approaches. As the home base of the case finding and screening personnel, the child and parent center would have "arms" to reach out, particularly into those homes where parents cannot be mobilized so that the children, at least, would be brought into service. Assistance would be given the mother in modifying her patterns of care for her children at home. Day-care programs for infants and young children would be housed in the center, and, where possible, the mother would be included in these.

The health services would combine with welfare to deal with the problem of adequate child and parent nutrition, beginning with the earliest possible prenatal phase. If a truly comprehensive preventive health and mental health approach is to be effected, it is apparent

* For example, the work of Dr. Susan W. Gray and associates in the project conducted at Peabody College, Nashville, Tenn., with parents in low-income groups. See "An Experimental Program for Culturally Deprived Children," *Child Development*, 36(4): 887–898, 1965.

that the current model of the well baby clinic is inadequate. Communication between the outside agents of the center and the various components within should continuously include the health teams. There should be no break in health care until late adolescence.

The Future

The thinking, researches, and conceptualization which the contributors to this volume make available about the earliest years of life in turn open vistas for the future in which every child could achieve his potential if we can put this new information to work in actual programs. It would be expensive if done well. The question is not, Can we afford to do it? Rather, we must ask, Can we afford *not* to do it?

Appendix A:
The Vulnerability Inventory

LOIS BARCLAY MURPHY

If we omit the obvious pathologies comprising diseases, marked damages, or defects referred to earlier and focus on the mild deviations from a hypothetical norm of well-balanced equipment and integrated primary functioning, we see a rather extended list of factors, no one of which need involve real difficulty for the child if the particular deviation is buffered by otherwise very well-functioning capacities.

Vulnerability can be considered at each of several levels which are not, however, mutually independent:

1. At the biological level: labile integration, tendency to decreased coordination, easy disruption of smooth functioning under strong stimulation from outside or inside.

    a. Exacerbation of the above by chronic environmental strain and/or absence of environmental help in reducing tension.

    b. Exacerbation by imbalances or other disturbances in bio-

364

chemical, metabolic, vegetative, autonomic functioning, or by too-high or too-low thresholds.

2. At the level of psychic structure: poor ego-cohesion, lack of stable integration:

   a. As an outcome of the influence of the biological lability referred to above.

   b. And/or low energy to invest in mastery or integrative efforts, selective organization of relations with the environment.

   c. And/or lack of effective defense maneuvers or internal defense mechanisms.

   d. Or as an outcome of inadequate input (due to sensory-perceptual defects) or output (due to interferences with motor discharge, expression and action) or interrelations between the two due to imbalances in maturity of different functional capacities.

   e. Or as a resultant of disorganizing anxiety or either severe or mild cumulative trauma.

Implied is the need to achieve—in part simultaneously and in part successively—integration of:

1. Vegetative functioning including gastrointestinal functions, sleep and waking rhythms; activity and rest rhythms.

2. Sensory functioning and its use in selection from the environment and increase of pleasure.

3. Cognitive functioning; perception, recognition, memory, differentiation of inner and outer stimuli.

4. Motor integration: first for management of the body and manipulation of objects, then for self-care and autonomous action in the environment.

5. Affective integration and the use of affect to support investments in the environment and for interaction with people.

6. Integration of self and of objects through the differentiation and organization of affective responses to cues of every kind, internal and external, proprioceptive, visual, auditory, tactual; and the cumulative investment of these and their integrated products with potentiality for gratification or pain.

7. Integration of the central organizing ego, which itself becomes an initiator of integrative functioning as well as a constantly modified product of it.

Any and every aspect of the individual equipment of the infant and of the young child in his environment and his attunement, fit, or difficulty in functioning in his environment plays a part—momentarily and cumulatively—in the emergence of these zones and levels of integration.

In presenting the vulnerability list, therefore, we are inviting consideration both of each item alone and of the kinds of interactions which may be seen when a number of difficulties are found in different areas or at a critical developmental phase, interacting with each other in such a way as to interfere with the basic well-being of the child, his ego development, his relationships with his mother and other people, and the over-all integration of the child's character as he develops.

While no item alone, unless severe, is likely to interfere seriously with development, the result of their interaction with each other and with independent or related difficulties contributed by the environment may lead to acquired retardation and other functional inadequacies, to delinquency, or to disturbances of mental health.

The vulnerability contributed by the interaction of these factors helps to define the nature and degree of stress. The coping resources, both innate and evolved from the child's struggles to master the environment and his own intrinsic and developmental problems, together with the presence of protecting or compensating mothering, support, soothing, etc., may contribute to decreased vulnerability as the child matures or even to a level of creativity and active attitude toward problem solving beyond that characteristic of more placid or less initially vulnerable children.

Almost any combination of oversensitivities, central perceptual handicaps, massive affective or autonomic overflow, or integrative difficulties affecting efficiency or speed of motor output may lead to one or another pattern or degree of giving up the effort to cope actively with the environment. Low-drive level generally or reduced increments to ego-functioning from frustrated oral drives as well as severe interferences with autonomy during the second year of life (as when a child is excessively confined due to illness or other causes) may also contribute to such renunciation of efforts in some children, although some others react with intensified compensatory effort which may be exhausting and contribute to fatigability.

The *retreat* may be of any degree: (1) adaptively, a mild delay to permit clearer orientation, inner rehearsal, then later active effort; (2) self-protective avoidance, by-passing specific unmanageable demands while remaining generally in contact with the environment; (3) narrowing the range of attention in a hermitlike seclusive way while carrying on some narrow but socially acceptable activity; or

(4) "autistic" withdrawal to sensory or symbolic repetitive activities which afford a slight opportunity for discharge while avoiding social involvement and genuine cathexis of the environment. Both (3) and (4), by reducing input and perceptual range, also reduce stimulus to cognitive activity and thus the level of mental functioning.

A child may show a circumscribed limitation of development in one zone or a mild regression or inhibition in several zones and still remain more or less within the normal range. But he may reduce his response to the environment in all zones—no longer exploring or reaching out motorically, nor searching the environment visually nor asking questions. If he loses interest and becomes apathetic or depressed, then this massive retreat or renunciation of response of expectation reduces his effective input and thus the amount of cognitive stimulation producing a cycle of interference with development. He fails to progress and thus becomes retarded.

Circumscribed inhibition or repression as a response to some combination of vulnerability and environmental deprivation may lead to any of the following patterns, among others, depending partly on how these are responded to:

1. *Renunciation of autonomy* and motor efforts toward self-care and use of the environment, thus becoming dependent.

2. *Loss of integration and control,* giving way to indiscriminate action, aggressive impulses as in some types of delinquency.

3. *Affective inhibition or regression*—inhibition of feelings of deep response or involvement; losing capacity for pleasure; giving up the expectation of gratifying interaction with the environment; becoming sad or emotionally flattened, resigned or apathetic.

4. *Cognitive inhibition or regression:* Inhibition of searching, analyzing, problem solving, or other cognitive efforts; disorganization of thought; regression to drive-dominated (primary process) thinking.

These and other inhibiting or regressing responses to frustrations arising from combinations of vulnerability and environmental difficulties in turn add a further level of vulnerability, a decrease or failure to develop coping resources needed at each developmental stage.

The Vulnerability Inventory

I. Primary tendencies (constitutional or acquired early in the first six months)

A. *Defects* (mild to severe)

1. Hearing (partial hearing loss affecting communication)

2. Visual (e.g., myopia, hampering quick orientation)
3. Manual (contributing to awkwardness, poor fine coordination)
4. Gross motor difficulties (due to flat feet, club foot, knock knee, or to poor coordination, which interfere with running, jumping, etc.)
5. Balance (in capacities or in control in relation to drives)

B. *Unusual structure and/or developmental pattern*
1. Body build
   a. Extreme ectomorphic (often a poor fighter, feels he can never win)
   b. Obese tendency (often slow, cannot keep up)
   c. Low center of gravity (short legs, etc.)
2. Peculiar appearance (asymmetrical face or head, stigmata)
3. Constitutional deviation from appearance and/or body build expected for own sex and family pattern
4. Extreme changes in body build at different stages, creating problem for child in accepting a changed self-image

C. *Sensitivities*
1. To extremes (inadequate stimulus barrier, hyperinput proneness, hypoinput proneness)
2. In specific zones
   a. Tactile (skin sensitivities contributing to complex, ambivalent, or anxious reactions to contact)
   b. Temperature
   c. Auditory (sensitivity to loud sounds or special qualities)
   d. Visual (unusually painful or pleasurable reactions to light, etc.)
   e. Pain
3. To specific qualities (e.g., shiny surfaces, rough textures)
4. To general stimuli (e.g., new situations, strangeness, sudden change)

D. *Imbalances*
1. Perceptual-cognitive pace more rapid than motor integration which contributes to greater intake than can be acted upon
2. Verbal-social areas (Gesell) outreach adaptive and discharge capacities, leading to overstimulation, flooding, etc.

3. Drives more intense than control capacities, leading to impulsiveness

4. Aggressive drives stronger than capacity for love, leading to difficulties in modulation of aggression

5. Sensitivities greater than protective and coping resources

E. *Deviant developmental rate:* Early or late onset of puberty, leading to peer group alienation. (*See also* B4.)

F. *Temperamental vulnerability:* Low threshold for irritability, displeasure, hostility, anxiety.

G. *Deviant arousal patterns:* Exceptionally slow or fast.

H. *Lability*

1. Autonomic as indicated by marked variability in pulse, respiratory rate, etc.

2. Tendency to disturbances of vegetative functioning: colic, diarrhea, vomiting, respiration, etc.

3. Somatic reactions to stress

4. Susceptibility to infection

5. Allergies; eczema, skin rashes, etc.

6. Low threshold for arousal of tension

I. *Perceptual-cognitive vulnerability:* Tendency to loss of integration or optimal level of functioning in cognitive areas that are under stress; fluctuating differentiation of fantasy and reality

J. *Motor:* Tendency to disorganized motor reactivity under stress

K. *Speech:* Tendency to loss of smooth speech under stress

L. *Social:* Tendency to loss of trust with resulting lack of direct contact

M. *Lack of resources for flexible active coping*

1. Passivity

2. Predisposition to restriction, inability to adapt body to environment or use environment for own comfort or satisfaction

3. Low "sending power" (limited vocalization, mimetic, affectionate and other expressive resources, and resources to evoke support, help, etc.)

4. Tendency for wide diffusion and overflow of affect as opposed to containment or confinement to specific time, space stimulus, and appropriate differentiation

5. Tendency to direct impulse-expression at the expense of delay, orientation, planning, sublimation, capacity, etc.

      6. Lack of flexible response to cues and comfort from caretakers

II. Emerging tendencies (reactions to birth and early infantile distress, developed during the period of patterning of perceptual-cognitive-affective functioning, and later)

  A. *Anxiety*
    1. Over own body
    2. Over object relationships
    3. Over separation or loss
    4. Over rejection, etc.
    5. Over failure or challenge
    6. Over self-functioning, etc.

  B. Hostility and aggression (in reaction to excessively interfering, frustrating, or painful handling)

  C. *Ambivalence and conflict*
    1. Rooted in strong positive and negative reactions to the same stimulus (tactile, visual, auditory, etc.)
    2. Resulting in early strong positive and strong negative tendencies in the mother
    3. Resulting from strongly satisfying combined with strongly frustrating ways of handling

  D. *Fatigability*
    1. Low energy reserve
    2. Poor energy management
    3. Inability to alternate activity and rest
    4. Progression and regression

III. Secondary outcomes of total infantile experience (learned or evolved after the first six months)

  A. *Failure to develop*
    1. Trust sufficient to withstand rebuffs and disappointment
    2. Nonverbal and verbal communication, imitation, identification
    3. Stable flexible relationships, capacity to communicate, cooperate, fight, love in the setting of the relation with the mother
    4. Resources for the discharge of tension, resolution of anger, and/or mastery of anger
    5. A range of affect, including capacity for fun, joy, interest in new experience, play, creativity
    6. Capacity to satisfy needs; or to maintain expectation or a capacity for delay

7. Ability to express drives through socialized activity
8. Reinforced capacity to exert effort or capacity to struggle against obstacles, keep on trying after failure, etc.
9. Capacity to "forgive and forget," tolerate frustration, renew positive relationships or let go and begin new relationships
10. Recovery patterns through temporary regression or withdrawal, self-comfort, compensation, etc.
11. Positive coping attitudes and resources, or to consolidate these with healthy defense mechanisms
12. Autonomy appropriate to the developmental stage and resources
13. Capacity to use the environment selectively, achieve goals, obtain substitutes, structure or restructure the environment
14. Clear concepts of objects, space, time relationships in the immediate and broader environment

B. *Persistent anxiety regarding*
1. Separation from mother
2. Doctors, pain, body handling by strangers
3. Other stimuli experienced in a traumatic context

C. *Residues of illness* (accidental or operative damage contributing to vulnerabilities similar to those under heading I, especially)
1. Temporary hearing defects etc. interfering with speech development
2. Dizziness or other anxiety-evoking reactions
3. Motor or digestive difficulties

D. *Cumulative conflicts* (arising from interaction of any of the above with problems of control and adaptation, in relation to)
1. Early feeding
2. Toileting pressures
3. Pressure for motor inhibition and control, etc.

E. *Depression, retreat* (reactions to loss, separation, frustration, or illness, which inhibit coping efforts)

IV. All of the aforementioned may result in expressions of vulnerability in one or more zones
A. *Motor*
1. Disorganization of motor control under stress (jerkiness, tremor, decreased accuracy and coordination)

      2. Inhibition, immobility or paralysis of action, stiffening, rigidity

      3. Loss of impulse control

      4. Other difficulties

B. *Speech*

      1. Loss of smooth functioning under stress, stammering, etc.

      2. "Whistling *s*," etc. under stress, infantile speech, etc.

      3. Inhibition of speech under stress, chronic speech inhibition

C. *Perceptual*

      1. Loss of perceptual clarity under stress (vagueness, confusion, perceptual distortion due to projection, displacement, etc.)

      2. Narrowed range of perceptual response (withdrawal, turning away, loss of curiosity, interest, response to environment)

      3. Loss of control of attention, capacity to select, etc.

D. *Affect*

      1. Loss of appropriateness of affect (extreme intensity or extreme flattening)

      2. Eruption of overwhelming affect; affect-storm under a strong stimulation

      3. Loss of affective investment in people, in objects, in activities

E. *Loss of integrative functioning* (decreased investment in the environment, loss of trust, initiative, problem solving, clarity of orientation, drive to learn, curiosity, creativity, etc.)

F. *Low level of self-confidence,* enjoyment of self and of others, capacity for participation, cooperation, and leadership in dyadic or group situations.

Appendix B:
A "Typical Day" for the Groups at the Children's Center

BETTYE M. CALDWELL
and JULIUS B. RICHMOND

	Infants (roughly 6-18 months)	Toddlers (18-30 months)	"Striders" (30-40 months)
7:30	Children arrive individually or in small clusters; same is true of staff. All early arrivals go into same group. Each child is greeted warmly, talked to, undressed (and changed if necessary). Although this is technically a free play period, there is a great deal of individual attention. Much lap-sitting, reading to one or two, taking child along while teacher prepares for day's activities, etc. As other staff and children arrive, children go to their own "home territory."		
9:00	Receive, greet, change babies. (All babies are changed upon arrival, with the hopefully clean diaper set aside for them to wear home.)	Nourishment and story (group together). In this group the only full-group reading is during the time the children are seated for their snack. At conclusion they move about, then are divided.	Greeting, establishment of group. Informal roll call and discussion of activities done the day before and planned for this day.
9:30	Nourishment (juice, milk, crackers, cookies, dry cereal, occasional full breakfast), conversation.	Special project (group divided), usually involving fine motor coordination--e.g. finger or chalk painting, stringing large macaroni, making pudding, playing with clay, shaking glitter on surface, making hand print, etc. Children leave table as they finish.	Story and snack. Snack is often a "buffet" with finger foods (carrot sticks, celery, apple slices), peanut butter or cheese and crackers. Story read after children finish eating.
10:00	"Special" project, usually one that can be done in feeding chair with all children in same area, (e.g., egg white painting, feeling hot and cold water, nesting blocks or cups, playing with toys having distinct textures, etc.).	"Surprise" period. Teachers show children something "spectacular"--blows balloon, offers turtle, lights and extinguishes candle, etc.	Special cognitive or creative activity. May be many things, will vary with topic being emphasized. Includes puzzles, art work, beads, cylinder blocks, mosaics, pasting cut-outs, etc. May also include demonstrations--e.g., pediatrician "examines" doll.
10:30	One-to-one period; activities arranged to fill individual needs. One child may be "walked" about building; 2 walked in strollers (outdoors in good weather); 2 to be read to; one to be encouraged with special puzzle; one to have "Baby's eyes, nose," etc.; one to have big spools--little spools, etc.	"Rambunctious" period. Large muscle toys are made available--roll toys, walking board, slide, wagon, trucks. Records may be played; children play with one another, interact with teacher in special individual ways. During this time all are toileted and dressed to go outside.	Free play, children all together, with wide range of toys available to choose from-- roll playing toys, books, blocks, etc. If field trip is scheduled, it will occupy both this and preceding period. Sometime during period, children will be toileted.
11:00	Change; play records; bring and serve lunch; clean up; prepare for nap.	Outdoor play, or play in basement. Wide array of equipment available.	Outdoor play, or play in basement. Climbers, tricycles, swings, push toys, sand box, etc. available.

Clean, toilet, and bib up for lunch. |

Time			
11:30		Change or toilet, wash, put bibs on for lunch.	Lunch. Children eat in one group.
12:00	Nap time; teachers and nurses have lunch. (Even though this period is thought of as nap time, not all the babies are asleep throughout the period. They go down and awaken at different times, with more variability in the time of waking. All are rocked either before or after nap. Babies who do not sleep receive individual attention—games, simple books, may sit in on teacher's meeting, etc.) Teachers fill out records, clean up play area, etc.	Lunch. The children eat in one group, sitting at small table.	
12:30		Toileting and diapering, clean-up, preparation for nap.	Washing, toileting, and brushing of teeth. Children lie down on cots as they get ready for nap. Teachers pat, sing softly, etc.
1:00		Nap period, wide variation in ease of going to sleep and duration of sleep. Some drop off instantly; others need patting or singing or rocking. Last one to sleep around 2:00, first one awake around 2:30. As children awaken, they are taken into adjoining room and rocked and cuddled, changed, read or sung to, etc. One teacher stays on observation duty. Teachers meet to discuss program, keep records, clean up area, etc. Only one room available, as one or two children might sleep until 3:30.	Nap time. Most children in group sleep very soundly for full period. One teacher remains on observation duty. Teachers meet to plan program, prepare for later activities, clean up room, etc. As children awaken they go into extra room, receive individual attention, rocking, special story, are toileted, etc.
1:30			
2:00			

	Infants (roughly 6-18 months)	Toddlers (18-30 months)	"Striders" (30-40 months)
2:30	Awake, "nuzzled," changed (diaper changing time is an important one for learning activities; adults consistently talk to, smile at, peek-a-boo with, hold up to windows to observe outside goings-on, etc.		Free play. Children are still "waking up." Large assortment of both small muscle and large muscle toys available for choice.
3:00	Nourishment	Individual learning activities—reading target (vocabulary) books, shape puzzles, cylinder blocks, nesting boxes, hide and find games, small table blocks, etc. These activities may follow rather than precede snack if all children awake.	Snack and group story. Also group singing.
3:30	"Floor play." (Activities vary with weather. Children may be taken outdoors for sand box, water play, swings, crawling in grass, etc. For indoor play, "large muscle" toys will be made available.)	Snack and story. May be offered outdoors in summer.	Structured active play. Activity record, ring games, bean bag game, marching, rhythm instruments. May go outdoors in good weather.
4:00	Children leave at different times during this period; same for staff. Older children are brought into baby area to wait for parents, driver, etc.	Individually guided play. By this time of day the children may be tired (as will be the staff). Some children will require outlets for vigorous activity, but often	Cognitive or creative activity. By this time, most of the children have gone. The head teacher who remains uses this as a time for playing special lotto-games,

Time		
4:30	Children are encouraged to play by themselves as much as possible during this time. Staff try to talk at least briefly with parents as they come to pick up children--exchange anecdotes, discuss problems, etc.	cannot take completely "free" play at this time. Thus action songs, marching and rhythms, ring games will be organized. Other children will want to be held and rocked.
		puppet stories, art activities, etc.
5:00 to 6:00	Preparation for departure or regrouping, changing and dressing. Children who stay late will be combined with children from other groups.	Preparation for departure. Toileting, practice in dressing, cuddling, and individual stories. Children who leave very late combined with other groups.

The amount of time during which children are free to select their own activities is under-represented in the table. E.g., though 30 minutes may be allowed in the schedule for toileting or changing, this takes only five minutes or so for any particular child. Thus these periods are also essentially free periods.

Index